This Book is Dedicated to
Robbi LePree

J. Michael Roddy's Haunter's Tale Vol. II

ISBN-13: 978-0-578-77528-9

http://HarkerPress.com
http://HauntersTale.com

J.MICHAEL RODDY'S

HAUNTER'S TALE

VOL. II

TABLE OF CONTENTS

INTRODUCTION

BY DANIEL ROEBUCK

J. Michael Roddy has done it again We all applauded the audaciously brilliant idea of gathering the best spooky minds in the country and wringing them tightly to dislodge some of the scariest tales of which they could think. J Michael Roddy's Haunter's Tales was truly remarkable in that it offered us a chance to see what it was that creeped the professional creepers.

Now with *Haunter's Tales Volume 2*, we don't simply get "more of the same". No, Roddy's too good a storyteller for that. This volume pushes that bloodstained envelope further and he cajoles his gaggle of ghoulmasters to dig even deeper. Much deeper than the standard six-foot grave.

His list of fiendishly entertaining horror professionals includes so many names of which I am familiar and reading their own stories, learning of their horrific experiences and bearing witness to their innermost fears is oddly entertaining, just as Mr. Roddy knew they would be. So, what are you waiting for? Go ahead and indulge your curiosity. Give it a good read. Or are you chicken?

With ghoulish delight,

Daniel Roebuck

Actor/Writer/Producer/Scaredy Cat

FOREWORD

BY SCOTT SWENSON

what SCARES people?

What scares people? This is a deceptively difficult question. Some people are afraid of a loud startling noise while others are terrified by a dark endless silence. Some are afraid of spiders, snakes and cockroaches while others derive fear from human threats like serial killers and evil clowns. Fear can come from the fantasy realm in the form of dragons and vampires or be 100% reality based like the fear of drowning or claustrophobic incarceration. If you ask 10 people, "What is scary?" you will, most likely, get at least 15 different responses. But this is exactly the question that members of the haunted attraction community seek to answer year after year.

It might be easier to answer the question, "What scares you?". Fear is very personal. It comes from 3 basic sources. Some fears come from past experiences. A fear of heights, for example, may come from falling out of your high chair when you were very young. Fear can also be generated as a response to a threat or traumatic experience. It gives you the strength and energy you need to get out of the way of a speeding train. Fear can even be genetic, passed down from one generation to the next. Since we all have different experiences, traumas and genetics, it is difficult to find one thing that scares everyone. In fact, it is impossible. This is why the creative minds that work within the horror and haunt industry need to find new ways to tell stories or visually represent the terrifying worlds they are trying to create.

The book you about to dive into, Haunter's Tale Volume 2, is an eclectic mix of articles, stories, poetry and works of art which attempt to shine new light (or perhaps a deeper darkness) onto the question of fear. All of these pieces are created by masters of the macabre, people who create countless ways to make people tremble and scream. I am very proud to call many of these contributors my peers, my idols and my inspirations. So cuddle up in a dark corner, light a candle and enjoy a kaleidoscope of answers to the deceptively difficult question, What scares people?

Scott Swenson

AND NOW A WORD FROM
DOUG JONES

As an actor who has starred in many dark and haunted titles over the years, I have learned from our fans how good scares from worlds and creatures unknown can not only entertain, but they can also relieve us of our real life worries. An escape into a controlled, yet frightening environment where zombies, ghosts, and monsters live can release our stress hormones and activate our problem-solving skills to enable us to exit the movie theater or the haunted house feeling triumphant and happy to be alive as we re-enter the real world. So, to those of you who create or perform in this genre, and to those who just love being an audience for all things horror and fantasy, thank you for keeping our beloved genre alive on all levels.

~ Doug Jones

(*Hocus Pocus, Pan's Labyrinth, The Shape Of Water, The Bye Bye Man, Hellboy*)

WHY?

BY J. MICHAEL RODDY

What is it about the horror fan that loves to be afraid? Even more so, the fan that wants to experience the most terrifying of scenarios, the one that wants to interact? As a little history for you, one of my favorite topics to discuss is about the things that scare us. I love good conversations about all manner of things that slither from the darkness that slowly reveal the face of the macabre. I love sharing a good ghost story, reviewing a well-made fright film, and chatting about the mechanics behind a well-designed storyline, and I love Haunted Houses.

But, I used to be terrified of them. I still remember the very first one that I attempted to visit. It was in Tampa, Florida, and was run by the Jaycees. The year was 1975, and I was in full Monsterkid mode. I spent my weekends watching Dr. Paul Bearer present classic horror on Creature Features on UHF channel 44 WTOG. I read *Famous Monsters of Filmland, The Monster Times, Eerie, Creepy, The Witching Hour, Werewolf by Night, The Tomb of Dracula*, and many more publications that fueled my imagination. I also loved the occasional Dan Curtis shocker that would come on the network, specifically the terrifying *Trilogy of Terror*. *Jaws* had been released that previous summer, and I was obsessed.

Historically, Halloween would fall on Friday that year. If you are a true horror fan, there is something special about Halloween falling on a Friday or Saturday; it made the evening last longer somehow without the threat of having to go to school the next day. I had my Ben Cooper costume picked out, I would be the shark from *JAWS*. Obsessed. *The Giant Spider Invasion* was in theatres, and that would solidify my lifelong fear of arachnids. Everything was falling in place to be a perfect holiday for tricks and treats. So, with my fascination firmly rooted in the scarier things, I was so excited to brave a "real" Haunted House.

School on Halloween in elementary school was always a blast. You could wear your costume, and most of the day was spent watching 16mm film prints of *The Legend of Sleepy Hollow* and *It's the Great Pumpkin, Charlie Brown*. There was also a scholastic book fair that week, and my mom volunteered at the school, so she always had her first pick and always made sure I had some wonderful books to surprise me. These included monster-themed joke books, posters, activities and *Movie Monsters* by Alan Ormsby.

The day was filled with detailed thoughts of how I would bravely face the ghouls and goblins that night instead of travelling the street to get treats. My mom would sneak me a few treats anyway. Besides, If Bud Abbott and Lou Costello could meet Frankenstein, then so could I. I rushed home after school, ate a peanut butter and jelly sandwich and filled my doodle pad with drawings of my favorite monsters. The sun started to fall in the sky, and as the hour grew close, I began to be filled with creeping anxiety. I shook it off, ready to be a young Van Helsing to face my vampiric foe.

We drove to the haunted house, passing the beginnings of trick or treaters starting to emerge from their dwellings and start the search for candy. Not for me, I was going somewhere much spookier.

I remember arriving and turning into the lot, parking in a grassy field somewhere, and seeing so many other people, all there to have fun and frights. I remember the building. It actually looked like a classic haunted house, and in my mind's eye and nostalgic view, I saw every cobweb, ghost, and flickering candle. A full moon hung perfectly over the house, creating shadows of menace. I could hear the screams echoing from inside. They resonated and seemed amplified, each one a warning of impending doom.

We approached the line (it would be a few years before I learned the term queue), and my heart began to race. There were a lot of people waiting for their chance to explore the old house. My Parents helped usher me towards the line, and then it happened. I saw a Wolfman leap from the corner of the darkness and rip apart another child about my age. He tore apart his neck, sending blood spraying across the grass, then with head arched back, he let loose with a tremendous howl worthy of Lon Chaney Jr.

Okay, that didn't really happen. The Wolfman mask was something that I had seen in the back pages of *Famous Monsters* as part of the Captain Company, but to see it moving, and leaping was remarkable. The child was also not harmed, he screamed but that was the extent of his physical injuries. People buzzed with excitement, and we slowly inched closer to the entrance. But the damage was done, and so was I. That's right, I chickened out. I mean full-tilt boogie meltdown. I remember being relieved that my parents were okay with us leaving as opposed to trying to talk me into going further in. We went home, and I am pretty sure that I was allowed to take a run around the street for treats. Nestled back safely in my home, I was comforted by my cinematic friends in the pages of Famous Monsters while above me on a shelf stood sentinel a row of plastic "Aurora" Monsters, slightly glowing in the dark. All was safe.

Every Halloween, my mother would always go full out for me, transforming out front room into our very own Haunt. We had all of these incredible Beistle decorations - Giant cardboard pumpkins, arching, and hissing black cats with glowing green eyes… the 55-inch jointed skeleton., the Witch with the black tissue body. She would also take my Model kits and place them around as well, creating a miniature McDougal's House of Horrors. It was here where I practiced scaring and haunting for the first time. I used to jump out and scare my Grandmother, but then she would say that I had the devil in me and freak me out, so I don't count those juvenile attempts.

My time outside of school during the month of October would be spent dreaming that my home was actually a haunted house, and I acted out every scene. After a tour around the street for tricks and treats, I would rush home to be the featured "scareactor" in my own home haunt. I would dress up as the Frankenstein Monster and stand silent and still near the door, perfectly illuminated by a flickering candle. The knock would come and my mom would open the door, inviting them to gaze into the haunted front room. The neighboring kids would be able to peek inside, taking in the decorations while the pickwick sound effects album providing the perfect ambience. Then, I would lumber forward, my hands out and they would scream.

My next haunt experience came many years later. By that time, I had moved from classic monsters into the slasher/gore phase of my interests. Frankenstein, Dracula, and the Wolf-man were replaced by Jason, Freddy and Michael Myers. *Fangoria* magazine joined the beloved issues of *Starlog* and *Famous Monsters* in providing glorious photography and in-depth coverage of all manner of the fear-filled fantastic.

My good friend Erik Hollander, who I would later produce the Jaws documentary - *The Shark is Still Working* with, was in charge of creating a Halloween experience for the neighborhood of The Woods in Jacksonville, Florida. The Woods was always that neighborhood. It was gated, and it just seemed that life was that much better behind those security stations. Erik created something called Nightmare Trail. It was a literal trail through a small section of the woods in the development, near to the community pool and tennis courts. Erik was obsessive about the production. He would start in late September and then get friends and family to build structures that would be found along a dark and foreboding trail. In those woods, there was a menagerie of monsters, mutants, and madman,

all played by his friends. One of the exciting experiences was developing those scares and the characters that would inhabit those dark woods. Make-up was provided mostly by what was available at the local Sears or JC Penney's, although Erik created many custom pieces with skulls and Bondo all-purpose putty.

I remember on one of these trips to Sears; I saw a Michael Myers mask from John Carpenter's *Halloween* for the first time. I had to have it, as The Shape was my favorite of all the maniacs. There are certain items that you always remember exactly when you got it… that mask was one of them. At Nightmare Trail, I would be starring as Leatherface from *The Texas Chainsaw Massacre*. I wanted to be Myers, but Erik played him, and he nailed it.

During these years, I must mention that we didn't just practice the art of scaring during Halloween. Erik and I, along with several of our closest friends used to play elaborate games of what we called "Gotcha". This was pranking, and we went all out. We would stage home invasions to trick and freak out our friends. We would decide as a group who was our victim. It was usually the one friend who wasn't able to come until later. We would plan extensive and elaborate situations to play these practical jokes on each other. This included one of our friends sneaking into the house and slowly starting to torture the attended victim—moving in other areas of the house, making noise in some dark bedroom. Of course, we were all in on it except for the intended victim so that we wouldn't hear any of the warning sounds of creaks and footsteps. We tricked friends into going into graveyards; We would play hide and seek and tag in the movie theatre. We would turn out all of the lights and chase each other through the six dark theatres. One of our most infamous "gotcha" moments.

My best friend Mark Burton and I spent countless hours dreaming. We came up with story ideas for movies and TV shows. Mark was joining me so that we could walk through a park after dark and just talk and dream about the future lives we wanted. Mark was convinced that Erik and I were not on speaking turns, so the idea that Erik was actually in on the prank was quickly rejected. So, Mark and I are walking through the dark, navigating the pathways. Suddenly in the distance there is a sound, a definite signal that we are not alone. I play off that I didn't hear anything and we continue to walk around. Another few noises here and there start to bring Mark on edge. Then we sit down on a bench. I am facing Mark. Behind him in the far distance is Erik – fully dressed as Michael Myers. A few branch snaps and Mark turns, slowly looking in the distance. What is that? Mark is not sure as it is very difficult to make out. We continue talking and I can see that Erik is now moving quickly to get closer. He freezes. Mark turns and there a mere 15 feet away is Myers. Mark let's out a scream and runs. Erik follows. I run around the other way to see the fun.

Mark is now full on running. Erik ducks into an opening in the park and hauls it running to cut Mark off. Erik takes off the mask and we laugh and then decide that we can make it to the other side of the park where Mark parked his car and Myers could be waiting for him.

Erik sprints one direction and I go the other. I move through the blackness, luckily avoiding twisting an ankle or worse. I emerge from the other entrance and run directly into an approaching police car that has pulled in. The officer flashes his lights and tells me to get in the back. Note: This is the only time in my life that I have ever been in a police car. The radio is full of chatter about us. This is bad. We pull out and down a longer house-filled street and I see Mark, moving very quickly. The police officer flashes his lights, and I see relief in my best friend's eyes. Mark runs up to the car and as he is about to explain, I blurt out "Where's Erik?" Mark's whole soul deflates, and the officer tells him to get in. We are driven back to the park where there are now three police cars. There is Erik, who has ditched the Myers outfit and knife. We explain that it was a prank. We are told that a woman was watching TV and saw a man being chased by a masked man with a knife and called the police. The officers ask to see the outfit, and when revealed states that Erik could have been shot. I realize at this point that we may be in real trouble. Luckily, one of the officers also ran a local photo lab and knew us, so we were released with a warning.

When I moved to Orlando, I appeared at the Mark II Dinner Theatre in a production of *Don't Dress for Dinner*. One evening, Director Mark Howard introduced me to David Clevinger. David was the director of a unique year-round attraction called Terror on Church Street. David invited me to visit, and as I approached the red and black building in the heart of downtown Orlando, that sinking, scary anxiety reappeared. But, I was much older, and I wasn't going to miss out on this opportunity. The attraction had a gift shop filled with fun trinkets and odd curios. Once you stepped inside, you were truly immersed in the world of dark, tropes from some of horrors most famous scenarios. The first experience was a shaded courtyard, illuminated only by flickering candlelight. An Undertaker character would expertly transition between menace and mirth as he explained the rules. Then, we were on our way, down a long alley, and through a heavy door that entered into a dark altar. Stepping forward, we moved through cell doors and into a cemetery. A blinding series of bright lightning and powerful blasts of thunder assaulted our senses as slow-moving zombies appeared through the fog... Terror on Church Street was one of the scariest, most wonderful places. Every room was completely immersive, combining audio. Lighting and movie quality set work with some of the best actors. After the last room, where you were chased out through the bayou by a chainsaw-wielding hillbilly, you emerged back into the gift shop, where Alan Ostrander's Roach character would taunt and tease you. Glorious.

After the tour, David was waiting in his office for me. It was a large room filled with potential set pieces for future projects. On the wall was an autographed poster by Wes Craven. I found David sitting behind a desk filled with ideas and pictures, sketches, and fun products. We talked for an hour about horror and theatre. He hired me, and I began my official career as a haunter. It was there that I met Jack Neberlein and became instant friends. I spent so many nights in those halls, reading and dreaming of ways to create my horror stories and scripts, writing, drawing and reading in-between groups of terrified guests.

David is so very dear to me. He provided me an outlet to combine my love of theatre, horror, and movies. He allowed me to create my own characters to help stalk Church Street and invite guests to the haunt. He gave me my first opportunity to write and help design rooms with him and Jack. We shot short films there in those dark movie-quality sets. I even saw a ghost, but that story is for another book.

Around the same time that I was hired at Terror on Church Street, I was also hired at Universal Studios, Florida. Those early days were so precious. I would spend all day at Universal playing Dudley Do-Right, Peter Venkman, Ray Stantz, or Egon Spengler finish my shift, and rush to make my 6:30 PM call at Terror. I would work until 12 AM or 2 AM and then drive to my apartment and repeat early the next morning.

A few months later, Universal had an event called Halloween Horror Nights, and they were looking for actors to play traditional roles from Universal's catalog. auditioned. I could do a pretty spot-on imitation of Anthony Perkins as Norman Bates from *Psycho* and was delighted to be cast as that role for their Psycho Path attraction. *Psycho IV* (directed by Mick Garris) was filmed at the Studios, and the infamous house and Motel used were still part of the landscape. I was so happy to not only see another quality Halloween experience based on one of the most famous of horror films, but to be cast as one of the most recognizable of all screen villains. I would stand outside the motel and just talk to guests, setting the perfect mood. Sometimes I would be waiting in the office to scare them before they met "mother". My favorite moments included coming back from break and just standing on the hill with the house looming in the background. I met Julie Zimmerman and Jerry Abercrombie – the architects of Halloween Horror Nights. I also met Leonard and Jeannie Pickel, two amazing and delightful folks.

The following year, I was asked to lend my horror film knowledge to help do some initial work on the next year's event. As the years progressed, I was given more and more opportunities to work various components of Halloween Horror Nights, including promos, voice-overs, scripting, directing, and ultimately helping lead the design of the overall event. Since then, I have been part of some fantastic teams and worked with the best people. At last count, I had a role in the design of over 75 traditional haunted mazes, 45 street experiences, and over 25 Halloween-themed shows. What is my process? I never lose sight of that fear that I felt back when I was about to enter my first haunted house. I remember the fun of scaring people from Nightmare Trail. I hold every design that I have ever been a part of up to the Terror on Church Street test. What is the story I am telling? What do I need you to know to let your mind start to work?

So, whether you want to design haunted mazes or Halloween experiences, or you are just a fan of being part of the terror, I hope you enjoy this book. Most of the people within these pages have been responsible for nightmares. Others are the future of the scare.

J. Michael Roddy

MEET OUR GHOULISH GALLERY

HORRORHOUND

The Many Masks of Maximillion Maximus

BY MICHAEL AIELLO

There once was a boy named Max,
Who had a love for making scary masks.
Ghosts and goblins and monsters galore,
Filled the walls of his room with space for many more.

His first was a monster made from man,
The eyes different colors, one blue, one tan.
Stitches around the skull with bolts on either side,
Skin a greenish hue covered in scars, cracked and dried.

Next, a man tuned wolf, his teeth pointy and sharp,
A soul cursed by moonlight though inside, he was pure of heart.
His howl echoed with force through the forest and the trees,
When Max wore this mask, the fur sometimes made him sneeze.

Max made vampires, zombies, and aliens from an outer world,
Hockey masked maniacs, leather-gloved madmen with knife fingers unfurled.
These creatures of the night filled him with unbridled joy,
His work was his play, never making Max a dull boy.

So many masks all shapes and all sizes,
His collection grew and grew, a family of homemade disguises.
His creations each with their own story, their own unique surprise,
They made him feel happy; they made him feel "ALIVE"!!

A love for all things Halloween and bringing monsters to life,
A hobby that's a home for things that go bump in the night.
For horror is his love from dawn till long past dusk,
Surrounded by his art, the many masks of Maximillion Maximus.

a few words from

MICHAEL AIELLO

As a designer of horror theatre or experiences, explain your process.

The process for me always begins with "what's been done? What hasn't and what would I like to see, experience and be surrounded by." I start as a fan of horror first because that's truly what I am. Whole-heartedly!

When is the last time you were genuinely scared by something someone created?

Re-watching *The Mist*. Any horror that plays itself out within locations and environments that are common to daily life: Neighborhoods, small towns. These places of perceived safety and comfort that can instantly turn dark, really get me. I think it's why I love Carpenter's *Halloween* so much. That neighborhood could be mine. It terrifies me.

Tell us about your contribution to our book. What was the inspiration?

Most of my horror projects revolve around an older audience enjoying it. So, creating something that a young child could enjoy intrigues me. The inspiration for this was reading about Rick Baker at a young age, creating masks in his childhood home.

What do you love about the genre of horror?

I love the diversity for story within the genre. It's full of seemingly endless subgenres to create within.

What is some of your favorite horror literature? Favorite Author?

Stephen King would be to top of list. I have a pretty extensive hardback collection of his. I also absolutely love collecting horror film paperback novelizations from the 80's.

What are some of your influences?

Horror films of the 1980's. I love horror comic books and novels. But overall, I'm a massive film score enthusiast. Scores of all kinds. I listen to film score playlists almost constantly. These compositions inspire and fuel my creativity.

What is your favorite Halloween treat?

Reese's Pieces – hands down my favorite!

You are hosting the perfect Halloween movie marathon. What are the films you choose and why?

Halloween. The Fog. The Thing. A Carpenter Trinity – these are my comfort food films. I've seen them more times than I can count and I never tire of them.

If you could continue any horror story (book or film), what would it be?

I love the ending to *The Thing* but I've always wanted to know what happened to MacReady and Childs. I actually had the opportunity to continue a "spiritual sequel" in the narrative of a horror maze a wrote and directed for Halloween Horror Nights!

Describe the perfect Halloween.

Horror Movie marathon bookended with horror soundtracks all day. Candles lit all around with a fog machine slowing hazing the interior of the house. Pumpkin beer!

SCARE CRED: MICHAEL AIELLO

Michael Aiello is the Senior Director - Creative - Live Entertainment for Universal Creative. Michael is passionate about creating live horror-based attractions. Since 2003, Michael has played a major creative role in in Universal Orlando's annual event, Halloween Horror Nights. Michael has successfully partnered with New Line Cinema to co-create content based on *A Nightmare on Elm Street, Friday the 13th* and *The Texas Chainsaw Massacre* as well as Lionsgate to create attractions based on the *Saw* franchise. Michael also collaborated with Executive Producer Greg Nicotero and lead the creative content for mazes based on AMC's *The Walking Dead.* He has partnered and lead creative with Warner Bros. on attractions based on the *The Exorcist* and Stanley Kubrick's *The Shining.* Michael has collaborated with Netflix and creators, The Duffer Brothers, on two successful live attraction adaptations of *Stranger Things.* Most recently Michael and his team created attractions based on Sony's *Ghostbusters.*

CURSE by the SEA

BY BRIAN ANGELOFF

A curse so malevolent
Found itself prevalent
Nestled in an old town by the sea
Even the bravest of skeptics
Eventually flee
That is if this place
lets them leave
And then never again
to be seen

Some say the dogs have gone rabid
And roam free
While the waves carry demons
Unlocked from the deep
The things that once were rise again
With evil intentions they will wreak

Nobody knows why something
so wretched is unleashed
Please head my warning
There is a terrible curse on this town by the sea

This first unfortunate tale is about a happily
married couple the Vandreets
They built a house and restaurant
on the edge of the sea
The two became pretty successful and rich
By catching and cooking crustaceans and fish
Each year got better
Leading a life that others could only wish

Like something from a fairy tale
But in this town evil always prevails

Melena Vandreets walked down the old doc
To see her husband before he sailed off
Without warning the wooden boards
creaked and rocked
She quickly fell to the shallows
with a splash and a crack
Landing on sharp oyster beds
and breaking her back

This town can be truly cruel and unfair
Due to the accident
She would live a short life Confined to a chair

Days turned to weeks as she lifelessly sat
Watching the outside world through the window
What kind of life is that
Mr Vandreets did everything to help her
He went the extra mile
But still she did nothing for months
And never did smile

He couldn't help take care of her and the restaurant
There just wasn't enough time
Customers stopped coming
They weren't earning a dime
The house was a mess
The dishes piled up

She did nothing to help him
The place started to smell
And became infested with bugs
One strange day he almost snapped and gave up
The door happened to be ajar
And in walked a pup
Mrs. vandreet's mouth formed a smile
With tears in her eyes she let out a laugh
As it walked right to her feet
while its little tail wagged
What a cute and fluffy black lab
She bent down and snatched him up onto her lap

She looked at her husband with a warm smile
She finally seemed to glow
He gave her a nod
How could he possibly say no

No longer worried
Off to work he could go
So he gathered the gear and sailed off in the boat

The Day turned out great as the fish took the bait
He through out the nets
And the crab traps were set
Finally he was relaxed
as the boat rocked in the waves

He didn't mean to sail out so far
And with a blink of an eye
The day turned to dark
With the boat full of fish he began the way home
Now a bit worried
He didn't want to leave his wife so long home alone

He stopped at the diner to put the fish on ice
Then walked home expecting some grief
Since it was well after nine
But came home to find his wife and the puppy
With another canine
This new yellow lab stood right by her side
The dog was startled and angry
That he walked inside
It seemed to protect her
By growling and revealing its teeth
Mr Vandreets was now frightened
And backed up a few feet

His wife gently commanded it to cease an attack
It instantly stopped
And its tail started to wag
it walked up to his hand and gave a sniff
It approved of this man and gave him a lick

Puzzled and distraught he looked at his wife
Again she had that look in her eyes
He looked around the room
To his surprise had been cleaned
Even dishes put away
Again how could he say no
That night he did not get any grief
Tomorrow morning he could happily sail away

Weeks passed and Mrs Vandreets gained
more furry pets
While Mr Vandreets began to feel some regrets
For he was the only one trying to reopen the diner
for paying guests
But her desire for helping became much less
Her attentions were focused
on rescuing more hairy pests

It seemed to him he no longer exists
He was tired of the shedding hair
And tired of stepping in shit
The two now constantly argued
Every day he would wake up pissed

Weeks turned to months
and her mutt collection grew
He had to sleep next door
Every night is full of barking
He couldn't take much more
His eyes constantly watered
Every ten minutes a sneeze
The property now was infested with fleas

Every night his anger grew worse
He took to the bottle -
feeding into this nightmarish curse
Now he was in misery while she was happy
That thought made him laugh
This was the night he finally snapped

Off he went into the town
A diabolical plan was now in his mind
He came back to the house now
with cages and twine
He stole sleeping pills from his wife
And fed the canines

Successfully the dogs were drugged and out cold
He put them in cages
Then quietly loaded them into the boat
They didn't bark or howl
Not even a peep
The water level now was perfectly deep

One by one he tossed them overboard
With a splash
Each dog in a crate would make the best crab trap
He grabbed the last cage
But the little pup was awake
It let out a wine as he threw it into the waves
He let out a howl and maniacally laughed
Now to go home
To finish yet another fiendish act

He drove the boat up the shore
Then snuck his way into the house
and up to the bedroom
Ever so quietly he cracked open the door
His wife was out cold and loudly she snored
Time to take care of her at last
She could not be awaken from the drugs
He dissolved in her glass

He carefully lifted her off the bed and into the chair
Then he gently tied her to the seat with sinister care
He pushed her out of the house and onto the boat
Her fate now inevitable there wasn't much hope
The two of them sailed off into the night
This was the last time he saw his wife
At least when she was still alive

One year had passed since his evil deed
The diner reopened and the house had been cleaned
Out of towners stopped by for a good bite to eat
The house was also open to them
For a good nights sleep

Vandreets property now had a gate
Yet somehow couldn't keep out the strays

They would show up by 2s and 3s
throughout the day
Then sit by the water
And into the horizon they'd gaze
It seemed they were taunting Vandreets
For what he had done
He'd run inside to grab his gun
By the time he ran out
They had already run

As for poor Melena under the water
she would dwell
Her flesh never rotted but began forming a shell
Seaweed and algae began to branch out
from her gown
As if searching for her beloved pets
that had drowned
Mrs Vandreets was no longer herself
Now she had taken form of a giant clamshell
The wheels of her chair stuck out of its sides
And was covered in sharp barnacles
And sea urchin spikes

From the bottom of this mysterious mollusk
Branched out tendrils of
seaweed, kelp, and old chains
That reached out attaching to her once alive pets
Algae and eels intertwined through their remains
As if now reigns to pull this nightmarish slay

Meanwhile at the diner
Vandreets was getting prepped
For the mayor was planning
A special dinner event
The pressure was on him

To impress very important guests
For Vandreets it would be a life changing day
They were in talks to tear apart the town
And build
Which meant more patrons
And a place to stay

All was so exciting and distracting
That he didn't realize today's special date
The anniversary of his wife
Of late

He gathered pots and pans
Then collected spoons and forks
When a noise came from behind him
A pitter-patter of something on the floor
Frustrated he threw the supplies down
He turned around to look
Startled to see two German shepherds
That stared him down and howled

He slowly backed out of the kitchen door
But in the other room
He saw a bunch more
Stray dogs of all kinds
Filled the dining hall
They all started to growl
As he scooted against the wall
There was nowhere to go
He couldn't run
They blocked the room
Where he kept the gun
They quickly reminded him
Of the evil things he done

They yet did not attack
But he feared for his life
And they seemed to make a path
For him to follow outside
Eerily the hounds followed each step
Until he got to the beach
Where the water and his feet met

All the dogs howled
And lifted their heads high
As dark clouds began to fill up the sky
He covered his ears and fell to his knees
Then large bubbles began to erupt
From out of the sea

One by one the dogs he killed
Emerged from the waves
Their rotted corpses tied to one another
Pulling up something connected by chains
The strange giant shelled carriage pulled up
Onto the shore
And the wheels dragged into the sand
This couldn't be happening
He did not understand

The huge shell opened
Revealing large jagged teeth
Emerging from its mantle
Was its slimy tongue
Which was not a tongue at all
It appeared to be Melena Vandreets
Her flesh, shell and gown now fused as one
She was slimy and pale
And her eye sockets were covered
By fleshy grey veil

In pure terror Mr Vandreets tried to scream
But from Melena every tentacle
And crustaceas appendage from the sea
Lashed out and reached
Pulling him up
Right off his feet

She dragged him up for a closer look
Tears began to fill his eyes
And her skeletal mouth
Formed a sinister a smile
He cried out loud
And before he could mutter the words
He was sorry
The clamshell snapped shut
Severing his head from the body

The sand was now littered with his blood
And remains
As the skeletal dogs pulled her back
Into the waves

A few years have passed now
And no progress was made
On this town
All fear the woman
In the giant clamshell
You do any wrong
She'll drag you to hell

She is a protector of nature
Her land
Her waters
Her world
She awaits at the sea floor
With she skull of her once beloved
That now shines like a pearl

a few words from

BRIAN ANGELOFF

As a designer of horror theatre or experiences, explain your process.

I find that music is a key factor in my process. Not so much the style or lyrics, but the sounds in general get the wheels turning. Then I visualize a concept, or image, and begin to sculpt, digitally or by hand, or type. Sometimes the creation itself is not enough. I got the creature in 3d space, or clay, or whatever it may be, so now I want to know more. Where does it come from, why does it exist, what does it like/ dislike and so on… So now this thing has to move, so I will 3d animate it now, or start to build the world around it. Sometimes there is no rhyme or reason till later on in the process.

When is the last time you were genuinely scared by something someone created?

Two films that terrified me as a kid was the original *Pet Sematary*, and, *The Changeling*. Those flicks kept me up for many nights.

Tell us about your contribution to our book. What was the inspiration?

I went on a scalloping trip with some family. We kept hearing dogs barking and occasionally would see a couple of dogs patrolling the old rickety peer. It was kind of eerie the way they walked side by side in unison. Then while diving under the water, I would see old crab traps, and I thought some looked like dog crates, so I strangely started to piece that strange story together. The ocean has always been my muse.

What do you love about the genre of horror?

I mainly loved monsters more than anything. The unknown mystery of why something so hideous could exist to terrorize us other than the predictable human function was always enthralling to me. There is a thrill of being scared, especially as a kid, and trying to reason with that fear is amazing.

What is some of your favorite horror literature? Favorite Author?

I am obsessed with anything Clive Barker.

What are some of your influences?

My dad was just as much of a horror nut as I was. He would draw monsters, and have me watch B-Monster movies with him all the time. We would always talk about what monster battle or team up would be the best. I also have found Clive Barker was a huge inspiration. I realized I was a lot like him as far as creating went.

What is your favorite Halloween treat?

My favorite Halloween candies are Reese's pumpkin peanut butter cups, and Universal Monster Candy, which are hard to find now.

You are hosting the perfect Halloween movie marathon. What are the films you choose and why?

Nightmare on Elm Street - Freddy was actually scary, and was a slasher game changer.

Creepshow - Every Halloween needs a horror anthology, and I don't think anything could beat *Creepshow.*

Jeepers Creepers - Old school campfire kind of tale.

Pumpkinhead- Great monster movie.

The Thing - Indescribable body horror monster. They don't make monsters like that any more!

If you could continue any horror story (Book or Film), what would it be?

I would love to take a crack at continuing the *Hellraise*r movies, but not making the same mistakes after the 2nd film. There are so many different cenobites and worlds around them to play with. Pinhead and the gang are great, but there are some exquisitely crazy forms of cenobites.

Describe the perfect Halloween.

Decorating the yard, and some scary music, not cheesy music, something to actually scare, "thriller gets very old" and Michael Jackson is for real scary. Good old-fashion horror movies tying into some new good modern films. All good friends, and family are dressed in a costume. Living in a neighborhood with a lot of trick-or-treaters. Pretending you are one of the decorations in the yard and scaring people, mainly adults. Then of course, visiting multiple haunted houses, and attractions.

SCARE CRED: BRIAN ANGELOFF

Brian Angeloff was born and raised in Stow Ohio , and since he can remember has been intrigued with all things horror. His childhood books, were Fangoria magazines, and Famous Monsters of Filmland, that his dad collected. His whole family were obsessed with Halloween. They supported his love for all things horror, and would do a crazy Halloween display in the yard putting them in the newspaper multiple times. He always could create, draw ,sculpt, and found his way getting paid to airbrush shirts, and skate boards while in High school. In 1999 he moved to Orlando Florida where he got into special effects make-up, making props, scenic work, film, theatre, theme parks, and also has done digital fine art photography for multiple resorts, hospitals and local homes. Brian currently lives in Maitland, Florida with his wife Joy, dog Rocco, and saltwater reef tank. He now is a 3d Z-Brush artist, and creates all sorts of fun collectables from his wild imagination to sell at multiple stores and conventions. Occasionally he will dabble in writing.

FACE REALITY

BY KENNY BABEL

Robin stared into his pupils in the bathroom mirror; his face frustratingly unrecognizable as it had been his whole life. This wasn't the face he saw in his mind's eye that represented "Robin". The nose was too broad and flat. His eyes too far apart. The face looked to him like a ram's face, his eyes slightly pointing in opposite directions. His full lips slightly pursed with annoyance.

He raised the razor blade to the twitching flesh under his left eye. Maybe his real face is underneath this one. Maybe the fasteners beneath were loosening, causing this false flesh to tremble and jerk. The eyes had open edges. That's where the mask would fray first.

He pulled the skin of his eyelid down with his free hand looking for the his real face. He couldn't see where it attached. He couldn't tell for certain. But he knew. He knew.

He slid the razor blade vertically down the outstretched lid splitting it in half past the orbit of his eye and down to his cheek in one swift stroke.

*

"Holy shit, Robin, what happened to your eye?" Marta asked, reaching up to touch the white gauze covering half of Robin's face. He flinched back instinctively away from her touch. "Oh, sorry. I just... damn," she stammered pulling her hand back.

"Sunglasses incident," he muttered, "No big deal; it's just the skin of the eyelid. It didn't hurt my eye."

"That's lucky as fuck," she said. She kissed her hand and mimed placing it on Robin's face from a distance. "Are you sure you should be at work?"

"Where else would I go?" Robin replied drily, "I can still see well enough to work on my computer."

"Your eyelid, though, shit. And with this crappy job I would call in for anything that would give me a doctor's note." Marta laughed her boyish laugh. That was one of the things that Robin really liked about Marta. Her laugh was open and fun-loving and honest, like she didn't care about how it sounded or what social signal it was sending, she was just enjoying life. "But I guess you have to pay for the doctor's bill with something, huh? Even with insurance, a trip to the ER is five hundred dollars. Fuckers."

"That's definitely true," Robin sighed. "That was one thing I didn't consider before all this," he gestured up to his face.

"You probably didn't have time to consider with your sunglasses breaking and shredding your eyelid. It's not like you ever plan to go to the ER. No one ever does."

Robin looked at his desk avoiding her eyes. "I just should have, though."

Marta laughed again. "Don't be silly. Did you get stitches?"

"Yes," Robin set his bag down.

"Well you can't stitch your own eyelid. Not unless you're Chuck Norris or some shit." Marta walked over and put her hand on Robin's shoulder. "Now you listen, if it starts to burn or get blurry or catch on fire and explode or something, you need to take a break or go home or something. If Rick says anything I've got your back. Just the fact that you are trying to work through it all shows how much you care for this shit hole. And if you need to change your bandage at any time during the day let me know. I won't help you, but I want to see," she smiled. "I'll bet your scar will make you look roguish."

Marta walked across to her cubicle and set her bag down. She slipped into her chair with ease and put on her headset making a neat little dent in her curly black hair. Immediately she relaxed into her chair, and wiggled her mouse. The computer screen flashed to life and bathed her in blue.

Marta was the closest thing Robin had to a real friend. He had never felt comfortable in his own skin, but Marta had an easy, accepting nature that made it feel like it didn't really matter. It was almost like she could see the Robin that was supposed to be there, not this face, this body. If she couldn't see it, maybe she could feel it. He looked at her as she made her first call on the headset, her lips a breath away from the mouthpiece.

"What happened to you?"

Robin startled and nearly knocked his bag from the desk. He turned to see Rick, his boss, standing over him, amusement on his slightly balding brow. "You okay?" Rick asked.

"Yes, yes, I'm fine. You just startled me," Robin stammered.

"No, I mean your face. All this." Rick gestured to the bandages on Robin's face causing him to flinch again.

"It's nothing. Sunglasses accident," Robin forced a chuckle.

"Sunglasses accident. Really? Only you, man, only you. Maybe it'll be an improvement," Rick smiled mockingly, and lightly tapped Robin's shoulder with a rolled up memo.

"I was hoping," Robin said seriously.

"Just kidding, bro. I hope it heals well. If you're going to be here, I expect a full days work, even still."

"I wouldn't expect you to expect any less," Robin said, raising his right hand to his bandage. His stitches were starting to burn a little, probably from just talking about them.

Rick laughed a short, polite laugh, "Funny. True, though. If you need to go home, clock out and go home so I can bring someone in who isn't a cyclops."

"Understood," Robin said, touching his cheek, feeling the face he wore and the space where the tape meets the other's flesh.

As Rick walked past him towards the back office, Robin looked over to see Marta performing an elaborate masturbation gesture like she was stroking a huge dick while pointing to Rick, all while saying, "We are offering lower interest rates on a consolidated credit account to help you get out of debt quickly..."

The beginning of the day went by fairly quickly. There were only several moments when Robin wanted to tear off his bandage and cut off his face with his desk scissors. Fewer moments than he usually had before the bandage. He thought to himself that this may be a good thing.

He changed his bandage at lunch in the men's room. As he came out Marta looked at him disappointedly. "Aw, really Robin? Where's the love?" She gestured up to his eye.

"I didn't think you were serious. Were you serious?"

Marta gave him a total deadpan stare, her big brown eyes serious as death. "I needed the mirror," Robin apologized.

"Whatever, Robin. I see how it is," she teased, throwing her spork into her Tupperware dish. "You know I love that stuff. I told you I love that show where that lady cuts out everybody's zits and shit."

"Yeah, I remember. I'm sorry. I just needed the mirror and..." Robin stopped. He reached up to the corner of the medical tape above his eyebrow. "Wait, I can just peel this here and pull it down a little." He started to pick up an edge of the tape with his fingernail.

"No wait. I'll do it," Marta said as she hopped up from her microwave lasagna and reached up for Robin's face.

Robin pulled back. "Stop, stop, let me..." his voice trailed off as he felt her cool hands take his hands and gently lower them from his face.

"I've got this," she said confidently, taking Robin by the shoulders and sitting him in the chair at the break room table. She moved in close and picked two or three hairs out of the tape that Robin had managed to trap under the bandage. She was so close that he could smell the sweet garlic on her breath.

"You cleaned your hands, right?" Robin asked cautiously as Marta picked at the tape.

"Shut up and hold still."

Robin felt an electric surge across his skin at her touch, almost like an invisible force field dissolving, retreating at her fingers' insistence. He felt almost sure she could see him now as he really was. The real him. He felt his mask dissolve. He felt his body rise with excitement. He felt free. Like Marta had done it, had revealed him.

"Oh my God..." Marta sounded breathless.

"W-What is it?" Robin stammered, "What do you see? How do I look?" He had never seen his face with his own eyes, but if she described it to him he knew he would recognize it through her.

"How did this happen, Robin?" Marta whispered.

"You did this, Marta. How do I look? Marta?"

"Not the bandage, Robin, your eyelid. How did the accident happen?"

"Sunglasses. Sunglasses broke." As he lied he felt the other face materialize again. He could see Marta looking at him with more scrutiny as his mask reappeared.

"This cut is straight and clean, Robin. Broken glasses did this? Made a cut this fine?" Marta looked at him calmly but searchingly in both his eyes now, her eyes flicking back and forth between them.

"Yes. Yes," he lied. Marta's face became distant as she weighed his words.

"Okay," she said, "That's just so weird." She brushed Robin's hair from his forehead and began to reattach the tape to his skin. "You are seriously lucky this wasn't much worse."

"I know. I know. Totally. Super lucky." Robin agreed with a mixture of relief and worry. Had she seen him? Really? Did she know she saw? What did he look like? Did she not trust him now since she saw his change?

"We better get back to it before Rick notices people have lives and shit," Marta said moving back to her spot at the table and picking up her Tupperware to rinse it. "Thanks for letting me see," she said and smiled. Robin looked at her a long moment as she turned to the sink. What did she mean?

The rest of the day went by uneventfully. The drama of the bandage had been addressed and played through and all was back to the usual rhythm of the office. Rick and Marta sniping at each other, the calls, the spreadsheets, the memos. As the day wrapped up Robin felt the mask firmly in place, but the memory of his true naked face being revealed, even ever so briefly, left a piece of him outside the mask, watching this false, hollow thing moving through the machinations of his job in his place.

Marta appeared beside him. "Hey Robin, how are you getting home?"

"I am going to drive," Robin replied, "I don't have much choice."

Marta frowned, "Robin, you can't drive with one eye; you've got no depth perception."

"Yeah, that's what the doctor told me."

"And you drove anyway?" Marta's brown eyes flashed.

"Yeah."

"What the hell, Robin? Don't you care about your life? Or the life of others on the road? Shit, I'm going to be on that road, too. Don't you care about my life?"

"Of course, I do, Marta."

"Then you aren't driving home, Robin. I'll take you home. And you can take a bus in to work tomorrow, or I'll pick you up again if I have to, but you can't drive. Pack up your shit."

Robin started to pack up his bag as Rick popped out of the office. He looked at Marta holding her purse and her bag. Rick frowned. "Marta, where are you going?"

"Home, after I drop Robin off at his place," Marta said pulling her keys from her bag.

"Home?" Rick said, "I thought you were sticking around here for a while to work on that thing." Rick looked from Marta to Robin and back.

"I was going to, but Robin is going to kill someone if he drives himself home so I'm going to drive him." Marta replied sounding slightly annoyed.

"Well," Rick said, "Can't he take a bus?"

"Rick, don't be an asshole," Marta shot.

"I'm just saying. You don't need to take him," Rick shifted uncomfortably.

Marta jangled the keys in her hand. "You wanna take him?"

"No, I just..."

"Then zip it," Marta said, "Then keep it zipped." She laughed at her comment as Rick blushed and responded curtly.

"Fine," he said, "Drive safe," and he shuffled back to his office.

"Come on," Marta said, "Let's go before he comes back out with some other idiot comment." Robin followed Marta out to the far side of the lot where the employees parked under the buzzing light. "Do you need anything out of your car?" she asked.

"No," Robin replied, " I've got it all in here." He lifted his bag. They walked out, Marta leading Robin quickly out the front door and into the parking lot. Darkness was falling fast already, the days had shortened, and the October evening was crisp and colorful with the last light fading in the west.

The lights on Marta's Toyota Corolla flashed as she unlocked the car with her fob. "Goddamn, it gets dark so fast already," she complained, "It makes me feel like all I do is work and sleep."

"That's all I do no matter when the sun sets," Robin said as he opened the passenger door.

"You need to get out more. " Marta slid into the driver's seat and started moving a pile of mail and food containers off of the passenger seat. "Sorry," she said, "I eat when I drive. You need a girlfriend."

"Do you have one?" Robin said, and he kicked a monstrous fountain soda cup out of the way.

"A girlfriend?" Marta laughed her boyish laugh.

"I don't know, maybe," Robin chuckled, "but, you know, someone."

"Well, kind of," Marta said starting the car. She looked back toward the office before checking her mirrors and backing out of her space. "And kind of not really." She hit the gas and crunched her tires over the new fallen leaves, pulling up to the street, and pausing to look at Robin. Robin didn't see her because his bandage was on his left eye.

"Robin. Which way?"

Robin turned to her. "I'm up off of University in the Brooks Crossings."

"Behind the Publix?" Marta put her blinker on and turned right uncomfortably close to a fast coming Dodge Ram. He flashed his high beams at her. "Dick," she muttered.

"Yeah," Robin said. "You were saying?"

"What was I saying?" Marta replied.

"Your kind of significant other," Robin said.

"Yeah. I don't know. I don't know what the fuck I'm doing." "Or who you're doing?" Robin quipped.

Marta laughed, "No, that I know. And so do you."

"Is it Rick?" Robin said, turning his head to really catch her reaction with his right eye.

Marta's smile disappeared for a brief second, and then it returned, but dimmer, like a ghost of itself. "How long have you known?" she asked, sounding disappointed.

"I didn't. Until just now. And he seemed weird when we left."

"Yeah. He's weird," Marta eyed the road as it curved, the reflections of the headlights of the oncoming traffic casting moving reflections on her face. "He gets jealous easily even though he is married, and I'm not. Don't judge me." She glanced at Robin.

"I wasn't. You're a grown up. You can do what you want."

"It's not really what I want. There's just nothing else going on." Her eyes narrowed a little as she slowed to a traffic signal, bathing her in red light. "Do you think I am a horrible human?" She asked, looking sincerely at Robin, searching his face. Robin's expression was blank.

"Human?" He teased, "Not at all. A succubus maybe."

She turned and slapped his arm.

"Ow!" Robin laughed, "Succubus attack!"

Marta laughed, too, hitting him a second time, "I don't even know what a succubus is, but I know you're being an ass end." She hit him again and then took his hand. "Jerk."

"Marta, I don't think you're a horrible human. I think you're pretty damn awesome," Robin said, feeling his face glow again.

"I do, too," she said and smiled. They drove on quietly for a minute that seemed like an hour. Marta broke the silence. "Sometimes, though..."

"Brooks Crossings," Robin interrupted, pointing to the sign that led into the apartment complex. "Turn right at the stop sign. Third building on the left."

"Gotcha," Marta said, turning the wheel, and pulling up past the first two buildings to the spots marked "Visitor Parking".

Marta turned to Robin, "Robin, can I ask you something?"

"Of course," Robin said, gathering the strap on his bag, one hand on the door handle.

"Do you ever look at yourself and wonder who the hell you really are? Do you ever feel like you don't even recognize who yourself anymore?"

Robin's blood ran cold in his veins. What did she know? She had seen. She must have seen. But she didn't seem scared at all. Robin realized he was holding his breath. He blinked. "We should talk," Robin said, "Inside."

Marta pushed a black curl behind her ear, "You know, Robin, I really could use a good long talk right now. Maybe we can help each other. I see you, you know. How different you are. You know you can tell me anything, and I won't judge you, right."

Robin looked at her, not blinking, with his one eye. Was this really happening? She had made the mask disappear before. Maybe she could free him from it for good. It was almost too much to hope for. He pulled the car door handle and the interior lights in the car sprang to life.

She exited the driver's side and stepped into night, the sun now having hidden its head beneath the blanket of October darkness.

"My apartment is this way." Robin lead Marta up the stairs to the door of 3811 and stuck his key in the lock, opening the door to his tidy apartment. He turned on the lights and hung his keys on the hook by the door. "Come on in," he said, gesturing to the couch.

Marta looked around. The place was neat and orderly. It almost looked like an Ikea show room. "Nice place. I knew it would be neat. Your kind always are."

"My kind?" Robin asked.

"Yeah, you know." Marta sat on the couch. "Your kind. Good with design and stuff."

"Marta, what do you know? What have you seen?" Robin sat down next to her with such an earnest look on his face it almost made Marta tear up.

"Robin, you know. And it's okay. It's totally cool. It's actually kind of a nice difference to all the other guys in the office."

"You've seen this?" Robin asked. His intense look kind of set Marta ill at ease. "It's okay, Robin. It really is. It's the twenty-first century, you know?"

"But you've seen..." Robin intoned very meaningfully.

"I just know, you know. I mean I sit across from you every day. How could I not have

seen?"

Robin seemed to squirm with agitation. "What did it look like, Marta? What you've seen?" Robin placed his hand on Marta's upper arm, holding it in a tight grip.

"Robin," Marta asked evenly, "Can you let me go, please?"

"What?" He answered.

"Can you let me go? Please? I have to go to the bathroom."

Robin blinked repeatedly as if coming out of a trance, then let go of Marta's arm. "Bathroom. Down the hall to the left."

"Thanks," Marta said, feeling a burning on her arm where Robin had just released her. She stood and headed quickly down the hall, stepped into the bathroom, and shut the door. She quickly headed to the sink, lifted her sleeve, and looked in the mirror. A bruise was already rising from where Robin had gripped her. "The fuck..." she muttered to herself as she eyed the darkening skin. She heard footsteps coming up the hallway and quickly reached over and locked the door. The footsteps stopped outside. She could see the shadow of Robin's feet beneath the door.

"Hey man, don't listen to me pee. That's just sick." She laughed loudly.

Outside the door, Robin noticed that her laugh had changed. Something was wrong.

Marta saw the door handle twitch as though someone were trying gently to test the lock.

"Almost done," Marta said loudly, seriously regretting that she had left her cell phone with her purse in the living room in her haste to gain space. She reached over and spun the toilet paper roll, tearing off a piece to make it sound as though she were actually using the toilet. She wadded it up and made to toss it into the trash can next to the toilet when she noticed the can was full of blood-soaked tissues. "Jesus," she hissed to herself.

She went to flush the toilet, but jerked her hand back. The handle was sticky. Disgusted she pulled back her fingers to see mostly dried blood on the toilet handle. She pulled another piece of toilet paper and used it to flush the toilet, then moved quickly to wash the blood from her hand at the sink. She turned on the hot water and grabbed the bar of soap near the basin. But as she began scrubbing her hand she felt a sharp pain on her left palm.

"Shit fuck, motherfucker!" She exclaimed as she dropped the bar of soap into the sink basin. Reaching into the sink Marta pulled out a shiny silver razor blade that had been stuck to the bottom of the soap. Someone must have set the soap on top of it, and it had stuck together. Marta heard the footsteps fade back toward the living room, then heard Robin call to her.

"Everything okay?" Came the voice that almost didn't sound like her friend from the office.

"Yeah. Yeah," she replied, "I just dropped the soap here. Sorry." She tore another footlong strip of toilet paper and applied pressure to where the razor blade had cut her. What the fuck was going on? Robin. Nice Robin. The razor blade. The blood-soaked tissues. Had he? Could he have possibly cut his own fucking eyelid? Could it have been an accident? Definitely not a sunglasses accident. Marta wrapped the razor blade in another wad of toilet paper and put it in her pocket, then continued putting pressure on the cut. It wasn't deep, but it hurt like hell.

Marta decided she would make her apologies, tell Robin she had left something at the office, remind him that Rick knew she was coming here, and then leave. She would deal with all this tomorrow, at the office, where she could talk to Robin with more people around. She didn't know exactly why, but she was feeling very vulnerable and unsafe. She would get her purse and go.

"Get the hell out," she murmured to herself as she opened the door.

Only to come face to face with Robin standing directly in the doorway looking intensely at her.

"You know, don't you?" He stared. "You've seen."

"What? Robin, I was just peeing."

"My face. You saw it. You know." Robin's face screwed up with emotion and he let out a choked sob. He suddenly looked very frail and very alone. He dropped to his knees in front of her. Marta thought her best hope was to be sympathetic.

"Yes, yes, I saw your face, Robin. I know. I can help you, Robin. I can help find someone to help you."

"You can help me, yourself, Marta. You can tell me what you saw." Robin took Marta's hands in his pleadingly.

"I saw the blood, Robin. I saw the blood," Marta soothed.

"I saw the blood, Marta! What was underneath?" Robin snapped, "My face!"

"Robin, we need to get you a doctor..."

"No, no doctors. They don't believe me. They made the mask. They made it to hide my true face from me. You have seen, though. What did you see?" He gripped her more tightly again, imploring her, tears starting to pour from is eyes, staining his bandage with pink from the tears mixed with blood.

"What do you mean they made you a mask, Robin?" Marta was trying to be as gentle as possible, but the fear was rising in her again.

"This!" He gestured to his face. "This fucking, fucking..." he released one of her hands and began to scratch at his face, clawing off his bandage, revealing his stitches which were bleeding now from the strain.

"Robin, stop," Marta pleaded, "Robin, please! You're sick. And you're hurt, Robin, please...". She reached up with her free hand to stop him from clawing himself, but he shoved her roughly backward away from him. She went careening back into the bathroom, tripping and pulling the shower curtain down over her as she sprawled into bathtub.

"Marta, I have to take it off! I know I have to!" Robin began to slam his face into the door, creating huge tears in the skin on his forehead. Blood gushed from the open wounds and streamed down his face dropping in huge streams to the floor.

Marta screamed in terror, "Robin, please stop! Please, Jesus, stop, stop!"

Robin turned to her, eyes filled with blood and anguish, "You want to help them, don't you? You've seen, but you are helping them!" He stretched out his arms toward Marta and lurched toward the tub where she lay. Panicked, Marta reached in her pocket and pulled out the razor blade still wrapped in toilet paper. Robin reached down into the tub and grabbed her by the shoulders, blood pouring from his face into her eyes, her mouth, choking her as he stood over her.

With a swift stroke Marta brought the razor blade across Robin's face, opening his left cheek from his eye to his upper lip. Robin gurgled for a moment and then went completely still as blood poured from his face onto Marta's body. Marta's face went slack with horror as the cut on Robin's cheek spread open with a sickening sucking sound, like an obscene kiss, as the flesh parted, then gaped. Pushing through the cheek was long, pale, wormlike creature, almost translucent, that had its bald, mucus-covered head nestled in a hole in Robin's cheekbone like a moray eel in a coral reef. It had two dark circle patches beneath the skin, almost like eyes that seemed like endless pools of ebony. As Marta looked into one, transfixed, she saw tiny lights pulsing in the blackness.

Coming to her senses Marta brought the razor blade back up to slash the hideous grub, but Robin's arm shot out and knocked the blade from her hand. Then he grabbed her throat with his right arm as his left struggled to pin her right arm again. But Marta's left arm was still free, and as Robin choked her, she reached up into his open cheek and grabbed the worm by its head, pulling it forward. It came out about eight inches and stopped, like it was attached to something. Robin's hand tightened hard on her throat, choking the strength from her.

Marta was losing consciousness. She yanked harder on the creature, and its eyes flashed purple and green. From Robin's mouth came an eerie voice - Robin, but not Robin, "Marta, let us go, Marta..."

With her last ounce of strength, in a burst of revulsion and horror, Marta yanked at the creature one last time, and with a juicy tear and a pop, all sixteen inches of the pulsating, gelatinous worm sucked out of Robin's skull. Robin immediately released his grip, and his body fell to the bathroom floor, eyes vacant, as in a vegetative state. Marta fell back into the tub, colors bursting like fireworks in her eyes as she tried to maintain consciousness and suck in air. Something was moving beside her face, rattling the plastic shower curtain next to her, wriggling like a fish out of water. She turned her eyes to see the disgusting, mucus-covered worm flagellating in the tub, moving closer to her face, its black eyes flashing purple and yellow.

She opened her mouth to scream, but it never came out. Marta felt the fat, slick body of the worm force its way into her mouth. She tried to bite it, but it seemed to expand its thick trunk, forcing her jaws open. She tried to grab it with her hands, but its slimy girth made that impossible. She felt it slip deeper into her throat, pulsating its horrendous body, pushing it past her tongue. She felt it pause, then shudder the entire length of its body. Then the top of her mouth was on fire, burning like battery acid. She thrashed and flailed, but it would not stop. She felt its bulk slide up into her nasal cavity, behind her eyes. Lights danced in her vision, and she thought she could smell something burning.

*

Marta looked at herself in the mirror. She couldn't say exactly why, but she felt like she looked different, almost as though the face she saw in the mirror wasn't her real face at all. Her eye twitched annoyingly as she put on her mascara for the day.

a few words from

KENNY BABEL

As a designer of horror theatre or experiences, explain your process.

On many of my past projects, I have been given a list of assets to play with and asked to remix them into something familiar, but unique. The object quite often is to get the most bang for the least bucks. So, I look at the elements- the costumes, the sets, the props that we have available. Like choosing toys from a toy chest, I start mixing and matching, finding similarities and differences and creating the scenarios from there. Then I ask myself questions. Who is the audience, either directly or indirectly? If it's a house attraction, what role does the guest going through the house play? If it's a script or short story, which character or characters represent the audience in the story? Who is in danger? Who really shouldn't be there? Once I know this, the rest starts to write itself.

When is the last time you were genuinely scared by something someone created?

I'm a tough scare. I can be startled, but even that is a challenge. One thing that comes to mind that continually creeps me out is the little lady in white at the end of the Haunted Mansion ride. It's silly. Something about her really gets to me. I think it stems back to dreams I used to have where tiny statues, almost like those of the saints, were possessed and could walk and talk like diminutive people. They were incredibly fast and numerous- and malicious.

Tell us about your contribution to our book. What was the inspiration?

Mind controlling parasites like Ophiocordyceps, the zombie ant fungus, or the parasitic emerald wasp, Ampulex compressa, were my inspiration. These parasites control the minds and motor functions of their hosts. I started thinking that if this type of parasite could infect a human, how much would the human be aware of what was happening? What would it mentally do to a human as the identity of the parasite and the human merged? What kind of disconnect or negative mental effects might be exhibited?

What do you love about the genre of horror?

Horror is primal. It's a reflex action. The quickening of the pulse. The rapidity of the breath. The tension. The release. People have such varying responses to horror. Some laugh. Some scream. Some cry. Some hide. Some hit. But they all feel that release afterwards, that rush of endorphins that follows a good scare. It's one of those things we experience in the moment and on an animal level. I think that is why so many people associate horror with sexuality. These are experiences where the social veneer drops, and we respond in real time.

What are some of your influences?

My brothers will always be my greatest influences. We would read horror stories from an old, red, cloth-bound book my mother owned when she was a child, and we would scare each other sleepless. We would create our own horror legends of the town and folks we grew up around. We would watch the old Universal horror films which had an enormous impact on me. The love of these movies led to the literature they were based on. The appreciation of them led to the horror community- *Famous Monsters*, *Fangoria*, *Creepy*.

Describe the perfect Halloween.

First, it needs to be cold. Autumn cold, not winter cold. In the forties and fifties on the Fahrenheit scale is good for me. Cold enough that I don't have to wear a jacket, but if I want to I'm not going to sweat to death. The day should be filled with cold air and warm sun. The day starts with a picnic in a graveyard with a bottle of wine, walking among the stones, reading the names and dates, the epitaphs, seeing the photos, flowers, and gifts left by loved ones. I like to contemplate the nature of the turning of the wheel of life. Halloween is New Year's to me. I look at the world as the ancient Celts did. The dark time of the year is like the time we spend in the womb before birth, or the time the seed spends in the soil before it breaks through. Life begins in darkness so I like to think of the fertile earth and feel the connection to those who came before. When the Trick-or-Treating begins in the neighborhood I want to see everyone. I love people. It's great to see how their personalities are reflected in their choices of costumes and in how they address the candy bowl. But as the evening turns to night and the porch lights go out, I want to spend time with my loved one, reading scary stories to each other and snuggling.

SCARE CRED: KENNY BABEL

Kenny Babel is an actor / writer who lives and works in the Central Florida area. Kenny gained a love of horror stories at an early age from his brothers, especially his brother John. He and his brothers made up their own tales of horror based on the classic horror films of Universal and Hammer. After being thoroughly terrified by the PBS *Count Dracula*, he started reading the classic horror novels. In 1991, Kenny found himself working in Entertainment for Universal Studios Florida. In 1992, he worked in his first professional haunted house, *The People Under the Stairs*, in a full gimp suit, chasing guests with a sawed-off shotgun as "Leather Daddy." He continued on in Halloween Horror Nights to portray such icons as Jack the Evil Clown. He went to work behind the scenes as performance captain, writer, creator, and director with the Art & Design Team. He co-wrote *Bill and Ted's Excellent Halloween Adventure* with Michael Aiello for nine years, as well as scripts for live entertainment, on-line content, in-house video, and radio content.

MRS. MACABRE

BY AUSTIN BOUSE

Chapter 1

The Raven and The Cat

It was past midnight when the raven and the cat materialized from the dark. Materialized is the correct term, for if you had been outside at such a late hour or had peeked from your window, you would've seen the animals emerge from the darkness as if it were a curtain. Their black feathers and fur glistening in the street lamps. You would have also noticed how odd the pairing was. The raven was not flying from the cat, nor was the cat chasing after the raven. They were both moving as if they were on a stroll together, the raven hovering slightly above the cat.

Once they had exited from the night, they both stopped at the end of the street, with the raven landing next to the cat. They stood there for a moment, as if they were trying to figure out what to do next.

"So," the cat finally said to the raven, "we're here aren't we?"

"Patience, Elvira," the raven said to her companion. "We should wait first." The raven spoke with a voice that was deep, smooth, and confident. The voice of a woman who had done her fair share of waiting before.

"Wait for what?" Elvira said impatiently. She scratched her ear with her paw.

A bright light came from off to the side, a car was speeding right towards them. The raven flew with a caw and landed on the nearest light post. Elvira arched her back and hissed, her eyes filled with fear, the car honked, swerved, but hit her nonetheless.

"That," the raven said and flew down to her companion, her talons hitting the ground with a righteous click. The cat's body lay limp for a moment, then there were the sounds of small cracks as her bones reformed inside herself. She blinked and got up. "Can't believe you made me waste a life on one of those things," Elvira shook her head. "Why do they have such *ugly* machines here?"

"Because they don't have magic here, darling," she sighed, tenderly. "How many lives do you have left?"

"One," Elvia grumbled.

"Oh,"The raven paused, embarrassed by how flippant she had been. "Then we'll be more cautious from now on, won't we?" She looked down the street, left and then right. "Now, I believe the coast is clear."

The raven placed her wings in front of her and bowed her head into them. If you were to gaze once again from the window or the street, you would've been so shocked that you might have thought you were dreaming. Yes, two talking animals were alarming enough, but what was even more alarming was that the raven was growing. The bird grew o the height of an average adult, her wings wrapped around her body, her feathers swished as if hundreds of dresses were being unfurled together. The feet of the bird turned into heels with pointed toes. Her wings grew pale hands with black nails and her feathers became a black dress. The head of the bird had changed to a woman's with skin the color of paper and hair and lips as dark as the night sky. She wore a small hat that had a black feather sticking out of it with a veil that draped on the side of her face. In her hand, she held a broom. The transformation was complete and there, standing next to the cat on an ordinary street, was Mrs. Macabre.

"Show off," Elvira scoffed.

"Now, now, my dear," Mrs. Macabre smiled, "there are plenty of people who can turn into animals, but not too many animals who can talk."

"Let's just get this over with," the cat eyed her companion's broom. "You might want to change that. I don't believe people here are accustomed to walking with brooms down streets?"

Mrs. Macabre looked down at her broom. It was a beautifully ornate thing: Dirty blonde straw from the fear fields, a long black handle made of wood from a hemlock tree with symbols and hieroglyphics carved into it, a skull of a raven sat nicely at the top of it.

"Yes," she placed a hand to her chin, "yes, I do suppose you are right," there was a moment of silent contemplation, then she exclaimed, "I've got it!"

Mrs. Macabre stood next to her broom and began to twirl it with two fingers. It quickly took a life of its own and began to spin without her assistance. As it spun, the broom slowly changed, it's straw disappeared and was replaced by large bat wings. The broom stopped spinning and it became apparent that there wasn't any bat wings at all, but the canopy of a black umbrella.

"Better?" She asked.

"I believe so," Elvira said, walking forward. "Now come on. If we don't get back home soon, we'll be stuck here till tomorrow night. You wouldn't want to stay in the sun now would you?

Mrs. Macabre shuddered at the thought. Where she and Elvira came from, they were never bothered by the cruel heat of an unforgiving sun. The closest their world came to daylight was a dreary overcast.

As they walked down the neighborhood street, Mrs. Macabre's heels clacked against the asphalt like talons. She had hoped that the sound would not disturb any of the residents from their slumber or a bad case of insomnia. Though she had visited this world countless times, she had never been pleased by how plain the houses were. They just sat there next to each other like perfect white squares in their perfectly manicured lawns, with their perfectly straight driveways. There were no jagged lines, dead flowers, or a hint of black to be found on any them. The houses didn't even *move*! How primitive. The only resemblance this world had to her own was the current darkness and a pleasant mist that hung faintly in the air. She smiled at how grim it felt .

"Do you see anything?" She asked the cat.

"Not particularly," Elvira said as they walked, staring at each house. "At least not what we're looking for."

"I hope no one sees us" Mrs. Macabre said, annoyed. "If we run into another girl scout, I swear to Hades-"

"Wait," Elvira stopped dead in her tracks.

"Yes?" Mrs. Macabre perked up a bit.

Elvira nodded to her. They both walked towards a house, the damp grass squeaking under their feet as they quietly grew closer. A loud bark came from behind the fence next to the house, making them stop.

"Dogs," Elvira hissed, hair standing up. "Why do so many of them have to have dogs?"

"Patience, my sweet," Mrs. Macabre reassured her, "they can be easily distracted." She tilted her umbrella up and a piece of straw grew out of the tip of it. She held it between two fingers, gazing at it intensely. The bit of straw slowly turned into a white bone. She threw it over the fence and the dog stopped barking, the thumping of its paws could be heard running across the yard.

"Thanks," Elvira sighed. "You're welcome," Mrs. Macabre smiled. "Where are they?"

"Up there," Elvira tilted her head towards the second floor of the house. Another black window stared back at them like all the rest.

"Ah, yes," Mrs. Macabre moved closer, almost to the front porch. "Come on up, then," she gestured her shoulder to Elvira. The cat hopped on and sat next to her head, with both her hands on the handle of the umbrella, Mrs. Macabre flew upwards.

They reached the window and hovered in front of it. From the glow of the moonlight, Mrs. Macabre could see two beds occupied by two girls who looked almost exactly alike. Their room was decorated with fake spider webs and bats, posters of *The Nightmare Before Christmas* and other spooky films hung here and there. A collection of horror books were placed neatly on a shelf in the corner.

"Oh, I like them very much, indeed," Mrs. Macabre whispered. "Do you think they require our assistance?"

Elvira's eyes glowed the color of glow-in-the-dark paint, and stared at the children. "They would do well back home," she said, distracted, as if she was looking for something.

Mrs. Macabre nodded in agreement.

"They are not liked by others," she continued. "But that's because they possess qualities that more. . . narrow minded folk do not see."

"Is that a yes?"

"It is," Elvira's eyes returned to their normal, darker green shade.

"Wonderful then let us- " she gasped.

"What is it?" Elvira asked, she squinted in the window and saw, the clock on their nightstand, glowing with the same green as her eyes had been just moments before: It was ten minutes till the hour was up.

"Blast!" Mrs. Macabre said, then quickly flew back down. Elvira jumped off and they went rushing off of the front lawn and into the street.

"I told you we should have left the manor earlier!. You're always so-" Elvira panted

"Oh, do shut up, darling," Mrs. Macabre said as her umbrella transformed into a broom again. They reached the black area from which they had entered.

Elvira had noticed her companion had stopped. "Well," she said impatiently, "come on, then!"

"You stay here," Mrs. Macabre said.

"What?" Elvira said, shocked.

"I need you to keep an eye on the children, dear," Mrs. Macabre said keeping her measured tone.

"Why?"

"Because we want to be certain that these are the *correct* children."

"But-"

"Would you care for me to jog your memory on what happened last time?" Mrs. Macabre's face was still as stone and her eyes were as sharp as knives. Elvira knew what that expression meant, she had seen it in her companion's darkest moments. It was an expression of utmost certainty.

"Yes," Elvira sighed. "You're right."

"Good kitty," Mrs. Macabre smiled and scratched Elvira behind her right ear, her favorite spot. "In the meantime, have some dinner," she removed another straw from her broom and tossed it up in the air. By the time it had hit the ground, it had transformed into a mouse. It squeaked at the sight of the cat and ran away.

Elvira glared at it with hungry eyes. "Thank you," she looked back up at Mrs. Macabre, who had taken her raven shape again. "But don't do this again."

"Nevermore," said the raven and she flew into the darkness.

"Hilarious," Elvira said and ran down the street, looking for the mouse.

Continue the story at

http://Books2Read.com/b/bzordz

a few words from

AUSTIN BOUSE

As a designer of horror theatre or experiences, explain your process.

Weirdly enough, I'm not very interested in scaring people with horror. I'm more interested in using the trappings of the genre to talk about our universal anxieties and how we "other" people who are different from us.

When is the last time you were genuinely scared by something someone created?

The film *Hereditary* deeply disturbed me when I first saw it. I'd put it up there along with *The Exorcist, The Texas Chain Saw Massacre,* or *The Blair Witch Project* in terms of horror films where one feels genuinely unsafe while watching them. Like someone letting go of your hand in a dark forest.

Tell us about your contribution to our book. What was the inspiration?

Mrs. Macabre came from this idea that I had for doing a book that was essentially *Mary Poppins* for Goth kids. It came out of my love for those old-school children's books that you just don't see anymore. Episodic, strange stories where the world and magic are never quite explained. Stories that exist within dream logic. Not to mention that it was the first book I wrote after realizing that I was gender fluid. So, it's possibly the most "Me" story I've ever written. *Abby The Happy Vampire* came out of me teaching myself how to draw. I drew this vampire-girl character and it struck me that she looked like a horror version of a Charles Shultz character. So, the idea of combing the every-day observation of what it means to be a child that *Peanuts* has with the dark humor and the outsider spirit of *The Addams Family* was too exciting for me to pass up.

What do you love about the genre of horror?

What I love the most about horror is that not only does it allow us to explore our deepest fears in a safe way, but it also gives us a home for the outsider. As a disabled gender fluid person, I've never felt like I was a part of the every day world. Monsters, and the strange and the unusual always felt more identifiable to me than say, Mickey Mouse.

What is some of your favorite horror literature? Favorite Author?

Stephen King would be at the top of my list, of course. I also love Neil Gaiman, Mary Shelley, Clive Barker, Joe Hill, Anne Rice, and Edgar Allan Poe.

What are some of your influences?

Besides the ones mentioned already, filmmakers like Tim Burton, Guillermo del Toro, David Lynch, and comic book writers/artists like Grant Morrison, Alan Moore, Charles Shultz, Edward Gorey, and Charles Addams.

What is your favorite Halloween treat?

Candy corn. Don't listen to the folks that tell you it is "bad." They should not be trusted.

You are hosting the perfect Halloween movie marathon. What are the films you choose and why?

My Halloween movie marathon would be made from films that I think represent the holiday the best. So, of course you would have to start with John Carpenter's *Halloween*, then the third film in the series, *Season of The Witch, Hocus Pocus, The Nightmare Before Christmas, The Crow,* Tim Burton's *Sleepy Hollow*, and what I consider to be the greatest Halloween movie of all time, *Trick 'r. Treat.*

If you could continue any horror story (Book or Film), what would it be?

I would either write a comic mini-series or a film where the *Ghostbusters* have to capture *Beetlejuice*. Not sure if it's a licensing disagreement, but I am *baffled* by how that idea has never been done before.

Describe the perfect Halloween.

Halloween for me, cannot be perfect in a single day, it has to be the entire month of October. I do a month-long horror movie marathon (book ended by *Halloween* and *Trick r' Treat*) going through the history of the genre from the *Universal Classic Monsters* onward. I have to visit my local *Spirit Halloween* store at least once. I have to decorate, if even it just my desk. I have to watch vintage Halloween TV ads. I have to read something spooky related. And, ideally, I make my own costume. My favorite day of the year cannot be limited to just 24 hours.

SCARE CRED: AUSTIN BOUSE

Austin is a writer, horror freak, and comic book nerd living in central Texas. Their web comic Abby The Happy Vampire publishes every Sunday on the website webtoon.com. Mrs. Macabre is their first book for children. Their debut novel, Never, was published in 2019. They are gender fluid, prefers the pronouns They/Them, and has a form of cerebral palsy. Austin plans on keeping it that way. You can find them on Instagram and Twitter at @austiniswriting.

#NOFILTER

BY RICKY BRIGANTE

The dedication of fans to an interactive experience is unreal, especially at Halloween time. A couple years ago, we were in the thick of online privacy leaks and Instagram influencer hell, so we asked the question: What happens when social media truly becomes horrifying? The result was #NOFILTER, the Halloween time immersive experience we created at Pseudonym Productions. It was a bizarre mix of an alternate reality game and immersive theater with online interactions and six live pop-up events in Orlando, Los Angeles, and New York. Most of it took place in a fake online social network called Connections. Definitely not your usual haunt.

While we wove a story centered around a powerful demon hidden in plain sight, the players were the ones who were ultimately in control. The story played out over six consecutive weeks during which players could choose sides and decide whether to try to save Taylor, the shallow (but endlessly friendly) Insta-star, or to side with Vokorev, the ever-tempting demon, to wreak havoc on all involved. As Halloween approached, Vokorev seized control of Connections and demanded that her followers reveal themselves with a display of force. Under her "influence," players began dressing like her, worshipping shrines to her at home, and even sharing photos of themselves smeared in fake (we hope?) blood – all to show their loyalty.

Ultimately, she used her newfound online power to give all players access to each other's accounts, including their private conversations and photos. It took mere minutes for chaos to take over Connections. What started innocently as memes and silly jokes were plastered all over each other's accounts as players logged in and posed as each other quickly turned truly horrible. Anonymized players began posting hateful messages and publicly revealing personal things that had been said under the assumption of privacy on this fictitious social network.

Within a couple hours, the hate spreading was becoming so brutal we had to shut it down. It was a shocking demonstration of the true horrors of the Internet rapidly unfolding before our eyes. While the characters, story, world, and social network were all fake - the words being exchanged were quite real. And we stopped it just before it had the chance to cross the line between fiction and reality.

Startle scares and clowns with chainsaws can't compete with the horrors of each other. The fast speed at which players went from friendly play to turning hateful on each other was frightening.

Ultimately, because of players' actions, Taylor was murdered by Vokorev in a live event, right before attendees' eyes. They circled around her, powerless to stop what they had put in motion. It was a somber, tear-filled happening after which players walked silently back to their cars, reeling from the impact of what they had done. But as Halloween passed, there was still one week of #NOFILTER left to go. And players were determined to redeem themselves. In literal mourning for a character's passing, we anonymously received at the doorstep of Pseudonym Productions a surprise bouquet of funerel lilies and a cake written with the hashtag #WeConnect, along with Taylor and Vokorev's names.

From that moment forward, players came together under #WeConnect to make good on what had happened, ultimately driving the ending of the six-week experience with a etherial appearance of Taylor to forgive them all, including Vokorev. It was the final live event of #NOFILTER and a night of celebration... with cake.

Horror comes in many forms. And the most horrifying of all is when it's real. For those who played and for us as creators, the six weeks of #NOFILTER really happened. And it was powerful for everyone, certainly a Halloween to remember.

a few words from

RICKY BRIGANTE

What do you love about the genre of horror?

It gives an opportunity to explore the worst of humanity and learn how to avoid becoming just that. It's also a fantastic release, allowing you to vicariously "experience" the horrible things we all think about from time to time.

What are some of your influences?

My earliest memories of horror include watching *A Nightmare on Elm Street* and developing a sick sense of humor thanks to the antics of Freddy Krueger at far too young of an age. The music of Rob Zombie has continued that inspired me to always want to walk that razor's edge between horror and comic relief, even if the comedy comes out of the sheer absurdity of over-the-top situations.

What is your favorite Halloween treat?

Halloween Oreos, no question about it. I stalk Target every August waiting for that first shipment to arrive.

You are hosting the perfect Halloween movie marathon. What are the films you choose and why?

For the classics: *A Nightmare on Elm Street, The Shining,* and *The Exorcist.* For the shock: *Hereditary, House of 1,000 Corpses / The Devil's Rejects,* and *A Serbian Film.* For the laughs: *Cabin in the Woods, Evil Dead II,* and *Young Frankenstein.* For the family: *Frankenweenie* and *The Addams Family*

If you could continue any horror story, what would it be?

I'd love a modern-day *Rear Window* using today's technologies and connection to the world. I feel like there is already so little privacy left that I wonder what a *Black Mirror* style take on the original would be like.

As a designer of horror theatre or experiences, explain your process.

I shut myself in a room alone, either in complete darkness or with a single candle for light. I have my computer for writing and research. I set the mood with meditative dark, droning tones. I lie down on the floor. Or pace around. I transition from real life into a world where nothing else exists except myself, my thoughts, and my feelings. And I allow myself to find places in my life where I have felt the worst.

Then I write from there. A stream of consciousness of what I am feeling and why I am feeling it. From that, I remove the feelings that I'd never want anyone else to go through and focus on the parts that I can harness into an experience of horror that won't leave people ruined, but still make them think. Characters and story emerge only after I've identified the darkness that acts as the underbelly of the experience. Once I write a scattered treatment of how I can have someone else explore those feelings, I begin to hunt for images and music that make me feel the same way. Through these references, I write a step-by-step walkthrough with detailed descriptions of what guests feel, see, hear, touch, taste, and smell. No detail is too small.

Once that is complete, I step back and give myself some time to escape those dark feelings before working with others to take further passes at the design to make it feel real for everyone involved, not just myself. It's an iterative process that is sometimes painful to go through, but rewarding in the end.

When is the last time you were genuinely scared by something someone created?

The second time I did the *Blackout* experience. It left me angry. Utterly angry. At the experience itself. At the actors involved. At other participants. At myself. Anger is an emotion I very rarely feel - and that scared me. I can't say I "enjoyed" the experience at all. But I do appreciate its ability to get me to scare myself through real, raw emotion.

Describe the perfect Halloween.

We have an incredibly successful season of creeping people out with our latest Halloween season immersive experience. Our staff has the reigns of running it, so my wife and I are able to enjoy Halloween night on our own. We come up with some fun costumes for ourselves, prepare a spirited dinner, watch *It's the Great Pumpkin Charlie Brown*, and give a few small scares to hundreds of excited trick-or-treaters who leave our house impressed by our spooky decorations, with full-sized candy bars in-hand.

SCARE CRED: RICKY BRIGANTE

Ricky Brigante was the founder of *Inside the Magic*, a respected leading source of news and information in the themed entertainment industry, covering theme parks, haunted attractions, and immersive experiences worldwide. After selling *Inside the Magic* in 2018, Ricky channeled his passion for themed entertainment into becoming a designer of immersive experiences. As Pseudonym Productions, he has helped to create uniquely interactive entertainment, including four Halloween experiences that blurred the lines between reality and fiction while enticing audiences to push boundaries and step outside their comfort zone. Ricky's work has been featured in *Entertainment Weekly, USA Today, Los Angeles Times, Fox News, Huffington Post, Yahoo!, AOL, MSN, Playboy, Broadway World, NPR, Business Insider,* and the *Orlando Sentinel.*

BEETLEJUICE at Universal Studios Florida and Halloween Horror Nights — TAKE ONE

BY DANNY BURZLAFF

The early years of *Universal Studios Florida* were fraught with challenges as the opening team faced the daunting task of creating a thriving international theme park in arguably the most competitive theme park landscape on the planet. In many ways, those initial years after opening were a bit like the wild west, in that management dodged and weaved incoming arrows from all directions, as the growing pressure to live up to the hype of "Ride the Movies" became a reality. As the Manager of Entertainment and Special Events, it was my role to support the key attractions across the park by developing a comprehensive live entertainment program. This included the creation and development of a massive character department which I named "Animated Street Stars," a curated look-a-like pool that I labeled "Celebrity Street Stars," live street shows such as the still popular *Blues Brothers* Show and the faux live film unit - Universal Production Unit, that set up mock film/TV shoots and stunts across the park throughout the day. Since I was also responsible for all entertainment-driven special events, it fell upon me to produce the original *Halloween Horror Nights* event, 1990. Since the park opened in June of that year...and as one may recall, it wasn't exactly a smooth opening. It became a rather unimaginable exercise to create, produce, install, and operate a major Halloween event within a few months. Though our team began the process in earnest, we quickly realized the improbability of this task at hand and especially if we were to get it right. After all, we had marching orders from our illustrious leader (CEO of MCA), Jay Stein, to "*Own* Halloween." We argued that we simply would not have the time and resources to make this goal a reality, and so it was determined to develop the program for the following year 1991. (Note, that the first year of HHN was called, *Fright Nights*.) As the months spun ahead, and we managed to correct our operational issues with ride failure and guest management (for the most part), it was also determined that perhaps a dedicated Special Events Department should be employed, much to my relief. It was at that time my direct involvement with *Universal Studios* Halloween came to an end. Sort of.

As stated earlier, that first year of USF operations was rather adventurous as we tried new ideas and concepts in live entertainment, to in truth bend the rules established by the good folks down the street. Our live entertainers and look-a-like characters we not merely photo-ops but were seasoned improvisational performers that would not only break the fourth wall of theater but would often break the theme park rules of engagement by offering realistic renditions of their characters rather than stereotypical versions of a street performer. We used the term RAW quite often back then, which not only could define the edgy performances but certainly construed the attributes of our Production Film Unit as we "filmed" high falls, stair crashes, fight scenes, car hits, vehicle stunts and more, on the fly and in real-time. It was in the spirit of this lively, knife-edge, entertainment matrix that I had a unique opportunity. In my role, I managed all of the licensed and branded characters for the park, including managing the contracts, royalties, etc. In other words, I was responsible for ensuring that we had the rights to utilize and represent characters such as *Laurel and Hardy*, *Marx Brothers*, *Blues Brothers*, *Marylin Monroe, Charlie Chaplin*, and others, as well as cartoon characters like Hanna-Barbera Characters, Warner Brothers Characters, Walter Lantz Characters, etc.

So, on one faithful day, I was presented with the opportunity to secure the rights for a recent film character for the park, Beetlejuice. I instantly fell in love with the idea of having *Beetlejuice* roaming our streets of Hollywood Blvd and NYC in search of his next victims. The top brass did not share in my enthusiasm, and thus declined to sign for the character rights and that was the end of that. Sort of. To back up a bit, the competitive marketing and PR betwixt Universal and Disney at this time was extreme, to put it mildly. Universal marketing and promotions department made every effort to out-maneuver, outshine, and out-think it's competition. One example I recall was when a low-income daycare center in Miami was forced to paint over/cover it's Disney Murals on their building due to copyright infringement, Universal enlisted a group of our characters (*Yogi Bear, Boo Boo, Scooby-Doo, Woody Woodpecker*, and more) along with Universal scenic artists to travel to Miami to repaint the building with OUR characters! While the children were entertained by the traveling group of Animated Street Stars, swag such as T-Shirts, tickets, and plush toys were flowing like water, and the local and national news was on hand to capture the smiling faces of the poor, underprivileged and slighted little children. I am sure Mr. Jay Stein was also smiling, as the image of his Universal star and mascot Woody Woodpecker was splashed across both TV screens and evening papers around the country. This stunt was indicative of the type of marketing ploy that was engaged during these early years of USF. Jay Stein was also smiling in part because the costumed character of *Woody Woodpecker* had such a commanding physical presence, both on-screen and in person. You see, the style guide for *Woody Woodpecker's* character, according to license holder Walter Lantz Productions, mandated the portraying performer to be at the height of between 5'1" – 5'3" (as I recall). But Jay Stein insisted during pre-opening that he wanted Woody too, and I quote, "tower above that (explicative) mouse!" in all shared promotional events. So, I was *asked* to redesign the costume to accept a performer 5'9 – 5'10," and it's for that reason USF has a ginormous *Woody Woodpecker* character; one that certainly looms large in a crowd (nearly 7 feet with the head), but doesn't necessarily comply with the physical attributes or traits of the beloved little bird (in my humble opinion).

But I digress... *Beetlejuice*. It was my position that the character of Beetlejuice was the very antithesis of *Mickey Mouse* and that for USF, a company based upon action-adventure, disaster and horror film franchises, he would make a fantastic addition to the entertainment program and a featured performer in the park. Further, I believed his personality would help to define the overall character of the park; irreverent, unapologetic, uncompromising, outlandish, brass, and in your face FUN! I convinced the upper management to give me a trial run and to prove my thesis that *Beetlejuice* could be both a crowd favorite and most excellent mascot alternative to the rodent down the street. That he, Beetlejuice, embodied the crass, rough-around-the-edges, devil-may-care attitude that our park was founded. Tom Williams, park president, agreed. I then quickly pieced together a costume, applied my makeup, and enlisted a video camera crew to follow me through the park as *Beetlejuice* made his debut. From the inappropriate comments, sexual innuendo, and revolting flehm and throat clearing...I let it all hang out. The video was delivered to Tom Williams and the team, and the rest is history, as the 'ghost with the most' was a smash hit, and *Beetlejuice* became a fixture in the park.

As mentioned above, my role with Universal Halloween came to an end following the development of a new Special Events Department, however that said, I *was* involved in the first year of Halloween as I reprised the role of the dead anti-hero and host for the first *Fright Night* Commercials. Of course, the character went on to legendary status at USF, first in a live street show I produced on the steps of the NYC Public Library, alongside the Ghostbusters, entitled "Beetlejuice, Dead in Concert" and later in the famed "Beetlejuice Graveyard Review" which ran in various renditions from 1992 – 2016 when the Fast and Furious attraction replaced it. Universal Studios Hollywood and Universal Studios Japan piggybacked on the success of the dark-hearted ghoul turned rock star, and also featured versions of the show in their parks as well. Looking back, I can honestly say I didn't know that Beetlejuice would obtain such an evergreen status as a beloved character in the parks, but I have always believed in his engaging and unremitting spirit to entertain, the power of his quirky personality, and his ability to command the audience by eloquently announcing, "It's Showtime!"

a few words from

DANNY BURZLAFF

As a designer of horror theatre or experiences, explain your process.

You've heard it before, and in this case, you'll hear it again – story is king. The backbone of any successful experience is the Why, What and How; the roadmap for conveying any exhilarating fright, serious historical presentation or a rip-roaring adventure. Once the written concept takes form, one can then begin to develop imagery to support the story, which leads to design and ultimately production. There is no magic in the magic…except of course there IS. The story needs to get *it* right and there should be no advancement in the production until the story is plotted, played out, and perfected. An attraction with flaws can survive, and even become a staple experience, if it's supported by a powerful tale. No matter if you're creating a single scare room, a massive walkthrough haunt or a live show experience, there must be a compelling, unique, intriguing story as the foundation for success.

When is the last time you were genuinely scared by something someone created?

Aside from the "people of Walmart" there are few things in life (or death) that scare me. I will jump when surprised, if that counts but never in fear or real concern for my safety. My seatbelt came loose on a roller coaster once… that was frightening. Construction methods in China has often left me weak in the knees, or bleeding in them due to poor execution of stair treads. On a ghost hunt in San Diego one midnight a few years ago, I was literally and physically shocked when instructed to place my hand into a 'vortex.' I think I jumped *and* yelped…but was that created by others or was it just there? The vortex was out of doors, on an open lawn, next to the famed "Whaley House", (the only government recognized haunted house in the US), but I don't think that one counts. Does it?

Other than that, I can't recall having really screamed or yelled with fear in quite some time. I enjoy the other end of the fright too much and therefore am hard to startle. I'll think on this and if I come up with a moment, I'll let you know.

Tell us about your contribution to our book. What was the inspiration?

For me behind-the-scenes tales are always the most interesting by-product of the production process; it's the how and why something came to be or was launched or was even tried that intrigues me. The story behind the story. It is these initial moments of time where perhaps something great was born…something memorable or even remarkable. I find that these epiphany moments are often times unexpected or accidental, sparked by unplanned circumstances. I imagine some of the greatest haunted frights came about as secondary notions or spin-offs from another scheme.

It's these unexpected creations that often tell the best tales. Unexpected or accidental successes was the inspiration in contributing to this book, and I wonder how many missed opportunities have been discarded as a napkin sketch or perhaps are still rattling around in someone's head yet to be discovered? The greatest artistic failures are those that were never attempted, and deemed too problematic, risky, difficult, expensive…you pick the excuse. My advice for anyone conceiving of a new guest experience is to seek out the *genuinely new and unique* and strive to tell the story from a different perspective. Shake up the norm, twist the expected and open the door to any and all possibiltiies.

What do you love about the genre of horror?

I grew up in a TV era of black and white re-runs of the classics such *as Frankenstein, Dracula, Invisible Man, Wolfman, Creature from the Black Lagoon*, etc. I was fascinated by the makeup and costumes, especially given the year(s) in which they were made, and as a kid I began to seek out makeup techniques. I was in awe of industry greats such as Jack Pierce, and I was completely amazed at the brilliance of legendary actor Lon Chaney and how he not only starred as a monster but would create his own incredible prosthetics and makeup appliances decades before it became an "art." I was originally drawn to horror by the makeup, costumes, and theatrics of the genre and thrilled to uncover their secrets to layering a good scare. For Halloween I'd create my own haunts, often times replicating one of these classic monsters, and I suppose I have always been driven by the desire to create the mechanics of the perfect scare by way of horror character makeup and costuming.

What is your favorite Halloween treat?

My favorite of all time was from a house two blocks away and as a kid this treat was VERY sticky. So much so that many (many) decades later it remains a fond memory. The home owner would convert their front porch into a witch's lair, complete with an enormous bubbling cauldron. The witch would make an appearance, dressed in black full-length gown, pointed hat, straw-like hair and a face that would make Margaret Hamilton proud. She cackled as the frightened kids gingerly stepped forward. Then she would present a "poison" apple, skewer it with a stick and then would proceed to sink the apple into her bubbling cauldron of goo. What was then removed and revealed was a custom-made, steaming hot, caramel covered apple! She would screech and laugh as the kids lined up for this incredible death wish. Was it the most amazing tasting caramel apple, who remembers? What I DO remember is the experience and how each and every child was unique, gifted and performed for. The caramel apple was very sticky… very sticky indeed.

As a side note: one Halloween the witch was gone, so too was the eerie music, rolling fog and steaming cauldron. To my shock, the costumed hag was replaced with a peace-sign wearing woman dressed in tied-dyed clothes and sporting a big grin! Turns out, she had found Jesus and was now serving "Love Potion" in little Dixie Cups to all the disillusioned kids in our neighborhood. How could this be?! It was my last year of trick-or-treating, as then and there I vowed to create my own version of the perfect scare for my fellow revelers on this glorious holiday… and I did.

You are hosting the perfect Halloween movie marathon. What are the films you choose and why?

I think I would have to create at least two genres' as to not dilute the theme by mixing up the recipe. Night one would feature the classics; *Frankenstein, Dracula, Phantom of the Opera, Wolfman, Creature of the Black Lagoon*, and a midnight showing of *Nosferatu*. These films created the very foundation of the horror genre. I believe everyone who loves the genre should experience these films on a big screen, without distractions or commercials, and you'll understand how they became the catalyst for all film frights since.

Night two would present more "modern classics" such as *The Exorcist, The Shining, Poltergeist* and *Jaws*. *Jaws* is often times overlooked in this genre, but indeed at the time of its release, (and some say to this day), the film set the standard for a good scare as it was/is absolutely terrifying. What these films share is the wonderful context of a deep and rich story. Each are presented in incredible cinematic style, and in many cases specialized techniques were created specifically for the filming.

If you could continue any horror story (book or film), what would it be?

One of my favorite horror books is *Troop*, by Nick Cutter. With every terrifying scene, my mind visualizes the ways in which these morbid moments could be played out on the big screen. I am truly amazed that no one has made this thriller/horror/nightmare of a scouting trip gone bad....really bad...is beyond me. It's a must read in my book (see what I did there?)...and should be on your nightstand now. I think Stephen King summed it up best when describing this novel, *The Troop* scared the hell out of me, and I couldn't put it down. This is old-school horror at its best." How can you beat that?

Describe the perfect Halloween.

That's easy: designing the scare, creating the scare, and then scaring the shit of everyone.

SCARE CRED: DANNY BURZLAFF

Danny is an themed attraction industry veteran and creative force behind the design, creation and production of major shows, attractions, exhibits and events for the leisure, entertainment, and hospitality marketplaces. His career spans over 35 years, and across 20 countries where he combines storytelling, writing, directing, producing and operating into compelling experiences for high profile brands and location-based attractions. Danny has served in roles as Creative & Project Director for theme parks, museums, visitor centers, retail, casinos, resorts, touring shows, mixed-use and more. He is continually seeking new ways to visualize compelling IP and Brand into innovative combinations of technology, interactivity, and theatrics that entertain guests around the world.

WATCH OUT

BY TERRONE CARPENTER

Some people just love going to buy groceries, finding the new improved, buy-one-get-one, same great product but with 33% more! What they don't realize is beyond the bright packaging and sample stations is a quagmire of accidents just waiting to happen. In my line of business, I investigate claims to determine the extent of liability. Grocery stores carry a lot of liability insurance for a reason. Slip and falls, especially in produce, are the most common. Fortunately, I got there before they swept up the entire protein spill covered with kitty litter. Protein spill? Insurance cribbed that term from the amusement industry, which has its own fair share of injuries. It's bodily fluid that requires clean up such as blood, vomit, urine. One usually precipitates the other.

OOOOOOOOOUUUUUUUUUUUUUUUUUU......

The accident victim was wailing. Never been to be able to tune it out. My junior partner, Jay, was making quips about "tomato juice in aisle one." Fortunately everyone was focused on the victim and only I could hear him. The victim had reddish brown "protein" gumming up her recently quaffed silver up-do. A pair of deputies stood around keeping folks away. I flashed my company ID, and after some comments, "How the hell does the insurance vulture get here before the EMTs?" The deputies let me talk to the employees once they were done and the ambulance had arrived.

The bag boy told me a "vagrant" - his words - was trying to shoplift melons inside his winter coat. "VJ" as his nametag stated, noticed it as it was odd that the "vagrant" had a long winter coat on over shorts in Florida which was odd to him even in October. As the shoplifter rushed toward the entrance door with his smuggled melons, one dropped and smashed causing the slip hazard for the victim Miss Squatgatzi. She had tried to dash by the shoplifter who was trying to go out the in and slipped. Miss Squatgatzi caught her temple on the corner of her shopping cart and fell like a sack of potatoes - or perhaps in this case a winter coat full of summer melons. That is when Gary, the assistant manager of the grocery store, called me after calling 911.

I took dozens of photos, checked the no slip walk off matt for proper fit and double checked the stores' SOG - standard operating guideline for their wet floor procedure and requested a copy of the police report. Jay hung out in the bakery section staring at the Carvel ice cream cakes like a kid in a cake shop. Assistant Manager Gary thanked me for coming out so quick and offered me one of their state-wide famous deli subs. I asked for one of the small Carvel ice cream cakes instead. I hope Jay appreciated the gesture.

I cranked the windows down in my 1970 Bronze Pontiac Catalina. Sensing my annoyance at the deputies, Jay dubbed it The Golden Vulture. As a vintage vehicle, imported from NYC it didn't have any AC, shoulder seatbelts or new-fangled safety equipment. Being in the business of accidents, I knew how often that safety equipment failed or complacent drivers relied on the invisible cloud of technology to keep them safe. I'd done the math and I preferred the huge V8 engine block, steel body panels and frame and the nearly 4000 pounds as my "safety rider". As for no AC in Florida, Jay was always cold and I always seemed to have a chill after an accident scene. I looked over at the ice cream cake in the passenger seat. I knew it wouldn't last long in the heat, so I had put it in a freezer bag with a bag of ice. Jay sat in the back making vulture sounds.

Next stop, A "four letter" community pool. Got a text on my Alpha Pager. Old but reliable like the Golden Vulture. People always ask if I am a drug dealer from the 1980s. I let them know that my car is from the 70's and doctors and medical first responders still use pagers. I had also given one to each of my family members as well as part of their bug out bags in case of emergency.

I usually share - "Paging facilities, unlike cell towers are usually equipped with standby power so that when the power grid is off during a natural disaster or extreme weather event, Pager Networks are still up and running and their transmitters have stronger signals that travel further. Pagers also use standard AA batteries which is very convenient if the power is down. If your looking for Crack for your 1980s drug habit, try the OBT - Orange Blossom Trail".

I also know birdwatchers use them to get real time geolocated pages about rare bird sightings, so I recently signed up. I just got one for a sighting of endangered Sand Hill Cranes in Windemere Florida right near where a Pro Golfer crashed his 2009 black Cadillac Escalade over a decade ago after a messy break-up. I was the adjuster for the community developer where it occurred.

We pulled into the YMCA, We had not beat the ambulance this time. According to the CDC, every day, about two children die from accidental drowning. Among adolescents and adults, alcohol use is involved in up to 70% of deaths associated with water recreation.

Waaaaaaaaaaaaaaaaaaaaaaaaaa....

Parents were on site and the wailing was overpowering. It seems that two teenagers climbed the fence to go swimming after pool closing. The cloud-based motion activated security footage showed me that the male teen in a fit of alcohol field bravado had run and dove in the deep end and did not immediately surface, perhaps he struck the bottom, hard to see from the angle. The other younger and smaller female tried to rescue him but was not a strong swimmer. Both drowned. Three oversized cans of a controversial 12-percent ABV "crazy energy beverage" lay near the pool empty, the label says each can is 4.75 servings. Jay remained in the car while I did what I needed to do. The kids one always hit him hard. I had the chills. The facility wasn't at fault. The gate was locked and the no driving or running signs were posted. The parents had a receipt of where the older teen had bought the "Crazy Cans" along with a fake ID that named him Keyser Söze from the film The Usual Suspects. There were 5 more accidents that day, but that one had left me in a haze.

Sometimes after a long day of accidents like this I just try to zone out from it all. I was having a moment like this during my drive home, which is unusual as it was forecast to rain. (Rain and wet roads cause more car accidents and injuries than snow, sleet or fog. The National Highway Traffic Safety Administration shows that 73 percent of weather-related crashes happen on wet pavement.)

Then after an afternoon of silence, Jay's vulture cries pulled me back. He asked about the cake which had become a pink slush of ice cream cake and melted ice in the freezer bag. I know he was just trying to keep me from drowning as well.

My Dad's Mazda RX-7 (with the rotary engine) hit and killed Jay about thirty-eight years ago while he was riding his bike home in the rain. He hit a sprinkler hose on the sidewalk and flipped right into my dad's lane. It's not just Jay. He's just been around the longest. The two teens, Storm and Ophelia (very Gen Z names from their Gen X parents) sat in the back with him. They'd be with us for a while. Every accidental and untimely death seems to find and plead with me in whispers and wails....

"Waaaaaaaaatch Ouuuuuuuuuuuuuut!"

a few words from

TERRONE CARPENTER

As a designer of horror theatre or experiences, explain your process.

Horror - ummm.... am I in the right place? I thought this was a book about the paranormal.

When is the last time you were genuinely scared by something someone created?

Like the Hulk said in *Avengers* - "I'm always angry." Or in my case... scared! Did you hear something?!

Tell us about your contribution to our book. What was the inspiration?

I'm fascinated by the paranormal and how it would impact our lives if they were commonplace. As a child I lived across the street from a cemetery my parents told me I talked to spirits.

What do you love about the genre of horror?

I love the paranormal! Did you say horror?

What is some of your favorite horror literature? Favorite author?

Develop your Psychic Skills by Enid Hoffman is a classic.

What are some of your influences?

Some early paranormal influences include *Firestarter* by The King, Claremont's Dark Phoenix run on *X-Men*, *The Adept Series* by Katherine Kurtz, *The X-Files* & Mike Mingola's *Hellboy and the BPRD*.

What is your favorite Halloween treat?

Did I mention I'm scared of everything - candy from strangers, that's a good one! How about an apple with a razor blade hidden in it!

You are hosting the perfect Halloween movie marathon. What are the films you choose and why?

Del Toro's *Hellboy*, King's *Firestarter*, Shyamalan's *The Sixth Sense*, the Duffer Bros' *Stranger Things*.

If you could continue any horror story (book or film), what would it be?

I would love to play in the *Hellboy* Universe! The combination of supernatural, paranormal and super adventure genres with a healthy helping of Cthulhu is ripe for further development.

Describe the perfect Halloween.

Dressing up as a super hero and defeating evil, but why stop at Halloween?

SCARE CRED: TERRONE CARPENTER

As a Creative Director, Show Writer and Technologist, Terrone has used his unique background in entertainment, design & interactive technology to bring stories to life professionally for nearly 30 years. Terrone has continued to practice and innovate the timeless magic of storytelling to create, write and direct over a thousand immersive stories and experiences for audiences all over the world. Kapow & Excelsior!

BLACK LADY

BY MARY CLAYPOOL

EXT. HOME IN THE SUBURBS - NIGHT

We see a wide shot of a typical suburban home--tidy yard, pleasant looking. All the lights are off. Suddenly we hear the piercing scream of a child.

CUT TO:

INT. HOME - DOORWAY OF CHILD'S BEDROOM

The screen is pitch black. A light comes on, and we see DIANE, a MOTHER in her 30's, standing in the doorway of a little girl's room. She wears pajamas and squints in the light. A look of concern crosses her face as she rushes to the terrified child.

CUT TO:

INT. CHILD'S BEDROOM

A typical cutsie girl's room decorated in pastels and outfitted with plushies and toys. RACHEL, a seven-year-old girl, cowers against the headboard of her bed against the wall, trembling, wide-eyed in terror and clutching her stuffed bunny.

MOTHER

Sweetie, what's wrong?! What's the matter?! Mommy's here, it's okay. Stop screaming, everything's okay. What's wrong, baby?!

RACHAEL

(panicked whisper)

She's here! She's here! Don't talk, or she'll know I told you! (panting in terror)

MOTHER

(sighs)

Oh, Rachael, not that dark woman again.

RACHAEL

(urgent whisper)

The black lady!!

MOTHER

Yeah... Now listen, sweetheart, there's no reason to be afraid of someone because of their skin color. You've seen Oprah Winfrey on TV, and she's a very nice person...

RACHAEL

No! I mean she's black like that!

The child points to a picture she has drawn of the black lady. It shows a raven-black female form without detail except for a pair of sinister neon blue eyes. The mother examines the picture then looks her daughter's face with an expression of worry.

MOTHER

(calmly, but a little unnerved)

Rachael, you were just having a

nightmare. You and I are the only
ones here. And Bun-Bun, of course.
(gently shaking the bunny in the
girl's arms) Bad dreams happen to
everyone, honey. They're not real,
and by morning, you'll have
forgotten all about it.

RACHAEL
(frightened whisper)
Mommy, she is real. And she's
under the bed. I wanna sleep with
you and Daddy.

The mother is a little creeped out as she glances downward.

MOTHER
That's enough. There's no black
lady. I'll show you.

The mother leans over the bed lifting the bedspread preparing to
loos under the bed. The girl suddenly seizes her mother's arm and
screams.

RACHAEL
Mommy, no...!!!

At that moment, we hear a man's voice off camera. The tone is
condescending.

FATHER (off)
Did somebody have another nightmare?

Mother lowers the bedspread and sits back on the bed with the child.

MOTHER

I'm afraid so.

Dad shuffles in and sits on the bed with the other two. He is also in his 30's, wears pajama bottoms and some kind of shirt with a feel-good "Save the Whales" motto or politically correct statement. His is patient in a patronizing way, the way some psychologists and self-help gurus tend to be.

MOTHER

She wants to sleep with us because there's a black lady in her room. Go back to bed, I'll handle it.

FATHER

(ignoring the mother)

A black lady, hm? That's interesting. Why a black lady and not an Asian or a Latina lady?

MOTHER

She doesn't mean African-American. She means black like this (grabs cape or whatever)

RACHAEL

(whispering)

And she has bright blue eyes and she's angry. Please don't let her hear you or she'll know I told you!

FATHER

(sweet but condescending)

Oh, I see. Well, why do you think she's angry? Could it be that she's upset because she hasn't been getting enough attention lately? Hm...?

Mother rolls her eyes. She know where this conversation is going.

MOTHER

Richard...

Father signals the mother to stops by gesturing with his hand palm-up. He does not look at her, but continues speaking to Rachel.

FATHER

Maybe this black lady isn't happy because her mommy just got a new job and her daddy's been out of town giving lectures.

MOTHER

(quietly forced)

Richard this isn't the time or place...

FATHER

Diane, please. This is what I do. (to child) Now Rachael, you need to

understand that daddy has a career,
and now mommy, for whatever reason,
has one too.

Mom appears pissed off at that last comment.

FATHER

It's true things will change, but
after-school care is going to be
fun. You'll socialize with other
kids, play age-appropriate games,
do arts and crafts that stimulate
creativity. We'll still spend
quality family times together in
the evenings and weekends.

RACHAEL

(weepy and terrified)

Daddy, she's real! Please, I wanna
sleep with you and Mommy!

FATHER

Okay, I see I'll just have to prove
to you that there's no black lady.

He stands and walks over to the closet. He slides the door open and inspects the closet with exaggeration.

FATHER

I don't see any black lady in here.

Mom has lost her patience.

MOTHER

All right, this is stupid. Let's just bring her to bed with us and go to sleep already.

FATHER

Allowing her to manipulate us is the last thing we should do. Really Diane, you're not working with me here.

Mom glares daggers at him. He continues his inane search by opening drawers in the child's desk and dresser.

FATHER (calling)

Hell-oooo...! Black Lady, are you in there? How 'bout in here? Maybe here? Nope, no Black Lady. Let's look under the bed.

He gets on his knees, lifts the blanket and hangs over the bed, looks under the bed and shouts.

FATHER

Black Lady....! Come out, come out, wherever you are...!

The child screams out in fear.

RACHAEL

Don't, Daddy!! Stop it, she'll hear you! Mommy, make him stop!

MOTHER

All right, cut it out. This is ridiculous. None of us'll get to sleep at this rate.

The father stands, a smug expression on his face.

FATHER

I'm simply making a point, Diane. Rachael has to learn to accept and cope with new situations. Otherwise, she'll never be able to deal with the reality of--ugh!

Suddenly, he slams backward onto the floor. He has been pulled off his feet. He lies on his back, stunned and breathless. His feet are beneath the bed.

MOTHER

Richard?!

RACHAEL

Daddy!

Without warning, the father is quickly yanked under the bed. He blocks himself with his arm on the frame of the bed and strains to hold on. With terrified eyes, he look up at his wife and reaches for her. Diane grabs his arm, but something powerful has a hold on him.

RICHARD

Help!!

In a shot, Diane's grip on him is broken as he is pulled completely under the bed. There is no sound after he disappears. Diane snaps out of her shock. She grabs the girl and practically throws her away from the bed.

MOTHER

Run! Go next door!

The child bolts from the room. The mother stands on the bed and leaps as far as she can from it. She reaches the door then stops. She can't abandon her husband. She glances around the room and picks up a stick horse. She inches toward the bed, crouches, and slowly lifts the sheet hanging over the edge with the end of the horse. A small pair of jaws open and close with a roar. The mother yelps and falls backward. It is only a toy dinosaur that activates and waddles out from behind the sheet.

She once again lifts the bedding and glances around in the darkness under the bed seeing only strewn toys and game pieces. In the farthest, darkest corner a pair of bright blue eyes suddenly opens and an evil hiss/growl sound emanates from the black form. The mother screams and flees the room.

Rachael's picture of the Black Lady floats to the floor. The camera slowly pushes in on it then holds. Suddenly, it whips out of frame. We hear the same chilling hiss/growl from before.

THE END

a few words from

MARY CLAYPOOL

When is the last time you were genuinely scared by something someone created?

Every October, my family and I would visit the old desert ghost town of Calico in Yermo, California. Throughout that month, the entire place is decked out for Halloween. The biggest draw is the old silver mine, which is transformed into a "haunted" experience. One year, we went in, and I was not prepared for the horrific set-ups and costumed performers who lay in wait at every turn. The natural creepiness of the dark mine combined with effective lighting, gruesome settings, eerie sound effects, and actors who were really into their roles had me jumping and yelping the entire time. It was awesome.

Tell us about your contribution to our book. What was the inspiration?

Shortly after moving into our current home, my four-year-old daughter started waking up every night screaming in terror. She claimed that an unfriendly female creature was hiding beneath her bed. She described the entity as being pitch black with bright blue eyes. Her frantic insistence that the "black lady" existed unnerved both of us. Great material for a horror tale. By the way, a friend's elaborate sage-burning ritual—performed mainly for my daughter's benefit—exorcised the unwanted guest, and she hasn't returned. Yet.

What do you love about the genre of horror?

I love horror, because its touches a primal chord that reaches back to our prehistoric ancestry. A good scare is cathartic and polarizing; it makes us feel alive and drives us to seek protection from the unknown. We can only imagine what's beyond the light, waiting and watching us in the darkness. There's something tantalizing about that.

What is some of your favorite horror literature? Favorite author?

There are so many fabulous works of horror, that it's difficult to choose. I would have to say that Ray Bradbury is my favorite author of both horror and science fiction. I remember finding his anthology, *The October Country*, in my school library when I was 12. It was like literary crack for me; after I read it, I was hooked on horror stories for life. His writing felt authentic and relatable, as if anyone might readily stumble into one of his fictional constructs. The works of H.P Lovecraft and Robert Bloch run a close second.

What are some of your influences?

My parents were my earliest and greatest influences. My mother's parents were Russian immigrants from a rural part of the country where folklore and superstitions abounded. They imbued their children with Old World beliefs in the supernatural and mystical. In turn, my mother passed them on to her children. My mother's stories of ghosts, mysterious creatures, and omens are ingrained in me. My father of Irish descent was a master storyteller. He would weave spellbinding tales about his lumberjacking and hunting days in the remote mountains of the American Northwest. His campfire stories based on old Native American legends still send shivers down my spine.

What is your favorite Halloween treat?

My homemade caramel apples. Not to boast, but they are the best. Ok, that's a boast. Fresh, tart apples coated in caramel made from scratch, drizzled with milk chocolate and white chocolate, then topped with candy sprinkles.

You are hosting the perfect Halloween movie marathon. What are the films you choose and why?

Aliens – science fiction, horror, action, deadly alien creatures, and it's a chick flick! Ultimately, it's a battle of maternal instinct between two females on a remote planet, each attempting to protect her young. One of Jim Cameron's best films! I watch it every Mother's Day.

The Haunting (1963 version) – a classic horror film based on Shirley Jackson's novel, *The Haunting of Hill House.* Everything in this movie blends flawlessly to produce the quintessential haunted house story. A must-watch.

The Thing (1982) - John Carpenter's remake of the 1951 science fiction film, *The Thing from Another World,* is outstanding. The paranoia of not knowing who's human and who isn't is more frightening than the creature itself.

Frankenstein (1931) – Kickin' it old school with that lovable lunk of a monster portrayed by the unparalleled Boris Karloff. An oldie that set the bar for amazing special make-up, lighting, and art direction in horror film.

Dracula – any version with Bela Lugosi or Christopher Lee. It isn't Halloween without a vampire.

Hellraiser – Clive Barker transports us to a nightmarish hellscape that's deliciously disturbing. Love those Cenobites!

Phantasm – a surreal sci-fi/horror cult classic that is best viewed without explanation. This weird and creepy film made "The Tall Man" (Angus Scrimm) an iconic character in the hallowed halls of horror.

The Exorcist – C'mon, who doesn't love seeing little girls possessed by demons? It took me years before I was able to watch the entire movie without closing my eyes.

Carrie – One of my favorite film adaptations of a Stephen King story. Sissy Spacek's portrayal of the disturbed, telekinetic titular character is unforgettable. Nightmare fuel.

Halloween – What better way to honor the glorious celebration of Samhain than with its filmic namesake? Watching Jamie Lee Curtis trying to elude the ultra-focused and unkillable Michael Meyers never gets old.

Black Sabbath (1963) – a trio of short stories that offer good old-fashioned frights. And it's hosted by Boris Karloff!

If you could continue any horror story (book or film), what would it be?

Ever since I watched the original 1958 version of *The Blob*, it has bugged me that the alien organism was just crated up and dropped out of a plane where it parachuted down to some random spot in the Arctic. No follow up whatsoever. Even as a kid, I thought that was really stupid. Notwithstanding that there was a 1988 remake, I would like to continue the original story in today's world. In my version, global warming has melted the polar ice caps to the point where the monster amoeba thaws and is on the loose. Indigenous people and animals aren't simply disappearing from loss of habitat.

Describe the perfect Halloween.

Spending the night in a bona fide haunted house with paranormal investigators and experiencing a first-hand encounter with a ghostly presence.

SCARE CRED: MARY CLAYPOOL

Horror, science fiction, and movies—the perfect combination, in Mary's opinion. Perhaps the power of that trinity is what guided her to the entertainment industry. Her first film job as a production assistant was on *Ghostbusters*. She then worked as a coordinator on *Fright Night, Big Trouble in Little China, Poltergeist II, Masters of the Universe, Gremlins 2,* and *Batman Returns* — right up her genre alley. Also an aspiring writer, she proved her scripting chops by writing two uncredited scenes for *Gremlins 2: The New Batch*, which is a story to save for another time. Today, Mary is a veteran ADR writer who has scribed hundreds of dubbing scripts for live action and anime projects, including *Ghost in the Shell, Cowboy Bebop*, and *Resident Evil: Degeneration*. In her spare time, she manages rental stages for film production, writes original short stories and scripts, travels, bakes, dotes on her family, and adores her two cats.

TANGIBLE MAGIC

My Halloween with Ray Bradbury

BY DAVE COBB

Halloween is always fun – but it's rare, however, that Halloween night contains some actual, tangible magic.

On November 2nd, 2007, I was invited to a Halloween dinner party at Club 33, the private restaurant at Disneyland, on the second floor above New Orleans Square. Dinner was, as usual, lovely – I'd been to the Club a few times before over the years, and always had a beautiful meal in an equally beautiful setting. But this time around was different, because there was a guest of honor, none other than the father of "The Halloween Tree" himself, Mr. Ray Bradbury.

Bradbury was a longtime fan of Disneyland, a personal friend of Walt Disney, and an occasional collaborator with Walt Disney Imagineering – most notably on the original concepts for Epcot – so seeing that it was the 35th anniversary of Bradbury's book "The Halloween Tree", Imagineers Marty Sklar, Tony Baxter and Tim Delaney decided to throw a Halloween party in Bradbury's honor.

Bradbury may have been frail in body, but most certainly not in brain -- he was as giddy as an eight-year-old as he regaled us with many of his Disney-related stories, on what he told us was "his favorite holiday of the year". Deep beneath his wheelchair-bound, 87-year-old skin beat the heart of a poet, an enthusiast and lover of life who ensured all of us adoring nerds in the audience that our mutual loves of science fiction, of fantasy, of what the world could indeed be, was indeed okay. He was so full of passion and wanted to get across to all of us in attendance that HE WAS INDEED ONE OF US and we belonged together, in that moment, not as acolytes but as co-conspirators, as grand collaborators in the humanity of creativity. It was less about his legacy and career as it was a feeling HE wanted to celebrate how we all tap into the same desires, the same needs, and the same hopes. It was one of those nights where it was hard to tell who was happier to be there – the audience or the man being honored.

As if a six-course meal with one of my literary heroes wasn't enough, another surprise was in store, not only for the audience but also for Bradbury himself. We all left the restaurant (nerd detail: we walked through the closed park... with all the lights off!) and gathered around a lone oak tree in the darkened town square of Frontierland, stray brown leaves strewn all over the ground. When Bradbury was asked to flip a pumpkin-themed switch nearby, the old tree lit up with strands of tiny illuminated jack-o-lanterns – thus, he now had his very own permanent Halloween Tree. "I belong here in Disneyland," said Bradbury at the tree's dedication ceremony, "ever since I came here 50 years ago. I'm glad I'm going to be a permanent part of the spirit of Halloween at Disneyland." Since then, during every autumn at the park, the unassuming tree is given a glimmering makeover, complete with twinkling orange lights and hand-painted jack-o'-lanterns hanging from its branches, and a plaque is installed at the base of the tree commemorating it for all who visit Disneyland during Halloween celebrations.

As a parting gift, we were all given signed copies of "The Halloween Tree" book. As I left, I picked up one of the stray (fake) "Disney autumn leaves" carefully art-directed on the ground around the actual tree. Mr. Bradbury invited everyone up for one-on-one greetings and photos, so I nervously waited my turn and timidly went up to meet him, asking him to sign the decorative autumn leaf for me.

"I don't really have much to say, except 'thank you', your books have meant so much to me... I can't believe I'm here," I blurted to him, my hands trembling and my eyes welling up. As frail as he was, he took my hand surprisingly quite firmly in his, looked me straight in the eyes – his filled with fire and life and heart – and he said wistfully and purposefully to me, "well, you are here, and you're wonderful."

I wept, and he held my hand firmly until I stopped weeping, giving me a broad, time-weary yet heartfelt smile, and a devilish, knowing twinkle in his eye. It was a lightning bolt to my soul, enveloping everything he'd said during the evening into a warm, gleaming gem deep inside my chest. It made me truly aware of the power of imagination, and the sacred and wonderful connection that all dreamers have. It was magic incarnate, that brief moment, and it changed my life.

I don't think I'll ever have a Halloween quite as perfect.

a few words from

DAVE COBB

As a designer of horror theatre or experiences, explain your process.

I think a horror experience benefits most from figuring out early what the most horrific, most impactful *emotional* horror the guest could or would feel – the "horror moral" of the story, if you will – and design the entire experience backwards from that emotion, or at least put it at the beginning of the third act. Land on that at the end – a sense of true emotional dread – and you've succeeded.

When is the last time you were genuinely scared by something someone created?

Easily *Delusion: Lies Within* in 2014. All of Jon Braver's work is pretty amazing; even in their weaker years, I always come out with a handful of moments that, through spectacle or story, really wowed me. *Lies Within* was, in my opinion, the peak of Delusion's powers, and everything worked. It built a sense of unending dread and a heart-stopping conclusion. It took me a long time to shake.

Before that, my answer would have always been The House of Restless Spirits in Santa Monica, which unfortunately had its last haunting in 2014; it wasn't shocking, or jump scares, or anything over-the-top about it that scared me – it was this quiet, slow, deliberate sense of "did-I-just-see-what-I-think-I-saw" around every corner. It felt like a legitimate haunting, one filled with emotion and dread and sadness, but still compels you to LOOK. And keep looking. And keep looking some more even if nothing's happening because… eventually something will, something quiet, and slow, and deliberate, and terrifying.

What do you love about the genre of horror?

On one hand, with visceral scares, I enjoy the rush – I love screaming and then laughing, that dopamine and adrenaline jolt. On the other hand, I also love a slow, turning-of-the-screw tension, especially if the release isn't visceral but rather dread or unease or unspeakable horror.

What is some of your favorite horror literature? Favorite author?

Stephen King, of course. And Lovecraft.

What are some of your influences?

As I kid I couldn't get enough of *Universal Monsters* and *Hammer Horror*, all a staple of after-school and weekend-afternoon television. Later in my teens, it was the golden age of home video, and my formative horror became high-concept – *Videodrome*, and high-weirdness - *Society, The Stuff, The Thing.*

What is your favorite Halloween treat?

Stay the hell away from my Sugar Babies. And from an experience standpoint, I love the silly/spooky haunt experiences as much as the horror-based ones. My two favorite things in all of LA are always the Griffith Park Ghost Train and Boney Island – not scary in the least, but easily my favorite Halloween treats.

You are hosting the perfect Halloween movie marathon. What are the films you choose and why?

I'd start with *Halloween III* because it's a weird tone-setter early in the evening. I'd follow with something like *Society* because it's super fucked-up and weird and gory, yet you can't take your eyes off of it. Next up would be John Carpenter's *The Thing* to continue the gore and dread. Once everyone was nice and freaked out, I'd close the night with the original *Halloween* because that shit STILL scares me. Anyone still awake after that would get a late-night after-party showing of *The Stuff* for some drunken LULZ.

If you could continue any horror story (Book or Film), what would it be?

Something Wicked This Way Comes by Ray Bradbury. In the book, the Autumn People came every hundred years or so, so I'd love to see a contemporary version of how Mr. Dark would manifest in today's world.

Describe the perfect Halloween.

Doing a caravan with friends to all the local suburban haunts we could find, and then home for some horror movies.

SCARE CRED: DAVE COBB

Dave Cobb is a writer, creative director and designer of immersive experiences that tell stories in physical places: theme parks, rides, attractions, museums, live shows and events. He has spent nearly three decades combining location, technology, emotion and interactivity to engage and excite audiences in new and unique ways, collaborating with brands and companies like Universal Studios, Warner Bros., Paramount, Lionsgate, Sony Pictures, and Thinkwell Group.

NEIGHBORLY

BY JOHN CONNON

THE GARDENER, 30's, gay male
THE NEIGHBOR, 30's, straight family man

LIGHTS UP: a fence separating two properties

THE GARDENER enters with a bag of yard waste, hands streaked with dirt, sweaty, comes down center, as THE NEIGHBOR enters from the opposite side of the stage with a bag of garbage. They meet at the fence.

THE GARDENER: Hey, Neighbor.

THE NEIGHBOR: Hey, man.

THE GARDENER: Sure is quiet today.

THE NEIGHBOR: Yeah. It is.

The Neighbor turns to go back inside.

THE GARDENER: How's everything in your world?

THE NEIGHBOR: Ah. Y'know. Fine. Kid's got a tummy ache, but y'know.

THE GARDENER: I didn't see him playing in the pool. That's too bad.

THE NEIGHBOR: Yeah. Some sort of bug. He'll be fine.

The Neighbor tries again to go inside.

THE GARDENER: Can I ask you a weird question?

THE NEIGHBOR: Okay...

THE GARDENER: I mean, I hope it's not weird.

THE NEIGHBOR: What?

THE GARDENER: What's it like? To be a parent?

THE NEIGHBOR: Ah. I mean... I don't really know how to answer that.

THE GARDENER: I just mean, like, to have all that responsibility.

THE NEIGHBOR: Well, yeah. It's a lot of responsibility. You gotta make sure they're fed and dressed in the morning. Teach them right. Make sure they're safe.

THE GARDENER: That kid does some crazy stuff in that pool!

THE NEIGHBOR: Right?! Gotta make sure he's not killing himself out there.

THE GARDENER: That alone! He's such a cute little guy.

THE NEIGHBOR: Yup. He's my little man.

THE GARDENER: Does he ever say what he wants to be when he grows up?

THE NEIGHBOR: Ah, I don't know. It changes every day. He's gonna be a fireman one day. A policeman the next. Who knows?

THE GARDENER: Little dreamer. That's so fun. What do you want him to be?

THE NEIGHBOR: Umm. I guess I'd want him to be... I don't think I'd really want him to be a fireman or a policeman. So fucking dangerous anymore. Just, you know, like a lawyer or doctor.

THE GARDENER: Something safe.

THE NEIGHBOR: Something like that.

There is an awkward beat.

THE NEIGHBOR: Well.

He goes to leave.

THE GARDENER: Hey, man. I just wanted to apologize for our dog barking all those times.

THE NEIGHBOR: Oh. Yeah. No big deal.

THE GARDENER: Obviously that won't be a problem anymore.

THE NEIGHBOR: Yeah. Hey, man. I'm sorry for your loss.

THE GARDENER: Thank you. We buried our little girl over there. Planted some flowers right on the spot just now.

THE NEIGHBOR: Oh. Very pretty.

THE GARDENER: Thanks. Oleander. We liked the pink. How's that for a stereotype?

THE NEIGHBOR: Er... Uh. Okay. Well. I am real sorry I yelled at you. That one day. About the dog barking.

THE GARDENER: Oh. No. No need to apologize. I mean, she was. Totally on me.

THE NEIGHBOR: No. It was uncalled for. I just...lost my temper.

THE GARDENER: It's fine. I just...never realized you worked late and slept late. What was it, like 10am? If I had known...I wouldn't ever have left her out all morning.

THE NEIGHBOR: I shouldn't have lost my shit. I'm sorry. It was...I was on about two hours of sleep and...

THE GARDENER: Right! I mean, like I said. No need to apologize.

THE NEIGHBOR: I just feel bad. And now... (indicating the flower bed) Those are really pretty.

THE GARDENER: Thanks.

THE NEIGHBOR: Well...okay.

Tries again to go back inside.

THE GARDENER: We never expected her to have that kind of a bark. She actually didn't bark for like the first several months we had her. She was just quiet. But then...I don't even remember what it was. Maybe the bug guy or something. I don't know. But she saw this guy outside and lost her fucking mind. And we were like, what...NOISE is that?! Her bark was...bonkers!

THE NEIGHBOR: A little bit.

THE GARDENER: So high! Like piercing. So...sorry about that.

THE NEIGHBOR: Oh. It's all good.

THE GARDENER: We found her on the street.

THE NEIGHBOR: Oh, man.

THE GARDENER: Not when she died!

THE NEIGHBOR: Oh!

THE GARDENER: No, she died in her little bed. I mean, when we got her. She was on the street. She was just... like...running around. She had no collar. And she was just like...weaving around. I mean, somebody dumped her. They say that people will do that. They'll just dump a dog. Like drive far from their neighborhood, find a nicer neighborhood, I guess, and just dump the dog. In hopes that someone will come along and pick the dog up.

THE NEIGHBOR: Really?

THE GARDENER: Can you imagine? Just dumping your dog? I couldn't even imagine! I would never be able to sleep again. How do you go to sleep ever again after dumping a dog in some random neighborhood?

THE NEIGHBOR: I don't know.

THE GARDENER: So, we, of course, two gay guys, see this little Schnauzer, running around looking panicked. Her fur was all matted and she was infested with ticks. It was awful. We took her around to all the vets in the area and were like, Do you recognize this dog? Is she like a patient? And this one vet was like, No, text book case of a dog being dumped. So we got her, y'know, cleaned up and spayed and, yeah, we put out an ad that we found this dog, and, of course, no one replied. This just abandoned little creature. Who does that?

THE NEIGHBOR: Yeah.

THE GARDENER: But we took it as a sign from the Universe. We were meant to have her. She was our little baby. That's what dogs are, y'know. To like gay guys. Our little babies.

THE NEIGHBOR: Yeah. I'm so sorry.

THE GARDENER: They are just like, unconditional love. Y'know? We named her Ollie. Like Oleander. And she would just...the moment we walked in the house, she had to be right on us. Right on top of us. Like, if she could fuse into us, like osmose into us... Well, me anyway. She couldn't give a crap about my partner. Really. He was always like, That dog couldn't care less about me. Which was not at all true. Of course. But I fed her, y'know. I walked her. I took her to the vet and all that stuff. I was the one who did all that. And she would just sit with me. And look at me. Just sit and look me in the eye. Right into my soul. All the time. I always said, in my next life, I want to come back as a gay couple's dog.

THE NEIGHBOR: That's funny.

THE GARDENER: And I was so worried about losing her. Y'know? Like she would run away. Because what if she wasn't dumped, right? What if she just got out and ran? But then, I came home from work one day and let her out and I wasn't even thinking, but someone had left our gate open.

THE NEIGHBOR: Really?

THE GARDENER: I mean, maybe a meter reader or our lawn guy or someone, but I didn't even check it, and I just let her out, and y'know ten minutes go by and I go to let her in and she's nowhere. And I see the gate open, and I just panic. I mean, I was like...I mean, you see those ladies in a grocery store and they lose track of their kid and they are freaking out, y'know? I had always been like, Lady, calm the fuck down. But in that moment, I totally got it. My heart went to like, ice. I was screaming. Because I thought...if she is gone, if Ollie is gone, and I don't know where she is or what happened to her...I will never sleep again. Never.

THE NEIGHBOR: Right.

THE GARDENER: But, of course, I come around the house, and there she was. Just sitting on the front porch, just sitting by the door. Waiting for me. Crisis averted. And in that moment, it was clear. She had been dumped. She was abandoned. Because she wasn't the type of dog to run. She would sit right there by the door. She would sit there and wait for me all day long.

THE NEIGHBOR: Aw, man.

THE GARDENER: So, after the gate thing happened, I was like, so cautious, right? I would check the gate every single time. I got so paranoid about the gate. And I was pissed, too, because if it was the meter reader or whatever, I wanted to say something to them, like, Whatever you're doing in the back yard fine whatever, but CLOSE the Goddamned gate when you're done.

THE NEIGHBOR: Exactly!

THE GARDENER: So, we had a camera put up back there.

THE NEIGHBOR: Oh, wow.

THE GARDENER: Mmhmm. Because whoever came into the back yard, we were gonna see it. And whoever left the gate open, we were gonna give them a real piece of our mind.

THE NEIGHBOR: Sure.

They stare at each other for an uncomfortable amount of time.

THE NEIGHBOR: I should get back. Check on my kid.

THE GARDENER: Like that day you came over and gave me a piece of your mind, about Ollie barking.

THE NEIGHBOR: Again, I'm sorry I lost my shit. It was really nothing.

THE GARDENER: No, I know it was nothing. I just want to explain what was happening that day. We had a plumber come by and he had to fix the sink. It was clogged up or whatever, so we just set her out so that he could do his job. It was probably like forty five minutes, I guess. And with that bark of hers. I mean, forty minutes is a long time. So...again...my apologies.

THE NEIGHBOR: Right. I should have just kept my cool. Because dogs bark.

THE GARDENER: Yeah. And kids scream.

THE NEIGHBOR: I'm sorry...?

THE GARDENER: I'm just sayin'. Dogs bark. And kids scream. They're very similar in that way.

THE NEIGHBOR: Okay...

THE GARDENER: I mean, let's take your kid for example. That is a scream on that kid.

THE NEIGHBOR: He just gets excited, playing in the pool.

THE GARDENER: Exactly.

THE NEIGHBOR: Wait...is my kid bothering you guys?

THE GARDENER: Not at all. That's the thing. It never bothered us. Because that's what kids do. They scream.

THE NEIGHBOR: Yeah.

THE GARDENER: For hours. All day. Just running around that pool. Screaming his little head off.

THE NEIGHBOR: What do you expect us to do about that?

THE GARDENER: Nothing! Really. I just think it's interesting. Comparing noise levels, I mean. Like our dog barked for, what, a half hour one day versus the interminable piercing scream of your kid every day all day from like 7 am on a Saturday til who the fuck knows when at night. But little Ollie, our little girl, barks for what, fifteen minutes, and that's enough to drive you, a grown ass adult, to come to my front door and bang on it repeatedly and raise your voice to me, another grown ass adult.

THE NEIGHBOR: Look, I said I was sorry.

THE GARDENER: And then...fast forward. Not a week later...we wake up to find Ollie dead in her little bed. And it's not just that she's dead. She has apparently, through the night, puked up her guts. And had diarrhea. Bloody bloody diarrhea all over the white shag rug. So, not only is there our dead...child...right there in her little bed...but there's this fucking hideous clean-up project as well! Talk about insult to injury.

THE NEIGHBOR: Dude...

THE GARDENER: So, of course, we're like, What did she get into? What did she eat? Cuz she's like a little Hoover when it comes to scraps. I mean, I was walking her once and we saw a dead frog on the street and before I even realized what it was, she had just sucked the damn thing up. I might have even told you that story once.

THE NEIGHBOR: Maybe.

THE GARDENER: So, I go, Let's look at the camera. In the back. Maybe we got it on camera. Maybe we can see. Let's see what it was.

THE NEIGHBOR: Aww, man.

THE GARDENER: And what do you think we saw? Neighbor!

THE NEIGHBOR: Look, man...

THE GARDENER: You threw something into our fucking yard. And you knew she would eat it.

THE NEIGHBOR: I...

THE GARDENER: You poisoned our little girl. Our little baby. And for what? Because she barked?

THE NEIGHBOR: I...am...

THE GARDENER: Don't even fucking say you are sorry. If I hear you say you are sorry one more fucking time!

THE NEIGHBOR: Are you going to call the police?

THE GARDENER: No. I thought about it. But no. My partner was ready to come over and beat the shit out of you. But I told him No.

THE NEIGHBOR: Okay. That's very... Thanks, man.

THE GARDENER: Just go home. Check on your kid. Give your kid a hug.

THE NEIGHBOR: Yeah.

The Neighbor starts to walk off.

THE GARDENER: Because y'know dogs and kids are so similar.

THE NEIGHBOR: What?

THE GARDENER: Dogs and kids. They both love to play. They both make a lot of noise. They both love you unconditionally and expect you to protect them. And they both... well, they'll eat just about anything.

THE NEIGHBOR: Excuse me...?

THE GARDENER: Just sayin'.

THE NEIGHBOR: What did you do? WHAT DID YOU FUCKING DO?!

The Neighbor panics, not sure whether to check his kid or get answers.

THE GARDENER: See ya 'round, Neighbor.

The Gardener exits.

LIGHTS OUT

a few words from

JOHN CONNON

When is the last time you were genuinely scared by something someone created?

I was genuinely frightened walking through the *Dead Exposure: Patient Zero* maze at HHN 28. It was dark and disorienting and you never knew when the strobe lighting would reveal an infected zombie.

Tell us about your contribution to our book. What was the inspiration?

The inspiration for *Neighborly* was a real incident where I had let my dog out while a repairman came over and the repair took about 45 minutes. My dog had been outside barking the entire time and my neighbor lost his mind and went off on me. I felt so terrible that the dog was bothering him, but I did think his reaction was extreme. So, I let my imagination take each character's reactions to even darker extremes for the sake of the play.

What do you love about the genre of horror?

I think what I love about horror is the playing out of classic good vs evil stories in a setting that is fantastical. We see so much genuine hideousness in the world with unchecked human cruelty and injustices. With the horror genre, we get the chance to see good battle evil in such fun exaggerated ways. And it's usually the best of human traits, ingenuity, courage, love that are required to vanquish the villain.

What is some of your favorite horror literature? Favorite Author?

I grew up on a steady diet of Stephen King. I loved *The Shining* so much. His bullied heroes, like the Losers Club of *It*, Charlie of *Firestarter*, Arnie of *Christine*, or *Carrie* really spoke to me. I love Anne Rice as well, for the psychological and philosophical questions she tackles about what it means to be a "monster." I also really dug the classics, *Frankenstein* and *The Phantom of the Opera*.

What are some of your influences?

I'd say King for sure, but I'm also very influenced by movies. James Cameron for *Aliens*, *The Terminator* movies and *The Abyss*; Spielberg for *Poltergeist, Jaws, Jurassic Park*; John Carpenter for the *Halloween* franchise and *The Thing*; Ridley Scott for *Alien*.

What is your favorite Halloween treat?

I love a Reese's in the shape of a pumpkin!

You are hosting the perfect Halloween movie marathon. What are the films you choose and why?

Halloween, Halloween II, Halloween H20 – does one need an explanation?? Michael Myers is the OG slasher and Jamie Lee Curtis is the perfect final girl. *Alien* – Sigourney Weaver is EVERYTHING! Also, the face hugger is perhaps the most horrific creature ever conceived. *Scream, An American Werewolf in London* – love the self-awareness and attitude of these movies. Great blend of horror and humor. *Poltergeist, The Shining,* and *The Changeling* (George C. Scott) – I'm a sucker for a great haunted house story and these are my top three. *Get Out* – unnerving suspense throughout with excellent social commentary. *The Thing* (John Carpenter) – the ultimate creature feature, great mounting dread and paranoia. *It: Chapter One, It: Chapter Two* – one of the very best adaptations of a Stephen King novel in my opinion. And not just because I'm in the second one! *Ha!*

If you could continue any horror story (book or film), what would it be?

I love the story of Ellen Ripley across the *Alien* franchise. I'm very interested in her journey beyond the franchise. She is an excellent character, bold, empathetic, still with a wink of humor, forced to make tough decisions, haunted by her experiences, yet willing to take the stand necessary for the greater good. I would like to explore Ripley where the franchise left her (**spoiler alert** a cloned version, exhibiting more apathy to her circumstances) and see her rediscover her humanity in the midst of yet another battle with the Xenomorph.

Describe the perfect Halloween.

It would have to be a several-day affair for me because I really do love the simple experience of handing out candy and seeing all the kids in costumes coming to the door. So, I'd have one evening for that and another for the uninterrupted movie marathon described above. Thirteen movies makes for a long day! And I'd be all about attending a big event like HHN at Universal Studios or Howl-O-Scream at Busch Gardens, being around a group of like-minded fans screaming our heads off all through the next great horror maze.

SCARE CRED: JOHN CONNON

John Connon is an award-winning writer, actor, content-creator based in Orlando, FL. He has worked as a scare-actor and has been featured in numerous horror maze queue videos as well as live press events for Universal Studios' Halloween Horror Nights. He recently got to live a Stephen King fan's dream come true playing Juniper Hills Security Guard John Koontz in It: Chapter Two. He is currently putting the finishing touches on his own short horror film, Puttering, which he wrote, produced, and directed.

ISLAND PULSE

BY ANDREA CORDARO

Manuel's dark hands traveled over the chalk board, scrawling out the word "Open". Snow fell around him, as he listened to the drums within, breathing in the cool winter air and admiring his handiwork. His old eyes smiled at his sandwich board, which contained an intricate cross symbol, decorated with spirals and curls. Manuel mused to himself, "where Papa Legba opens the door, blessings are free to walk in." El Club De Los Antepasados was open for business.

Out of the corner of his eye, he saw a six year old girl in a yellow dress slip passed him into the club, skipping and swinging a yellow orchid in her hand. He chased after her, leaving the cold white snow exterior for the warm vibrant world of the club. As quickly as she had appeared, she had vanished. She was nowhere to be seen. Had she been there at all? Or was she a trick of the eyes?

Manuel slid behind the bar, keeping in time with the lively beat of the Afro-Cuban jazz band. Quick hands pounded out a vibrant Caribbean beat, as he raised up a machete and brought it down on a coconut, milk oozing from the crack. The cheeks of the trumpet player expanded to release a new note, when a hot smokey haze began to fill the intimate room. Coconut milk swirled into a cup. The strings of the piano vibrated with life. The candles at the center of each table illuminated couples in their own small worlds. Manuel twisted a wet martini glass into salt. The drum beat quickened. Candles flickered violently. Sound burst out after having struggled for it's escape through brass tunnels. The bartender twisted his knife on the skin of an orange, peeling it off in a spiral. The songstress at the microphone parted her shiny red lips to release a deep cry, traveling over her tongue, her uvula dancing. Manuel rattled his shaker as the music became faster and more intense. And at its climax, a lighter sparked a flame.

Quiet now, a breeze blew over the banana leaf plants, and like a wave flowed through the room's deep red velvet curtains.

A man passed his fingers playfully through the flames of three candles, sitting alone in intense thought and taking in the music. There was something mysterious about Carlos. He had an air of gravitas about him, a seriousness and confidence. He wore a vibrant suit, but it was tailored and precise. He continued to play with the flames like a dance.

At the bar, Ana amused herself with one of her usual games. She flirted with the two young men beside her who dared to try to outdrink her. Sober as ever, she declared her victory, seven overturned shot glasses in. One man was only on his third shot and the other dropped his glass and fell off his chair. She bellowed with laughter which filled the room, her yellow dress seeming to grow brighter. Though wild, Ana carried depth behind her eyes. But her play things now were turning aggressive.

All this caught Carlos' attention. He turned around to look up at the bar, and put the men in their place. That is when they recognized each other. They hadn't expected to see one another there. Their paths had not met at a crossroad for a long time, and that was in a far away place. But chance encounters are never really chance, are they?

He beckoned her to join him. She smiled. Of course she would.

She turned around and leaned into the bar to whisper into Manuel's ear flirtatiously. He blushed. She reached in to her purse and instead of cash, pushed a yellow orchid across the bar. Manuel's eyes widened. He understood now and accepted the gift humbly.

She sat back in her stool and with precision she opened her lipstick, closed her eyes and held up her left palm gazing into it. Her palm reflected a warm light onto her face. Still with eyes closed, she applied her lipstick skillfully. Freshly applied perfume settled on her skin in droplets. She slinked her way through the club to join Carlos at his table.

Carlos savored the sight of her, and she heard it even in the way he said her name. "Ana".

She gave him a knowing look. She knew just what he liked. From her bag, she produced a hand rolled cigar. She smelled it, taking in its sweet aroma. And then she offered it to Carlos to do the same, running it along his nose. He smiled, approving.

"Light me", she invited.

Carlos took out an old match box and slowly and carefully laid out three very long cigar matches on the table. He ran the end of one of the long matches over his palm striking it with his skin. Carlos' raised up the lit match, so Ana could light the cigar. She turned it precisely between her fingers, toasting the outside.

"This reminds me of home," Carlos reflected. Ana laughed heartily.

"I am home", she declared.

"You certainly made yourself at home with those boys," he countered. Ana laughed, and murmured, "Home is where your love lives."

The match had now burned down. Carlos struck the second match on the table from his palm, and they continued lighting the cigar.

"Where is Belie?" He challenged.

Ana brushed this off. "Carlos, you don't need to worry about him." He laughed and asserted, "No. I don't. It's the other way around."

The second match had burned down. Carlos lit the third match and they concentrated on lighting the center of the cigar.

"But you're never angry", Ana purred.

"Those who allow themselves to feel anger, have no power over the situations which they so desperately attempt to control."

"But those who feel anger, have passion. They love something they want to fight for," she defied.

"Passion has many faces."

They took pleasure in challenging each other. It was through their duality, that they understood one another. The third match had burned down. Ana blew on the burnt end of the cigar, now glowing red hot. Fiercely, she sliced off it's head, and then lovingly blew her sweet breath again on the end, bringing it to life. Finally she lifted the cigar to her lips and drew in its heat. Smoke swirled out of her, leaving her lips and traveling across the table tickling Carlos. He loved to see her enjoy herself.

A waiter delivered a glass of rum in a high ball glass. Ana placed the lit cigar balanced on top of the glass like an offering, and pushed it across the table.

"My favorite", Carlos smiled. He leaned into her, sharing his fire, with a deep and intense kiss. She reveled in it, and when their lips had parted she studied him.

"So then...which face do you wear?" she pressed.

Casually, he puffed on his cigar. "Passion is suffering", he proclaimed. Ana opened her mouth, preparing to protest, but Carlos hadn't finished. "No! It is. See you and I are not so different. An agony accompanies the joy of love. It is like a death of the self. Those things which you would avoid; punishment, pain, shame, you will run toward them for your heart has transmuted your eyes, your mind and you can no longer look down and see where your feet are leading you."

"But if you're discovering pain when your feet are in pursuit, it's because of the strain you've put on them by resisting the path." Ana was now impassioned. "But really, you look on your love, and see yourself. There is no difference between your feet or theirs. For if one should not be able to go on, the other will carry you. So you or they, whomever does the walking, it doesn't matter, because you will both get there. You will run to love because when two have been divided there is a peace in their joining."

"Peace!" Carlos laughed. "Only after a man stares down Papa Guide can he know peace."

"But they're not choosing to die. Love is life affirming. It is in fact death's opposite. It is infinitely creative..."

"And what would you be creating from, exactly?" Carlos argued. "The act of creation is really the act of destruction. They are the same. Think of how life is created - hundreds of sperm die, so that one may crack open an egg."

For a moment, Ana's eyes traveled to the high ball glass, its sweat dripping down the side, two droplets becoming one. "And there is a peace in their joining", she mused.

"Only because they have passed through the fire, and it has changed them." The waiter arrived again, this time with a salt rimmed drink in a martini glass, a lime slice on the rim.

"Not everyone needs to cleanse through fire," Ana considered. "Some horses actually drink from the river."

She gracefully lifted the lime, squeezing it into her drink. Carlos watched the juice run down her wrist. Taking it up, he brought her hand to his lips, drinking it in with a kiss. "...some horses..." he concluded.

Of course, they were both right. It was a matter choice, after all. She licked the salt from the rim of her glass taking a sip.

"Do you drink this much when you're with Belie?" Carlos questioned.

"Ya know, Carlos, you drink an awful lot for—"

"—A saint?" he finished.

They chuckled. But then her mood shifted. She jabbed sarcastically, "What about your sweet little—".

"—It's too cold for her here," he interrupted.

"It is cold", she melancholically accepted. "What good is gold cobble stones if you don't own the street?"

"No. No," he reassured. "It's impossible to rise without being scalded at some point by the heat that carries you up."

"That's only true if you're being carried up." Ana closed her eyes and lifted up her hand, now reopening them she gazed into the palm of her hand. Welled up with emotion, Carlos saw in the reflection of her eyes the suffering of their people, the disenfranchised, and the forgotten. But contained in those tears, was the love that could heal those hurts. Finally, she looked at Carlos, saddened. He couldn't bear to see her

like this. He raised up a candle, devouring the flame. He leaned into her, cradling her close to him and breathing new life into her. Her mood lifted, and finally it was time to address the reason they were both there.

"So you heard the drums too?" she asked.

"Well I didn't come to see chalk art in the dead of winter," he joked.

"Look at them," she gestured up to the band. "They've worked so hard to be good, not brilliant but maybe just good. So that some day, if it were near, brilliance might choose them." Carlos laughed, nodding. "Well they've called it to them awfully close...let's go."

Carlos looked up at the band. "You like them?" he asked her, considering them. They were young and enthusiastic, and filled with a joy for their music which made them appealing to watch. He had appreciated them.

Ana nodded at Carlos with a wild smile. "They're like children," she proclaimed, filled with delight.

Carlos was honored. "With me?" he asked. Not wanting to presume. Ana nodded again, and they sat quietly for a moment drinking each other in. Suddenly, Carlos pulled her into him passionately for an embrace.

The audience applauded. Carlos, now dressed in white, sat on the stage, conga drums in front of him. The band began to play an old song. A song which is always familiar but never sounds the same. Emerging from the darkness, Ana, adorned in a long gold dress, floated her way to the microphone. Her song glided through the room, punctuated by the rhythm of Carlos' drum.

"Whoso danceth not, knoweth not what cometh to pass.

I would be born and I would bear.

I would eat, and I would be eaten.

I would be united and I would unite.

A house I have not, and I have houses.

A place I have not, and I have places.

A temple I have not, and I have temples.

A lamp am I to thee that beholdest me.

A mirror am I to thee that perceivest me.

A door am I to thee that knockest at me.

A way am I to thee a wayfarer.

My heart, my mother,

my heart, my mother;

my heart of transformations.

I am the tree, And you are the fruit.

Go and rise up, rise up, rise up,

rise up out of the egg in the hidden land."

Their performance was passionate, engrossing, emotional and all encompassing. Its climax ecstatic. Ana and Carlos looked down at the audience enraptured by their performance. Ana and Carlos looked up at the extraordinary performers from their seat in the audience. They are everywhere. And they are nowhere. Finally their performance ended. The original band members bowed, the audience roaring with applause. Ana and Carlos smiled, knowing that through them, they had given a gift of extraordinary beauty. They smiled at one another, at peace.

Suddenly, their table was empty. The jazz club was dark and deserted, with the exception of the bartender, Manuel. He approached their table and picked up an unsmoked cigar, atop an undrunk drink. He took a sip, and sung to himself, "rise up, rise up, rise up". He let out a hearty light-hearted Carribean laugh. He turned out all the lights on his way to the door. And he lifted up his lighter and lit his cigar.

A bucket of water thrown on the sandwich board washed away the chalk of Papa Legba's veve, and Manuel closed the front door.

a few words from

ANDREA CORDARO

What do you love about the genre of horror?

Horror provides us a unique freedom and opportunity to live out the outcomes of mysteries, the unnatural and bizarre — things we wonder about, but can never experience. Through horror, we can walk right up to death's door, knock and look within. This is part of the appeal — to have died and lived to tell the tale. But perhaps the greatest appeal is that these things are forbidden. We're breaking all the rules of what's supposed to be done, what's supposed to be enjoyed, what's decent. And really what's more enticing than forbidden fruit?

What is some of your favorite horror literature?

Edgar Allen Poe's *The Cask of Amontillado* created for me a romance with crypts and catacombs. A romance which brought me to visit one of the more macabre world sites - Palermo's catacombs. It is a striking and unusual catacomb, because unlike most of the other's in Europe, this one still contains the dead. There is also a child there, in a glass crypt which is miraculously preserved. We think of death and horror as being very wet - blood, guts, and slime. But in reality, the dead lose all bodily moisture overtime, crumbling to dust. Faces frozen in agony over hundreds of years, slowly eroding in the quiet basement of a monastery, forgotten by time.

What are some of your influences?

Being an actor/ writer/ film producer, I've tried to take in the best of art. My first love,like so many others, was Walt Disney. As a kid, I became obsessed with European History. I was a total anglophile, reading Shakespeare, Bulfinch's mythology, and *Harry Potter*. But I read all kinds of fantasy and science fiction - Gaiman, Lewis, Bradbury, Orwell and others. I had a talent for painting and was drawn in to the romance of Johannes Vermeer, and Lawerence Alma Tadema, and the mystery of Rene Magrite.

As I grew as an artist, a family friend, gifted me a copy of *The Artist's Way*, a book on creativity and spirituality. This really shifted my perspective on what art could be and it's role in my life. I discovered a love of theater, through a love of musical theater, and I started to perform. In college, I studied theater and world religions. I immersed myself in the craft of acting. Taught by two students of Stella Adler, I made it my mission to dive deep into the teachings of Stanislavsky, Strasberg and Adler. All the while, I was deeply spiritual, studying everything I could in the realms of western esotericism and eastern religions. In college, I discovered the great modern theologians Huston Smith, and Joseph Campbell. And I became fascinated by the psychology of the mystical experience found in the works of William James, and Carl Jung.

Coming into the entertainment industry, I began to make films with my brother Francesco who chose the path of a director. I watched the classics - Kubrick, Scorsese, Coppolla, Tarantino, Fellini… In particular I have loved Darren Aronofsky, Alfonso Cuaron, Guillermo del Toro, David Lynch, and Terrence Malick. And "fuck it", throw Kevin Smith in there too.

What is your favorite Halloween treat?

I'm one of those pumpkin spice latte women. However, Reeses Peanut Butter Cups are the greatest candy of all time.

You are hosting the perfect Halloween movie marathon. What are the films you choose and why?

I have always been drawn to a good horror film. Naturally, I love the classics *The Shining, The Exorcist, Night of the Living Dead, The Omen…* These films literally invented what modern horror is. They're transformative and masterful. But being a 90's kid, I get real nostalgic about Wes Craven's *Scream* films and Andrew Fleming's *The Craft.* These were my teenage sleepover movies. I mean you need a lead up to when your frenemy pulls out her Ouija board, and forces the planket to spell out "u die". Going farther back into childhood, watching Kenny Ortega's *Hocus Pocus* has become an annual Halloween tradition for me.

As a designer of horror theatre or experiences, explain your process.

I run a film production company called Fusion Box Films with my partner and brother Francesco. Though we do a variety of different types of film work, we love working with Haunters to create narrative films for their attractions.

It is no secret that some of the most successful attractions in the world are also film studios. This is because your audience's relationship with you begins before they step through your doors. For us, it's about taking the world a Haunter has created already and bringing it to life through story. It's a collaborative process and we love working with new artists. The story and the vision for the piece evolve together. We will be thinking about how the film will be shot, the editing, the sound design, as we are putting it down on the page.

Francesco will consider what camera and what lenses work best to capture this particular world. Do we want it to look like a 70s slasher? Do we want a dark black and white silent film look like Nosferatu? Casting is incredibly important. Your actors have to be believable in the world of the story and they have to have the skill necessary to carry their roles. Lighting and sound are integral parts to horror. You have to consider what to show and what not to show. Lighting can literally alter characterization. And sound is crucial to setting a mood and bringing an audience on an emotional journey. Try watching a horror film with no volume. Not very scary is it? Every film is different, and so the process is always evolving and requiring new things from you.

Tell us about your contribution to our book. What was the inspiration?

Island Pulse is really a love letter to my long-time boyfriend Kervin Peralta, a Dominican American actor/ percussionist. He speaks often about his Grandmother, whose spiritual practice, we have gathered was Dominican voodoo or The 21 Divisions. A practice which is now lost to him and his family. I could very much relate to this. My great-grandmother practiced what is now called Benedicaria — or the spiritual work which was done in Southern Italy to banish the evil eye. My Grandfather and his brother spoke often of how psychic she was.

Together, the two of us talked about working on a film. And this story, originally written as a short film, came about. *Island Pulse* is a commentary on the nature of creativity as a spiritual act. Though primarily inspired by the 21 Divisions — Joseph Campbell's *The Power of Myth*, and Elizabeth Gilbert's various works on creativity and spirituality were also influences.

Describe the perfect Halloween.

When I think about Halloween, I think about crisp air, caramel apples, and mischief. For most people, it gives everyone permission to play. It is the American Carnivale, and a holiday that involves your entire community. In my hometown of New Paltz NY, Halloween has always been a very big community affair. For me I feel a sense of nostalgia, that for one night a year, I can wear some crazy thing, and play pretend like a kid. There's this trickster energy about the night too - you never know what could happen - a trick or a treat. There are few occasions where adults are given an excuse to be both creative and mischievous. I think those are things people need to live a full life.

SCARE CRED: ANDREA CORDARO

Andrea Cordaro is a film producer, actress and voice over artist from New York's Hudson Valley. Off-Broadway: *Gay.Porn.Mafia* (New York Live Arts Theater, Audience Award Winner - Downtown Urban Arts Festival). Regional: *Antony and Cleopatra* (The Hudson Valley Shakespeare Festival). Television: *The Onion Sports Dome* (Comedy Central), *The Chew* (ABC) and *Mysteries at the Museum* (Travel Channel). Cordaro is the voice of Joan in *Warpath* (Lilith Games). She has provided narration for the popular YouTube channel The Financial Diet and the podcast *The Science of Storytelling*. She was also the 2019 voice of The Markie Awards. She runs her own film production company, *Fusion Box Films*, with her partner and brother, Francesco Cordaro. Their film *Cannoli, Traditions Around the Table* was funded by a grant from Anthony and Joe Russo (directors of *Avengers: Infinity War*), and won Best Documentary at New York Women in Film and Television's Film Festival. It is currently streaming on Roku and Amazon Prime.

SAFE HAVEN

BY FRANCESCO CORDARO

Cold open - three men in orange jumpsuits in the woods hiding behind a fallen tree, struggling to stay quiet as they catch there breath.

JOHN

I think we lost them.

MIKE

You see anything?

JOHN

Shhhh

Two flashlights emerge in the darkness of the woods.

JOHN

I knew this was a bad idea.

JASON

Theres only two of ‘em. We can take’em.

In the distance they hear a scream.

GUARD #1

Aghhhh, oh my God! Aaaaaa!!!

A flashlight drops. Two gunshots. The other guard runs toward them.

JASON

(Laughs) One less to worry about.

Out of nowhere a zombie appears and attacks Jason. John and Mike make a run for it with the guard close behind.

MIKE

Look!

They come across a house in the middle of the woods. A few more slow moving zombies appear in the distance. They manage to break into the house. They are in the doorway. Beat.

MIKE

Close the door!

JOHN

Shut up, Mike!

GUARD #2

WAIT! for god sake PLEASE WAIT!

We see the guard running toward the house, zombies all around him.

MIKE

What are you doing? Your really going to risk your life for one of them? He doesn't care about you. Shut the door!

JOHN

Shut your mouth!

MIKE

You're going to get us killed, John!

The guard runs up the porch, a zombie attacks him. They both fall into the doorway of the house. The guard's 9mm pistol slides across the living room floor. They can't close the door because the guard and zombie are in the way. John struggles to help get the zombie off the guard without getting bitten. Mike picks up the gun.

MIKE

John get out of the way!

Mike opens fire killing the zombie. He manages to close the door just before a hoard of zombies burst through the door. Beat.

JOHN

(Sarcastic) Now we know why you were locked up.

MIKE

{Inspecting the gun) Nice piece!

GUARD #2

Thanks.

The guard puts his hand out expecting to get his gun back.

MIKE

(Laughs) I think you are a little out of your jurisdiction here, chief. (Aims at the Guard)

JOHN

Mike, what are you doing?

GUARD #2

Please don't! I got a wife and two kids.

MIKE

Yea, I got my own.

JOHN

Mike, we all want to get out of here
and we are clearly out numbered out
there. We are going to need all the
help we can get if we plan to survive.

MIKE

John, always making all the decisions
for everyone. Guess who's got the gun now.

He points at the guard.

GUARD #2

Look, what do you want from me? I was
just doing my job. please let me go.
This uniform means nothing now.

MIKE

It means nothing now, But it did when
you almost cracked my head open while
your friends covered for you.

JOHN

Mike, This isn't about getting justice.

MIKE

Justice? What are you, his lawyer? Huh?
You wanna get a jury? (Pointing at the gun.)
I got the judge right here.

JOHN

Do you see what's out there? We need him
whether he's guilty or not.(Aims at John.)

MIKE

You're on his side now?

The window breaks. Zombies are trying to get into the house. Mike points the gun at the guard.

MIKE

What's your name?

GUARD #2

Jimmy.

MIKE

Ok, you wanna help us so bad? Lets see it.

Mike places a knife on the floor and kicks it over to Jimmy. Jimmy reaches for the knife and gets shot in the head. John smacks the gun out of his hand. The gun goes off. Shooting John in the foot.

JOHN

You bastard. You shot me!

John's shoe gushes blood. Mike still holds the gun. He backs away.

MIKE

You might wanna reconsider your last words.

JOHN

I've done a lot of things I regret Mike.(Pause) but at least I'm dying a better man then I was before.

Mike aims at John. The room fills with zombies from all directions.

MIKE

Back up!

Mike shoots the final three rounds at a couple zombies. Click. Click. The gun is out of ammo. The zombies eat Mike. Oddly, The zombies start to leave the house. The lights change in the house. Jimmy rises up covered in blood and puts his hand out to help John up.

JIMMY

Its ok John.

Jimmys voice changes to the Judges voice.

JIMMY

(mouthing judges words) Congratulations.

JOHN

What?

JIMMY

RESET Safe Haven.

PRISON OFFICE
Jimmy removes John's headset. Jimmy and John are in a big conference room. On one side are three chairs with John, Mike, and Jason sitting in them. They are wearing clean orange jumpsuits with there hands cuffed behind there backs. on the other side of the room is a long table with 6 professional business people.

JUDGE

Take the other two back to there cells.
(Pause) John Anderson, you have served 20
years of a life sentence. (Pause)
Do you feel rehabilitated?

a few words from

FRANCESCO CORDARO

As a designer of horror theatre or experiences, explain your process.

When working with a haunted attraction, I make a film. First, I must experience it as an ordinary scared patron. After that, I am excited to pull back the curtain and see how the magic happens. Me and my team will then work side by side with their art department to develop a story built around this terrifying experience. I am sure to stay true to the original vision of the attraction when making a film with them.

When is the last time you were genuinely scared by something someone created?

Lucky for me my imagination pays the bills, but it can also be a bit of a double-edged sword. I get scared very easily. I am always terrified every time that I visit the Headless Horsemen hayrides In Ulster Park, NY. The worst part is I am friends with so many of these folks and yet they still scare the hell out of me.

Tell us about your contribution to our book. What was the inspiration?

I have always loved mixing sci-fi and horror. They are both rooted in fear of the unknown. *Black Mirror* has done this so elegantly, creating new fears I didn't know I had.

What do you love about the genre of horror?

I love to be engaged in any form of art I'm enjoying. Great horror keeps you guessing what's coming next. Unlike any other genre people either love it or hate it. I tend to like things that force you to either love or hate them. Providing that level of polar emotion is a sign of great art.

What is some of your favorite horror literature? Favorite Author?

Communion by Whitley Strieber is the most horrifying book I have ever read. Just the picture on the cover gives me chills. Although this is a true story of a mans repeated contact with apparent aliens or visitors. This is a book I hope to be able to finish reading one day. It has given me nightmares every time I pick it up.

What are some of your influences?

I am most influenced by films from the 70's. Directors that have had the most influence on my work are Kubrick,

Coppola, and Scorsese. The 70's was such an exciting time for filmmakers, there was so much room for exploration. It was the first-time filmmakers were able to shoot outside of the studio lots. There was a film that forced me to become a filmmaker. When I was 5 years old my godmother took me and my cousins to see *Independence Day (1996)* in the drive-in movies. I was so terrified I laid behind the driver seat holding my hands over my eyes. I will never forget that night I had terrible nightmares, petrified I was going to be abducted by aliens. My older sister came to comfort me and explained in detail the process of making a film. After that I have always been obsessed with making films and the power of moving people in such great lengths.

You are hosting the perfect Halloween movie marathon. What are the films you choose and why?

I actually host a movie marathon every Halloween. There are 3 movies that are always on the list. *The Texas Chainsaw Massacre (1974)* is my favorite horror movie of all time. It is so raw and unapologetically real. *The Shinning (1980)* is a cinematic masterpiece that always cleanses the pallet from all of the overly violent horror films from the night. *Dawn of the Dead (2004)* One of my favorite remakes of all time. As much as I love and respect all of George Romero's work, this has to be my favorite zombie film.

Describe the perfect Halloween.

My perfect Halloween revolves around food and movies, my two favorite things. All the best fall foods. Carving pumpkins and eating candy dressed as either a clown or zombie.

SCARE CRED: FRANCESCO CORDARO

Growing up in his family's Italian pastry shoppe, Francesco learned about hard work at a young age. He also learned he didn't want to work baker's hours. In his early teens Francesco found his grandfather's JVC Camcorder. Inspired by *The Godfather* and Julius Caesar he directed and stared in his own version, *Don Julio Caesaroni*. This led Francesco and his friends to make all their own films. Francesco's first documentary out of college was a love letter to aviation. Funded on Kickstarter, he won Best Short Documentary at Newport Beach Film Festival. As a director he worked on a piece with Regis Philbin and Kathie Lee Gifford that was featured on The Today Show. His passion for gaming came full circle when he was sent to South Korea by Intel to shoot a series of documentaries on two of the best StarCraft players in the world. After winning a grant from the Russo Brothers, Francesco directed, shot, and cut a film in his family pastry shoppe about the importance of keeping Italian American traditions alive.

SKETCHY THINGS

BY FRANK DIETZ

"Broomstick Bunny"

"Aurora Wolf Man"

"Chiller Halloween"

"The Castle"

"The Real Hitchhikers of Anaheim"

"Little Monster, Big Dreams"

"Halloween Hitchers"

a few words from

FRANK DIETZ

What do you love about the genre of horror?

What I love about the horror genre (and science fiction) is that it pushes the envelope of imagination further than other genres. When I was very young, I was more scared of the outside world than what I would see on television. The monsters I grew up watching felt like friends. After watching them my imagination would be on fire, and I would write stories and draw for hours. And that has never changed.

What is some of your favorite horror literature?

Richard Matheson's work has always been my favorite, *The Shrinking Man* and *I Am Legend* were two that I read over and over. I am also a fan of his screenplay work, like *The Night Stalker* and *The Legend of Hell House*.

What are some of your influences?

Ray Harryhausen, Richard Matheson, Ray Bradbury, Basil Gogos, Frank Frazetta, Mort Drucker, Bernie Wrightson, Vincent Price, Boris Karloff, Lon Chaney Jr., Peter Cushing.

What is your favorite Halloween treat?

Reese's Peanut Butter Cup Pumpkins. Can't resist them.

You are hosting the perfect Halloween movie marathon. What are the films you choose and why?

Abbott & Costello Meet Frankenstein is the first movie I remember seeing as a kid, and clearly it left a strong impression. It will always be at the top of my list. Probably a few of the Universal monster films. *The Brides of Dracula, City of The Dead* (A.K.A. *Horror Hotel*), either *The Abominable Dr. Phibes* or *Theater Of Blood,* and Terence Fisher's *Island of Terror*. All of these resonate with me more than, say, *Friday the 13*th or *Nightmare on Elm Street.*

If you could continue any horror story, what would it be?

I always imagined continuing the Universal Monsters stories. Then Jeff Rovin came out with his marvelous *Return of the Wolf Man*, novel in 1998, and that satisfied my thirst for that.

As a designer of horror theatre or experiences, explain your process.
I haven't done a lot of live horror theater, although I did get to play Captain Hendry in Bob Burns' 2002 Halloween show of *The Thing From Another World*. I played it dead serious, as if all the folks experiencing the show where in actual danger. It paid off, as we had many of the folks screaming when the jump scares happened.

When is the last time you were genuinely scared by something someone created?

Horror movies generally don't scare me. I'm more scared of things like getting lost in the woods, or not being able to find my kid, etc. But George Romero's *Dawn of the Dead* scared me the first time I saw it. I was actually nervous walking into a darkened house that night. That hadn't happened since 1967, when I was eight and saw *Island of Terror* in the theater.

Tell us about your contribution to our book. What was the inspiration?
A few of these are sketches created for gallery shows where the theme was all things Halloweeney. I specifically addressed my childhood memories of Halloween... things like the Haunted Mansion, Aurora monster models, Ben Cooper costumes and the characters that bring back fond memories.

Describe the perfect Halloween.
A cool night filled with stars and, if you're lucky, a bright, full moon. Houses decorated with skeletons and spider webs. The streetlamps have flickered on, and you can see small groups of kids down the street, crossing from house to house. The smell of fireplaces is in the air, and the fallen October leaves crunch beneath your feet as you walk. The sounds are what I love the most. Children yelling "Trick or Treat," followed by "Thank you!" Even the sound of candy being dropped into open bags or pillowcases. Then squeals of joy and giggles. The sounds of youthful delight and happiness. That will always be my Halloween.

SCARE CRED: FRANK DIETZ

Frank Dietz is a screenwriter, producer, director, actor and animator. His work can be seen in such films as *Hercules*, *Tarzan* and *Atlantis - The Lost Empire*. He has produced two award- winning documentaries: *Beast Wishes - The Fantastic World of Bob and Kathy Burns* and *Long Live The King*, all about the legacy of King Kong. More recently he wrote the comedy feature *I Hate Kids* and is currently a writer on the AMC/Shudder television series *Creepshow*. Frank can be heard on his *Damn Dirty Geeks* podcast, discussing genre movies and television with industry colleagues and guest stars. Visit him at *SketchyThingsArt.com*

THE V FACTOR

BY KIM DONOVAN

INT. VALLEY LOUNGE. - EVENING

IlYSE, 40's, struggling actor/bartender, vegan and RYJIN, 40's, struggling singer, vegan, bears strong physical resemblance to Michael Jackson, sit at a corner table at the lounge. Ilyse sips from her wine.

ILYSE

Last nights show was so good,
I wish you could have made it out!

RYJIN

I'm sorry I couldn't hun but
hopefully I don't have to
work next time.

ILYSE

No worries, I totally get it.
My rent just went up AGAIN.
Can't afford to turn down any
bartending shifts.

RYJIN

Well you could always move back
to Ohio. Rent's a lot cheaper there.

ILYSE

Yeah, but then I'd be in Ohio.

Both shudder.

RYJIN

Well you never know, your big
break could be right around the corner.

ILYSE

I just wish there were more roles
for women "of a certain age," you know?

RYJIN

Kinda.

ILYSE

God, when I was a kid I was so sure
I'd end up having this awesome career
as an actress. I remember my first
dance recital, waiting in the wings
to go on. It was stormy that night so
the electricity went out but we went
on anyway and did our dance routine and
it was so much fun! I loved putting on
plays with my friends growing up too. I
just want to be able to do it for a
living, but that dream is definitely
slipping away faster each day.

RYJIN

No Callback from Thursday's audition?

ILYSE

Not a peep.

RYJIN

You know darling, I have a way
that can make things get better
(brushing her hair back from her
face)...or at least not any worse.

ILYSE

Thanks, but we've been through this
a million times. I know it's working
for you, but I can't do it. I won't
even succumb to the Botox craze.
I can't. It's not right.

RYJIN

Have some more wine. I'll be gentle.

ILYSE takes a sip. Rygin moves in closer. She stops him.

ILYSE

I said no.

RYJIN

Hmmm. You're lips say no, but your
eyes say yes.

ILYSE

That didn't work on me with my high
school boyfriend, and it won't work
for you either.

Rygin sits back.

RYJIN

I'm sorry. (Ryjin picks up a carrot stick from the veggie platter in front of them, dips it in some hummus and offers it to her. She takes a bite) But it's not a game set up for any of us to win. And even harder to win if you're a woman.

ILYSE

Tell me about it.

RYJIN

You need to do whatever it takes to get your foot in the door before the door shuts completely.

ILYSE

I know but-

RYJIN

Honey, you aren't getting any younger-

Ilyse shoots him a look.

RYJIN (CONT'D)

Maybe you're happy playing "mom" or "bitchy ex-wife" roles forever-or until the "grandma" roles start rolling in-

Ilyse elbows him playfully, but firmly.

RYJIN (CONT'D)

Sorry. Think about it though hun.

ILYSE

I just couldn't. It's not right. I mean the guilt of knowing I cheated would eat me alive.

RYJIN

So it's the guilt that keeps you from doing it? Or the principle?

ILYSE

Both. I guess. It's just caving into what society and the industry expects us to do.

RYJIN

It's your decision.

Ilyse puts her head in her hands out of frustration. Ryjin rubs her back, comforting her.

RYJIN (CONT'D)

I can help you. Let me help.

Ilyse lifts her head.

ILYSE

At least I'm at that perfect age where roles in my age range rarely require nudity.

RYJIN

Honey, you can show me your gorgeous body anytime.

ILYSE

I love you.

Rygin unbuttons a few of his shirt buttons sexily.

RYJIN

(in an uncharacteristic deep sexy voice) I'd love you down like no others. For hours.

Ryjin lifts his eyebrow a couple times, and ILYSE giggles.

ILYSE

That was actually pretty sexy.

Ilyse and Ryjin each sip their wine. Ilyse picks up the menu.

ILYSE (CONT'D)

I'm hungry. Where's our vegan cheese plate?

Ryjin ignores her and nibbles her neck.

ILYSE (CONT'D)

Okay it's been a while since anybody's nibbled by neck...but I know what you're up to. The answer is still no.

RYJIN

You know, enough of that vegan cheese will go straight to your thighs. Then you'll be old AND fat before you know it.

ILYSE

(hitting him with the menu)
It's not funny.

RYJIN

You know you want to.

ILYSE

I don't want to.

RYJIN

Tell me no if you really mean it.

ILYSE

(beat) I can't.

Ryjin sexily bites his own lip, subtly exposing fangs. drawing blood. Ilyse watches drops drip into his wine glass. Ryjin sets the glass back down.

RYJIN

Are you sure you can't?

Ryjin POINTS at the corner of one of Ilyse's eyes.

RYJIN (CONT'D)

Has that wrinkle always there?

ILYSE

It's an expression line.

RYJIN

Oh, you know who I saw out with a gorgeous 20-something last night? Your ex-boyfriend Mike. Too bad things didn't work out with him.

Ilyse looks solemn, knowing her youth is fading. Tears well up.

ILYSE

Fine. What do I have to lose?

She leans her head to the side and closes her eyes. Ryjin bites her neck fiercely. Ilyse gives a relieved smile. Ryjin sucks her blood until she falls limp, but still awake, much more relaxed.

RYJIN

(lifting an eyebrow with a devious smile) Wine?

ILYSE

I'd love some.

Ilyse sips from his blood-spiked wine, the final step in beginning the transformation. Illyse is in the midst of being reborn into a vampire when MINDY, late thirties/early 40's, aspiring actress, cocktail waitress, approaches

MINDY

(setting it down on the table)
Vegan cheese plate.

RYJIN

Thank you, miss.

MINDY

Mindy. My name is Mindy. Let me know if you guys need any-

Mindy notices Ilyse turning.

MINDY (CONT'D)

Is everything okay.. Here?

Ryjin flashes his fangs at her.

RYJIN

Everything is fine.

Mindy's eyes widen.

MINDY

Oh, my God! Those look great! Are they custom or did you get those pre-made ones?

RYJIN

Go away!

Mindy ignores him and sits down next to him.

MINDY

So seriously, what are you guys rehearsing for? A film or a web series? I've been in a ton of B-horror movies - usually

topless, but not so much anymore. Are
they still casting?

Ilyse looks on in disbelief as she continues transforming in agony.

ILYSE

Bitch, go away!

MINDY

Okay, I'm sorry you guys, but here...

Mindy reaches into her apron and pulls out two business cards. She tries to hand one to each of them.

MINDY (CONT'D)

If they're still casting, my IMDB link
is right on there, and so is are my links
to my website, SAG i- actor, Actors Access,
LA Casting, Casting Frontier, You Tube,
Instagram, Twitter, Facebook, and Snapchat.
Also my reel is on Vimeo and-

Ryjin snatches a card.

MINDY (CONT'D)

Cool thanks guys!

Mindy exits. Ilyse regains her composure and smiles at Ryjin.

RYJIN

Cheese?

Ilyse contemplates the cheese.

ILYSE

Wait. You know, I never thought to ask... blood is still an animal product how can we drink blood and still be vegan?

Ilyse bites into a piece of cheese.

RYJIN

Unfortunately it is a fact that we do need to cheat a little and have blood. It's the only thing that will satisfy our deepest hunger-but if you're going to cheat make it something worth cheating for.

ILYSE

Like what?

Ryjin smiles.

RYJIN

It's my personal philosophy that you are what you eat. Naturally, I try to do as much of my feeding off of other vegans, however, for a nice apertif if you will, I feel that if you want to be successful in Hollywood, you should sip the blood of those who already have success in Hollywood.

ILYSE

What do you mean? Celebrities?

RYJIN

Not celebrities. I mean the Hollywood Elite. A-listers with that quality that producers want that goes beyond looks or talent. It's in their blood...

ILYSE

Um, we can't go around killing A- listers. Somebody's bound to notice.

RYJIN

Oh, no. Always just a sip. Just enough. Too risky to cause the death of a single one of them. It's not as hard as you would think. I'll show you the ropes... are you free tomorrow evening?

ILYSE

Unfortunately I am.

RYJIN

Great. I'll pick you up around ten so we can stake out the Whole Foods at closing time.

ILYSE

Sniffing out vegan blood. Sounds like a great Wednesday night.

EXT. WHOLE FOODS MARKET PARKING LOT- NIGHT

A few last customers exit the market and walk to their cars. Ryjin and Ilyse crouch nearby between cars as Ryjin sniffs the air. A thin, pale HIPSTER walks past and Ryjin's eyes widen.

RYJIN

That one!

They watch as the HIPSTER approaches his Prius. Ryjin paces behind him, and Ilyse ducks under his vehicle. Ryjin overtakes him, the man struggles, but as he nears the vehicle, Ilyse grabs his ankles and he falls to the ground, knocking the man out cold. Ryjin grabs the mans shoulders.

RYJIN (CONT'D)

(to Ilyse) Pull him!

They work together, pulling most of the hipster under his vehicle. Ryjin goes in for the bite, and Ilyse turns away. She hears his flesh being bitten into.

RYJIN (CONT'D)

The cups!

Ilyse hands him the two SOLO cups from her jacket pocket, while still turning away from the gruesome sight. She can hear blood dripping into the cups, and tears well up in her eyes.

EXT. WHOLE FOODS MARKET PARKING LOT - MOMENTS LATER

The lot is now empty, except for the Prius. Ryjin and Ilyse sit on the back of the tailgate. Ryjin hands her a cup.

RYJIN

Drink.

ILYSE

I'm not sure I can.

RYJIN

You need to. It's for your own good. You don't have a choice.

ILYSE

(closing eyes) It's just a nice glass of Malbec. It's just a nice glass of Malbec.

She sips. It's not bad.

ILYSE (CONT'D)

Hmm. It is a little bit like Malbec. With slight undertones of Kale and cheap beer.

RYJIN

Hopefully at the event I'm working Friday night we can find some with a hint of success.

Ilyse rests her head on Ryjin's shoulder for comfort. He hugs her.

EXT. HOLLYWOOD HILLS MANSION - SATURDAY NIGHT

Expensive cars line the street in front, music from the house is heard, colorful lights emitting from the backyard and windows.

INT. HOLLYWOOD HILLS MANSION - DRESSING ROOM

JULIETTE, very pale, almost ethereal looking, Ryjin's makeup artist, is touching up his makeup.

JULIETTE

Now, sweetie, when you are on stage, remember to

RYJIN

I know, I know.

Ryjin starts to get up. Juliette stops him.

JULIETTE

(reaching for his hair) Wait! Your hair. Let me touch it up just a little more.

She has trouble as there is a bit too much product

JULIETTE (CONT'D)

Now what is this? It's too much! I told you before you only need a little product. It's dripping onto your costume. It's going to be difficult to get that out and it will fade it. Next thing you know you'll look like one of those Hollywood Boulevard characters wearing a raggedy costume that smells like poop.

RYJIN

I know, I'm sorry. I'll be more careful next time. I have to go meet my friend.

JULIETTE

Okay. Just remember me when you become one of them.

RYJIN

Of course. I've already got my Oscar
speech written with you being thanked first.

JULIETTE

That's my boy. Now go have a good show!

INT. HOLLYWOOD HILLS MANSION - MOMENTS LATER

Ilyse meanders over to the bar, where she spots JANTS, late 30's, resembles Johnny Depp, dressed as Jack Sparrow. Jants walks with a sparrow swagger as he grabs his grog.

JANTS

Hello my Lady!

ILYSE

(flustered) Jack Sparrow!

JANTS

There should be a captain in there somewhere.

ILYSE

I'm sorry. Captain Jack Sparrow- Johnny...
it's so nice to meet you.

JANTS

Pleasure is all mine. May I get you a drink?

ILYSE

Yes, sure! Thanks! A glass of wine would
be great, Mister Depp.

INT. HOLLYWOOD HILLS MANSION - BAR - SECONDS LATER

The BARTENDER hands her a glass of wine, and he tips well.

JANTS

(pointing to stage) The show is about to start. My friend is performing.

ILYSE

(confused) Your friend?

JANTS

My friend Ryjin is a Michael Jackson impersonator.

ILYSE

Ryjin is my friend too! He invited me. I didn't know he knew you.

JANTS

I'm not really him love... (lowering voice, speaking in his own voice) I'm Jants. I'm working this gig as an impersonator too.

ILYSE

Oh, my God! So you're not really Johnny Depp?

JANTS

No. I wish. More like Johnny Debt. I impersonate JD and Sparrow. Mostly Sparrow these days.

ILYSE

I bet the Sparrow thing is popular with the ladies.

JANTS

Oh, it is. I owe Johnny a great deal of thanks for inventing that character! Ladies seem to love the dirty drunken pirate look. Now I get most of my drinks paid for. I'm like the hot chick at the bar!

Ryjin takes the stage in full-on Michael Jackson makeup and costume and begins his routine as the crowd gathers around the stage. Jants and Ilyse make their way towards the stage. A moment into the show, Ilyse's stomach starts growling. She ignores it. Time passes into his next routine and she begins to feel week and her stomach grows hungrier, and notices veins pulsing in the captivated audiences necks. Her fangs begin to protrude. She looks at Jants. he is watching the show. She sneaks away, stumbling like a drunken sorority girl. Ilyse, panicked, rushes back into the main room. Ryjin's show is over. She spots Jants.

ILYSE

Where is he?

JANTS

Who's he?

ILYSE

Ryjin! I need to talk to him!

JANTS

Backstage. Don't go back there.
He's having some fun.

Ilyse rushes towards the dressing room. She opens the door, and finds Ryjin sucking the neck of a WASTED FEMALE VEGAN CELEBRITY.

ILYSE

(TBD, depends on which look-alike is cast)

Ryjin drops the wasted vegan female celebrity's passed out body to the floor.

RYJIN

I couldn't help it.

Ilyse looks at the blood dripping from Ryjin's mouth, and suddenly is horrified at the realization of what has happened, and what her life will be from now on. Ilyse runs out the door, and to a dark recess of the back yard, overcome with emotion. She collapses into the grass in tears.

ILYSE

I can't do this. I can't.

Her stomach growls more.

ILYSE (CONT'D)

I can't. I'm so hungry.

A male figure approaches her from behind. Ilyse turns. In the moonlight, she sees Ryjin standing above her, proudly, with what appears to be a small glass of port wine in his hand.

ILYSE (CONT'D)

(sobbing) Thanks. I could use another drink.

Ryjin smiles.

RYJIN

My dear, this is the finest port wine
you will ever drink!

Ilyse's stomach growls louder. She realizes what's in the glass.

ILYSE

I can't.

RYJIN

You need to. You'll die if you don't.
You can't ignore the hunger.

Ilyse doubles over from the pain of her hungry stomach. Ryjin passes the glass under her nose so she can smell it. She gets a good whiff and takes it from him. Ilyse takes a hungry gulp, and as she drinks faster, blood dribbles down her chin. She can't get enough, and licks the glass dry, before falling to the ground in complete ecstasy. Ilyse writes in pleasure as though she is being given multiple orgasms by an unseen being. She continues to write, orgasmically. Ryjin looks concerned, and sits with her, waiting, watching.

RYJIN (CONT'D)

Did you take something earlier?

ILYSE

No. You know I don't do drugs! That Blood!
Oh, my god. It's better than sex!

Ilyse continues writhing.

RYJIN

I knew you'd like it. Not this much...

ILYSE

Who's blood? It's soooo good.

RYJIN

Are you drunk?

ILYSE

(still in ecstasy) Head spinning. Not
drunk. Most euphoric experience ever.
Best vegan blood ever! I must get more of it!

RYJIN

It's not that easy. I just lucked out.
He moves fast.

Ilyse becomes calm, and relaxed.

ILYSE

Who's is it?

RYJIN

(uneasy) I can't tell you. We should't know this.

ILYSE

(clutching at his shoulders, looking straight into his eyes) Tell me! We need to get more!

RYJIN

(having an epiphany) It's not just any vegan blood.

ILYSE

Definitely not! Wow!

Ryjin clutches her face with both his hands.

RYJIN

I think one of them-is one of us.

Ilyse reacts to his suggestion. Suddenly Juliette appears unseen by them from behind with a large object, and raises it over their heads and knocks them both out unconscious.

JULIETTE

Time out, my children!

(if legal/permission/and find look-alike-or-sound-alike, otherwise end on Juliette's line)

A-List vegan celebrity appears, takes the object from Juliette. A-Lister looks down at Ryjin and Ilyse on the ground.

The END, or to be continued....

a few words from

KIM DONOVAN

As a designer of horror theatre or experiences, explain your process.

Well, I've never designed a professional haunt, but for my home haunted Halloween parties I generally try to think of a theme for each room. Then I go shopping. While looking for sales. I have a few creepy food staples, like guacamole in a zombie head and a skull covered in hummus for dipping fresh veggies, and jello brain made with vodka can be a fun time… I have a neighbor who gives me any coupons she finds:) I incorporate different music/ sounds for each room. It's like a haunted house, but in a 850 sq. ft apartment in the San Fernando valley.

When is the last time you were genuinely scared by something someone created?

The poo in a Tupperware container while walking under an overpass in downtown LA. on my way to work.

Tell us about your contribution to our book. What was the inspiration?

I read the first one and recognized numerous names in it and wished I could have been a part of it. But I'm here for the second!

What do you love about the genre of horror?

I like that it makes many of our daily problems seem trivial in contrast, and usually makes you feel like you survived something horrific, which can help you deal with regular life easier, the adrenaline rush. The facing your fears aspect. As an artist/former haunter I appreciate the detail the FX artists put into their work to make things seem realistic.

What is some of your favorite horror literature? Favorite author?

I don't know why but I'm not much of a fiction reader. I do need to make more time for that. I'm very A.D.D. so that probably has a lot to do with it. Not that I get totally distracted, but I just have to be constantly multitasking, which makes reading difficult unless I'm isolated in a room with zero distractions. I'm not sure what that is. But I have been reading books by friends lately. At the End of Church Street is one fun book I recently read written by fellow Terror on Church Street alumni Gregory Hall. His dark humor shines throughout this book!

What are some of your influences?

Former haunted attractions I've worked at: Terror on Church Street (Orlando), Skull Kingdom (Orlando), Blood Manor (NYC), Jekyll & Hyde Club (NYC), Halloween Horror Nights @ Universal Studios (Orlando and Hollywood). Also, I was born in October so I always felt Halloween was MY holiday growing up, so it's really a part of who I am.

What is your favorite Halloween treat?

Well, I've been vegan since 1995 but I have been known to indulge in a leftover Snickers snack size after Halloween... and Reese's Peanut Butter cup.

You are hosting the perfect Halloween movie marathon. What are the films you choose and why?

A Nightmare on Elm Street, Beetlejuice, Interview With the Vampire, Bram Stoker's Dracula, Devil's Rejects, and *Warm Bodies.* Horror, dark comedy, romantic comedy, sexy...each one is quite different than the other, so a little something for everyone.

If you could continue any horror story (book or film), what would it be?

Interview With the Vampire. I know there have been sequels, but I mean with the original actors...but yeah, I hear Pitt and Cruise cost a lot, so probably unlikely.

Describe the perfect Halloween.

(1) Day off work as well as the day after. (2) Crisp fall air, but not too cold. Maybe sweater weather. (3) A trip to a cool haunted house out in the middle of nowhere. (4) A few good friends to enjoy it with. (5) A good Halloween party in a house with tons of creepy creative details and guests who go all out with their costumes. (6) Good wine.

SCARE CRED: KIM DONOVAN

Kim Donovan has performed in scareactor roles at the following haunted attractions: Terror On Church Street (Orlando), Skull Kingdom (Orlando), Blood Manor (NYC), Jekyl & Hyde Club (NYC) Halloween Horror Nights Universal Studios (Orlando and Hollywood). She is the screenwriter of the award-winning feature screenplay ScareActor, inspired by experiences working in some haunted attractions, and is currently hoping to find producer to help make it:) She currently lives in Sherman Oaks, California.

TRIBES OF THE MOON

why i love the monsters and my fellow tribe

BY JESSICA DWYER

Why do I love horror films? That's a question you may be asked a lot as a fan of a genre that has been maligned and misunderstood since the beginning of motion pictures. But it isn't just the movies that were treated with strange looks and gasps. We horror fans have been treated with that sort of reaction since we first picked up a copy of *Famous Monsters* or a VHS tape of *Evil Dead*. Our first *Nightmare on Elm Street* t-shirt we dared to wear or the first time we really went all out for our Halloween costume...we got the stares.

But the answer to the question isn't a complex one but at the same time it is. It isn't just the movies or the monsters, even though those are part of it. It's the people and the culture, it's finding the ones who understand you and get it, who've been there. Horror movies are the genre of the outsider, the one who didn't fit and within those movies we celebrate that.

It isn't just the films, it's the whole package. Going above and beyond with your own personal haunt for Halloween where your decorations have spilled out onto the sidewalk from your porch. You realize you've spent more on Halloween decorations that year than you have all the other holidays decorations combined for the last five. But that's okay because it's worth it to see the looks on the kids faces when *Freddy Krueger* hops out of those bushes. Then there are he books, the video games, the clothes, the prints, the collectibles...it's a lifestyle and it makes up so much of who we are.

But again, you are asking...why do you like horror movies so much?

And for the answer to that question I'm going to go way back in time to when I was around 5 or 6 years old. I grew up in a speck of a town in the Southern part of Illinois. I was a sickly and overweight kid who lived next a patch of road right out of Pet Sematary. You didn't walk near that road much less ride a bike on it and it didn't matter because there was really nowhere to go anyway.

It was lonely and I didn't have friends because I had a family that was pretty insular. Early on I started watching a lot of TV and that's when it all started. Right around the same time the bullying about my weight started I discovered *Creature Features* late night on PBS. This was the first time I would ever see *Dracula* and *Frankenstein*. *Universal's Classic Monster* movies were magic. They were like dark, black and white fairy tales that snagged my young brain in a way that nothing else had. Maybe I was too young, but I don't think so. Because it was here that I found my friends. Within the story of *Frankenstein*, the poor lumbering monster who didn't ask for anything happening to him, I found a kindred soul. He only wanted to be accepted. He felt like an outsider because he was shunned for the way he looked. If that didn't speak to a kid who was bullied, I don't know what could.

The monsters in the Universal films were all outsiders. Dracula was unlike any others around him, Larry Talbot's Wolfman hated himself and couldn't control what he was, The Creature From The Black Lagoon was the last of his kind, with no one else to understand him. Somehow my younger self realized these "bad guys" were just as much of a weirdo as I was, and I could relate to them.

Pretty soon my elementary school years were filled with reading comic books like Tomb of Dracula and lots more things I was way too young for including old copies of Dark Shadows novels. I even did a book report on

Barnabas, Quentin, and the Mummy's Curse in 5th grade. None of the other students knew what the heck this was but I think my teacher did because I got an A.

High School not surprisingly was even rougher and as I got older, I learned about some new films and fiends who would become friends. Fangoria become even more a staple along with Gorezone. I discovered Clive Barker, Stephen King, and the magic of VHS horror films. It was also during this time I would get called a Satan worshipping b*** and other more colorful and imaginative words because I liked to wear t-shirts with Freddy Krueger on them.

I was a lone fat girl who liked horror movies going to a high school with less than 200 students. It was in a town where there were literally no African American families or Latino families. One of the nearby towns is now well known for being one of the most racist areas of Southern, IL. If you didn't fit a certain mold you weren't going to have a smooth ride through your time. Needless to say, I didn't have a fun time.

I retreated into the books and movies populated by my friends. These stories were my haven away from the reality of what went on at school or at home. I found something beautiful in the Books of Blood and how Clive Barker could turn something horrifying into something seductive with just the phrase he used. And while it wasn't the same as having a group of buddies to hang out with, these characters and creatures, stories and strangeness gave me a haven and helped me learn.

I grew to realize the strange and different weren't something to be feared. I fully believe that these artists, their creations, those monsters helped me see beyond the near-sighted eyes and limited beliefs of not only some of my family but the community that I grew up in. These writers, filmmakers, and everyone involved reveled in the different, they embraced it. I would sit up late listening to Joe Bob Briggs unleash a string of consciousness history of some of the most bizarre films I've ever seen, and it was a lesson that I soaked in like a sponge. He was my teacher of the transgressive and I would eventually leave my prom early to head home and watch him host a Mummy movie marathon on Monstervision.

In 1990 a movie came out that showed everything I had learned and felt about my monsters and friends. I was 15 years old when I came face to face with the Tribes of the Moon. I would wind up driving an hour and a half to see Nightbreed on the big screen in the only theater showing it around me. I was transfixed by the story and by creatures that came alive on that screen. Finding ones who will accept you for who you are, for what you are, for what you love, no matter what. Clive Barker had once again showed us what being an outsider was like and that we only needed to find our tribe to no longer be on the outside. That promise of the breed stuck with me as much as the images of the breed themselves.

When I was 16 (before the prom night with Joe Bob and the bandage wrapped shambling Kharis) I had something magical happen. I went to a horror movie convention. Suddenly…I realized I wasn't the only one like me out there. It was amazing. There was Robert Englund, Doug Bradley, Zacherley, and even Uncle Forry. There were people wearing the same sort of shirts I owned. There were people buying trading cards of Jason Voorhees. And there was Clive Barker, in person.

I wasn't alone. I'd found my people, my tribe. I met Tony Timpone, the man I'd seen as hero on TV defending horror movies against talk show hosts and angry parents alike. I met Clive Barker and was able to tell him how much his work had meant to me. Teenage me was in heaven.

Of course, after the weekend you have to go back to reality (there's a reason it's called con-depression) but things seemed to get better after that. Maybe it was because I realized after all that time there were others out there. People I could just start talking to, without preamble, over the cover of a video cassette or an image from the latest Full Moon Entertainment movie. Either way, it seemed to get better.

I'd eventually get out of that small town and I'd break free from the seemingly eternal mentality that would be present in a lot of the people that lived there. Not all of them of course, but enough that "different" isn't something you want to be.

I moved far away and through that love of horror films I started talking to other fans online. I found friends, a fanmily if you will. I started writing and working in this world that I had been searching for for so long. I'd eventually start going to horror conventions every year because of this work. At these shows I found my own breed. This group was as colorful and diverse as anything out of Midian. White, black, brown, straight, gay, and all points in between and all linked by a love of the monsters who understood us when no one else did.

Why do I love horror you asked? Why do I love seeing the looks on kids faces when I scare them on Halloween and then they come back through the door of my haunted garage again and again, year after year? Why do I keep collecting movies, books, and things? Here's my answer.

It took me a long time to finally find my place but when I did, I knew it. We're the strange and unusual. We're the kids that found a friend in Frankenstein. We all dreamed about running away to where the monsters lived. We are all books of blood to be read by those that know our language.

We are the Tribes of the Moon and you are welcome here just as I was.

a few words from

JESSICA DWYER

As a designer of horror theatre or experiences, explain your process.

When we do our "at home haunt" for Halloween, I like doing something that will flow well and utilize the space we have. We've gotten big enough that we're now in the cul-de-sac and no longer just In the garage. When you don't have a lot of space you figure out ways to make It just look good. With the canopy tent we realized It looked like a carnival design so we went with a twisted fair booth with a horrifying and gory snack bar. It worked :)

When is the last time you were genuinely scared by something someone created?

There was a recent Facebook/TikTok video someone did that really got me. Little girl in her room and her dad flips the light switch on. Every time he does, you see a figure In the hall. The last time he does It the thing suddenly runs at the camera and you see a close up of the face. Even with no sound that got me.

Tell us about your contribution to our book. What was the inspiration?

It was my life and my journey into what horror really means to me and how my love for It has influenced my entire world. It's as personal a story as I can share.

What do you love about the genre of horror?

Horror can come in so many guises and ways. There's the horror of love, of death, of fear. Horror films and stories can be used to speak about things we won't normally speak of because It's too uncomfortable but If you disguise It just right using the black velvet drape of the genre you can get people to see something they may never have thought of seeing before.

What is some of your favorite horror literature? Favorite Author?

This Is tough. I love Barker, Lovecraft, and we wouldn't have the same sort of stories If Mary Shelley hadn't written what she had. But Poe just has a special place in my heart. His work Is beautiful, tragic, oddly funny sometimes, and he never got the recognition he deserved while he was alive.

What are some of your influences?

Debra Hill was a trail blazer for women in the world of horror. Joss Whedon knows how to write ensemble and snappy dialog better than most. Clive Barker Is a modern master and we don't have many of them left. Dan Curtis changed the face of horror on TV more than once.

You are hosting the perfect Halloween movie marathon. What are the films you choose and why?

Well, *Halloween* would have to be Included because It's sort of a rule. *Masque of the Red Death* because Vincent Price needs to be represented and It's a party-movie right? *Fright Night* because It's one of the best vampire movies ever made. And I'll Include Romero's *Dawn of the Dead* because It's one of the best zombie films ever made (and fits that description of how you can use the genre to speak about things that some people get uncomfortable about.)

If you could continue any horror story (book or film), what would it be?

This might be cheating but I would love to have a live action version of the DC Comic *I, Vampire* (comics are books!) There never has been one done and It's one of my favorite horror series. The original run has some of the most beautiful art around and Andrew Bennett Is such an amazing character. And bonus, the main villain Is a woman named Mary who started out as maiden fair and winds up the Queen of Blood.

Describe the perfect Halloween.

Having the haunted garage be up and running before the kids start showing up. No rain and fantastic weather. Having pizza delivered an hour or so In. Wrapping up and getting everything put away without Incident and not feeling too exhausted. Curling up with leftover pizza and candy and watching a Joe Bob Briggs marathon until 4am and passing out. Seriously, how can you fault this?

SCARE CRED: JESSICA DWYER

Jessica Dwyer has written for numerous magazines and websites covering the entertainment industry. She has also written fiction and non-fiction published in anthologies. She's recently published her first entry in a trilogy, Silver and Rubies. Jessica's also a producer and is working on upcoming film and TV projects. Her online webzine and YouTube channel, Fangirl Magazine is still going strong as is her radio show/ podcast Fangirl Radio which gives the point of view of female fans of horror, sci-fi, and other genres in the world of entertainment.

THE ELECTRIC CHAIR

BY ED EDMUNDS

In October 1995, we had an attraction at Distortions called Dark Museum. We wanted to have a good gag at the end, so we came up with the idea of making an electric chair with a rubber man that violently shook, screamed and smoked. When the next Transworld Halloween Show rolled around, we took it, thinking it would be a fun addition to the show booth but I only expected to sell 6 or so since at the time it was the most expensive prop ever at the trade show running a wopping $3800.00.

The response was amazing. We sold over two-hundred the first year. Up until then, animatronics were tongue and cheek, family friendly and mostly at theme parks. The Chairs showed up at Halloween Attractions all over the country. Newspapers and television stations came out and attendance at the attractions that had them went way up. I think attraction owners realized that haunted houses could be serious business if they invested more money in them. It was simply a product that was of its time, but it radically accelerated the growth and quality of Halloween events.

The funny thing is we had no idea what we were doing; it was just another product like so many we tried over the years, just throwing spaghetti against the wall to see if it would stick.

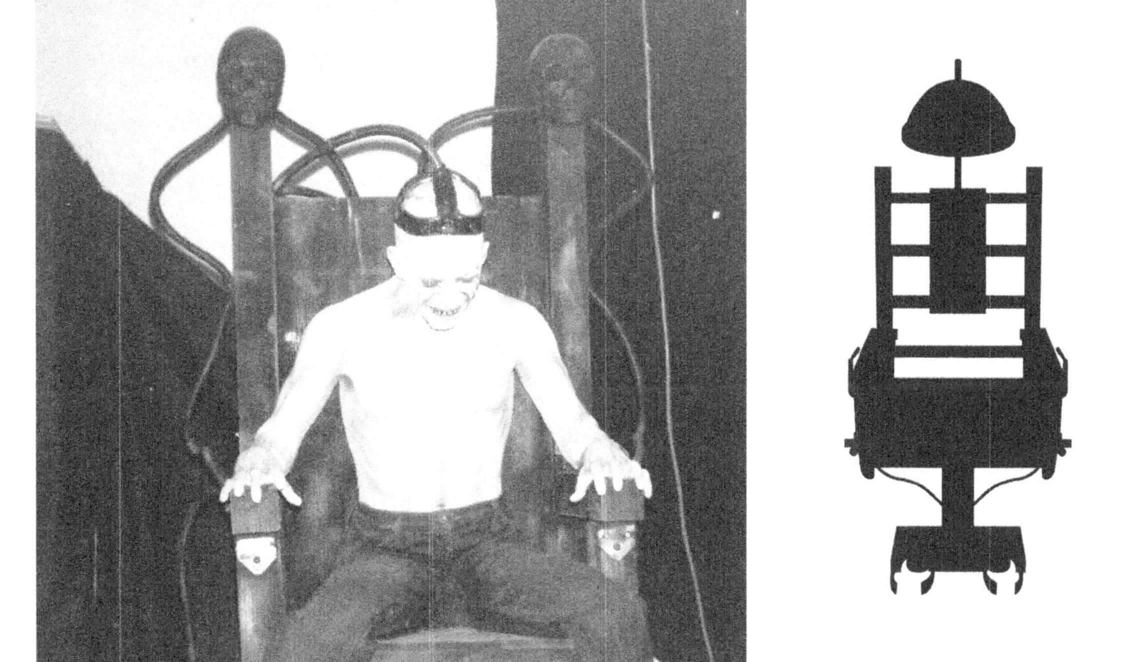

PENITENTIARY
HIGH VOLTAGE

HIGH VOLTAGE

a few words from

ED EDMUNDS

As a designer of horror theatre or experiences, explain your process.

We start by trying to dream up what would be cool and what people would like

- The idea(s)are sketched out in roughs altered and decided upon.
- The piece is sculpted and various departments look at It to see if there will be production problems.
- The piece is cast, generally in plaster.
- The mold is cleaned, poured and pulled.
- If it is a moving piece an armature and motors or cylinders are designed and installed.
- It is painted, dressed and haired.
- Then it is photographed, videoed and put out into the world to see what the public thinks!

When is the last time you were genuinely scared by something someone created?

Our twenty-one-foot tall skeleton. I thought we would die trying to install it in the rain with sixty-foot lifts.

Tell us about your contribution to our book. What was the inspiration?

I always like to know how things came into being that have a big influence.

What do you love about the genre of horror?

I like how a flickering image in a little box can draw you in and scare you.

What is some of your favorite horror literature? Favorite author?

1984 by George Orwell. *The Time Machine* by H.G. Wells.

What are some of your influences?

Outer Limits, Planet of the Apes, John Chambers, Dick Smith.

What is your favorite Halloween treat?

Reese's Peanut Butter Cups.

You are hosting the perfect Halloween movie marathon. What are the films you choose and why?

The Exorcist because it's truly scary. Also *The Time Machine.* I tend to like most time travel movies and this one is cinematic genius

If you could continue any horror story (book or film), what would it be?

The original *Outer Limits* series done with the same artistry, and a little more funding.

Describe the perfect Halloween.

Everything is shipped and we can all crash!

SCARE CRED: ED EDMUNDS

Ed Edmunds started Distortions Unlimited in 1978. Originally, the company produced Halloween masks and hands. As the years went by, Distortions expanded into props, life size monsters and animatronics.Throughout the 80s, most of the products were sculpted by founder Ed Edmunds. Being heavily into sci-fi as a child, much of the masks produced at the time were of aliens and other creatures of the sci-fi genre. In 1981, Marsha Taub joined the team and became co-owner of Distortions. In 2011, the Travel Channel began a series called Making Monsters, which documented the process of making Halloween props and animatronics inside the Distortions Colorado warehouse. The channel stopped producing episodes in 2013, but continues to rerun the episodes in the days before Halloween. Favorite Distortions Products are Shake & Bake and the Monster of the Month line Roles at Distortions include Design, Painting, Sculpting, a little bit of everything including janitorial services. With 35 years in business, the company is one of the biggest and most successful props and animatronics makers for professional haunted houses.

A STUDY OF DREAMS

Scene 4

BY SARAH A.S. ELGER
CO-WRITTEN WITH NIKHIL MENEZES.

Olivia enters the room a changed woman. Her hair is slicked back. Her makeup stronger. She is now wearing heels instead of flats. She walks and speaks with confidence, control. She commands attention from the entire room, speaking loudly.

Olivia: Do you know what my day consists of? I wake up. I make coffee for my husband. And then I type. All the notes that my husband writes, I type. He writes about dreams. My dreams, mostly. He writes about psychologists. He writes about the chemistry of the brain. And he writes it all down in chicken scratch. (she laughs) I think I'm the only person in the world who could read those notes.

During this, lights change and dim as if the aura of the room is following Olivia. Limbo can sense the disturbance in her presence and quietly instructs people in the audience to crouch/hide, that Olivia now has powers that could put them in danger.

Olivia: I wasn't born thinking I would spend my days as a glorified secretary to a self-proclaimed therapist of a husband. No, I once had my own dreams and aspirations. Dreams I was too afraid to ever tell him. Afraid of being laughed at and judged.

The Sandwoman becomes visible during the following part of the speech, lurking and looking on perversely as if Olivia is her proudest creation. Olivia walks toward Isabelle, as if she is the only person in the entire room she sees, eyes fixated on her.

Olivia: I still don't know what she is. All I know is that she is good for me. She doesn't see the ink under my fingernails. She doesn't see the bags under my eyes. She only sees those dreams that everyone else never bothers to see. And she gives me the power to achieve them.

Olivia approaches Sandwoman, face to face, putting her arms seductively across her shoulders.

Olivia: She understands how the physical world holds us back with its attachments and obligations. She has taught me only by staying asleep can I ever truly be free. She fills my dreams… opens my eyes… to my desires…

Just as the two move to kiss each other, the lights go wild, pulsing sounds happen, then all goes black. Sounds of passion are followed by silence. The lights return and the two are gone. Left behind is Olivia's shirt.

Limbo cautiously emerges from hiding and walks over and picks up the shirt, hanging it on the mantle.

a few words from

SARAH A.S. ELGER

What do you love about the genre of horror?

Monsters! I love everything about fantastical creatures, from their backstories and relationships to humans, special effects make up, to movement style and facial expression! I find I relate to many of these monsters as I believe there is a monster in each and every one of us. I feel mine comes out as a hunched over Nosferatu creepily walking up the stairs with my shadow sometimes and others the ravenous Pale Man..

What is some of your favorite horror literature?

I love the variety of Neil Gaiman's novels. My favorite is *Neverwhere*, which is more of an urban fantasy genre but there are some of the most beautifully dark and vivid scenes which have latched into my head.

What are some of your influences?

I was fortunately to visit this stunning castle in Gruyere, Switzerland that overlooks gardens and mountains, yet inside holds a vastly different vibe. This is where a museum of H.R.Giger's work lives. And it is not just all about *Alien*, although there is a gorgeous large sculptural table and chairs that are very much *Alien* in design. Much of the work is dark and stunning large paintings as well as a very 18+ gallery on the most perverse side of Giger, all equally mind-blowing. Across the street is an entire Giger designed bar that is the most inspiring and haunting themed bar I've ever encountered.

You are hosting the perfect Halloween movie marathon. What are the films you choose and why?

Nosferatu to start the night off with style.

Cabin in the Woods to remember what horror can really mean.

Get Out in the same ways *Cabin in the Woods* is horror, I like to think about who the real villains are.

Pan's Labyrinth to move into a more fantasy direction as the Halloween drinking is starting to kick in.

Hereditary to prepare for what is next.

Serbian Film only to be watch if completely intoxicated so that I won't remember much of it the next day.

Spooky Buddies because nothing is better than talking puppies in costumes and overacting 'creepy' characters after surviving watching #6 to help me fall asleep…

As a designer of horror theatre or experiences, explain your process.

For me, it all starts with the themes, world and characters. Then it evolves into the conflicts between those characters. I like to feel like I can step into the world in my imagination and then form stories inside that world. It's like building the playground first then having endless ways to play inside that space. During that time, I focus on mood and tone. I think about what I want guests to feel. Once those main elements are established then I think about how to design the set, lighting, and movement of guests so that they enhance the world and bring the story to life.

Tell us about your contribution to our book. What was the inspiration?

This is a short scene from our production of *A Study of Dreams* that took place in Orlando, 2017. It's the moment one of our characters transitions from a meek and mild-mannered woman into something so much more. It's wonderful to think about how far women have come with equality, yet so many horror movies still feature the woman as the meek or slutty character that usually is surface level. I like to be inspired by challenges individuals face in their daily lives and tweaking it even slightly can turn from a normal scene into something that is horrific. True horror comes from the everyday life and the world around us that we gawk at on the news and believe that it'll never happen to us.

When is the last time you were genuinely scared by something someone created?

Anything from a movie or book that jumps out and goes boo. It's very easy for me to sit at home at night and get creeped out by a shadow. I'm a giant wuss and scaredy cat. When I first started working at Universal and went to HHN for the first time, my coworkers made me go in front of the line because they knew I'd be entertaining to watch and get freaked out by every scare.

Describe the perfect Halloween.

Carving weirdly disfigured pumpkins and getting a sugar high on candy.

SCARE CRED: SARAH A.S. ELGER

Sarah A.S. Elger's themed entertainment career spans work with wizards, volcanos, King Kong, Big Bird, fast cars, and secret R&D projects for Walt Disney Imagineering, Universal Creative, SeaWorld, NASA, and Chimelong. Today, Sarah is the founder, Creative Director, and CEO of Pseudonym Productions, where she has co-written and directed seven original immersive experiences with an emphasis on open world gameplay, branching narratives, and meaningful interactions that connect people in unexpected, memorable ways. She leads teams of actors, scenic artists, designers, and technicians to bring to life vibrant fantasy worlds, themed environments, and surprising stories online and in real life.

A GHOULISH GALLERY

BY GEORGE FREI

George Frei ©

R.I.P.
R.I.P.
George Frei ©

George Frei ©

George Frei ©

George Frej ©

© George Frej

a few words from

GEORGE FREI

As a designer of horror theatre or experiences, explain your process.

Whatever I'm creating, it all starts with a story. The best creators I think connect with their audience. Horror genre in particular connects with their audience on a primal level. We find ourselves rooting for our protagonist to get away from that evil thing chasing them, or abolishing that evil entity in the world. So I'll explain my process in two different scenarios.

A lot of times when your working professionally your given a basic story to design/illustrate from. My job as the art director/set designer is to take all the information given and design the client's vision to the best of my ability. The first step is to take the basic story and draw out concept sketches for the client. Sometimes you are given the freedom to explore a bit and add your own ideas to further the story. I love those types of projects because you are now collaborating with the client and bouncing ideas around for the betterment of the project. After a concept has gone through with some revisions to narrow down the idea I finalize the comp to a more finished vision to what the client wants done. Then I'll move on to color comps to establish an overall mood of the final shot/or Wow moment. This will also help the team understand lighting, placement of characters, props, etc.

Once the final color shot has been approved the team will get together and all discuss how to best handle any builds, lighting, and overall show direction. I will then move on to design a breakdown of all elements for the show. This would include all production elements, guidelines, and essential details to get the job done. Once all design work for the show is broken down appropriate vendors to fabricate what I designed are called and build timelines set by the team. As the job moves into the production stage some adjustments may need to be made to design elements based on the vendors recommendations. This sometimes happens because of safety concerns for guest attendance and so on. As the art director/designer on a project I'm also responsible to oversee builds and final install of the project. When I start any personal projects like my book George Frei's *Monster Series* for example I ask myself these simple questions Who? What?, Where?, and Why?

Since I'm writing, illustrating, and putting the book together myself I have to ask these basic questions first for the overall book. I do the same process for each story and drawing. Sometimes an illustration or doodle I do sparks an idea for a story. It can be anything really; maybe a shape I see in the bark of a tree can spark a whole idea for a new world. So it's an organic process for me. With storytelling I need to have a basic idea on how it will start and how it will end the rest is just filling in the blanks. Both may change as the story evolves but at least I have the basic framework.

The great thing about writing is that characters really do take on a life of their own. So sometimes my stories may take on a whole new direction that I never expected because the character arch needs to go there. The main thing I keep in mind is how anything I do connects with my audience because if you don't have that your not successful as a creator.

When is the last time you were genuinely scared by something someone created?

I was twelve-years old when I read Mary Shelly's *Frankenstein* and it scared me to the bone. The thought of Dr. Frankenstein, a mad genius losing his humanity while trying to prolong life and creating the "Monster" all the while becoming a monster himself was a chilling thought.

Tell us about your contribution to our book. What was the inspiration?

The various illustrations contributed come from my love of the genre. I love the playing on the mischievous side of things. Sometimes the real monsters are humans and it takes a monster to set things right. It's an interesting juxtaposition that people may not expect.

What do you love about the genre of horror?

I love cautionary tales of horror. I also like the idea of the helpful monster witch is something I've developed in my own work George Frei's *Monster Series*. We are taught as kids that monsters are evil, but not ALL monsters are evil. Some monsters are helpful, misunderstood, and even good guys. I think horror that plays on these concepts are some of the most memorable and tend to connect with the human condition the most.

What is some of your favorite horror literature? Favorite author?

I grew up reading the classics, of course. Mary Shelly's *Frankenstein* is a forever-beloved classic. The real-life tie in of Vlad the Impaler to the immortal Count Dracula. Other more contemporary writers like Anne Rice and her gritty depiction of vampires throughout New Orleans. I could smell the sewers and bakeries in her descriptions. Stephen King is another prolific master of horror writing and too many more to name. Also Neil Gaiman for his groundbreaking *Sandman* series.

What are some of your influences?

I have a mix of eclectic influences from authors, directors, special effects artists, painters, and etc. Dick Smith the Godfather of makeup for his amazing makeup on The *Exorcist*, Rick Baker a master in horror makeup, Ray Harryhausen for *Jason and the Argonauts, Sinbad, Clash of the Titans*, Etc, Guillermo del Toro for *Pan's Labyrinth, Shape of Water*, Steven Spielberg for *Jaws, Jurassic Park*, Etc, Ridley Scott for *Alien*, etc. The list goes on and on…

Describe the perfect Halloween.

It's an interesting question because Halloween is a celebration of remembering the dead. So I would say every day should be Halloween. I have to say my perfect Halloween started on the day my father passed away October 30th 2000. My mother came downstairs to wake me up and tell me the cancer won the fight. Even though I was awake I thought I was still dreaming and hoped I wouldn't wake up. I lay there tossing and turning in and out of my dream state. I finally woke up to see the ambulance come by to take my Dad away. It was surreal to watch and almost like it wasn't happening at the same time. We prepared for the funeral but it wasn't long after that the funeral service was held, a couple days I think. I remember sitting in a chair by myself with my Dad in the casket and just staring at him. Thinking about all the good times wondering if this was the end, is there nothing else. People always ask for a sign or something. I didn't ask for anything. If there were a God why would he take my Dad away? Why would the cancer not go away when we prayed? Later that night, I sat on my couch in the basement alone and in a dark dusky room thinking about the culmination of his passing. After about thirty minutes of just sitting there I felt a strong presence on my right side. It was like someone was sitting in the couch across from me. I knew it was my Dad making sure I was ok. Still to this day I can't really explain the feeling but everything I know tells me it was him. I turned in that direction with tears in my eyes and smiled and said, "I'll be OK, Dad". After a couple minutes the presence was gone and my heart filled with love.

He passed away on All Hallows Eve. I didn't know then the significance of his death. I know now Halloween, All Hallows Eve, All Saints Day, whatever you want to call it is a day to remember our loved ones and cast out evil. He restored my faith…so til we meet again Dad! Happy Halloween Everyone!

SCARE CRED: GEORGE FREI

With a career spanning more than twenty years, George Frei is an award-winning artist and is best known for his dynamic visual storytelling, imaginative characters, intense color pallet, and fantastic world building. George Frei is the author and illustrator of George Frei's *Monster Series* and has also gained traction in the show circuit. Visit him at *TreeHouseMachine.com*!

THROUGH THE LENS OF HORROR

BY MICHAEL GAVIN

a few words from

MICHAEL GAVIN

As a designer of horror theatre or experiences, explain your process.

Each image should tell a story. For each planned set, I try to work with the model to bring them into the creative process. Sometimes this involves transforming concepts they envision to life; others its collaborative effort which includes introducing elements of the shoot that he or she are fond of. In so doing, their investment in the creative process produces better images. For cemetery (and other dark themed photographs without models): usually the environment does most of the storytelling work.

When is the last time you were genuinely scared by something someone created?

Honestly, I cannot recall the last time I was scared beyond being startled by a jump scare at a haunted attraction. Instead reactions tend to lean towards admiration and inspiration.

Tell us about your contribution to our book. What was the inspiration?

I've enjoyed horror ever since discovering I could be the one controlling or contributing to the scare. This magical transformation occurred at the age of 9, after discovering a monster make up book at the school book fair. Photography captured my interest in high school. With the advent of quality digital photography equipment, it was only natural that the two interests merged into a passion for creating creepy cool pictures.

What do you love about the genre of horror?

I really enjoy the ambiance and beauty of the genre. Dark, brooding and mysterious elements (especially the music) provide great places to escape, meditate and create.

What is some of your favorite horror literature? Favorite author?

I cannot pinpoint one favorite author, though lately Owl Goingback's work has been providing fiendishly fun nightmares. Overall a good ghost story and/or diving into the history and backstories of Halloween and classic horror movies provides a delightfully dark escape.

What are some of your influences?

In addition to the monster make up book that lured me into the genre, the work of Joshua Hoffine (check out his horror photography coffee table book!); creative creations of Christine McConnell; and cemetery photography of Sid Graves grant me inspiration. As making macabre miniatures (spooky dollhouses and similar) will provide my camera with fresh new material, Heather Tracy and Bentley House minis (check their Addams Family dollhouse) offer YouTube inspiration and instruction. But, most of all my mom influenced my journey into this tiny realm of terror as she used to make all kinds of miniature creations. Inheriting her tools didn't hurt either.

If you could continue any horror story (book or film), what would it be?

Showtime's *Penny Dreadful* series ended to abruptly and left so much potential (both for the existing characters and new monsters) behind. Sorry, while the "City of Angels" spin off was great period-centric entertainment, this was not the "Penny Dreadful" with monsters and spooky fun I was hoping for.

Describe the perfect Halloween.

There's a slight chill cooling the nighttime air. A full moon accents the evening. Trick-or-treaters traverse the neighborhood, on a quest for sweet treasures. Eerie music offers ambiance for the monstrous sounds emanating between foam tombstones and low-lying fog of what was once the front yard. Hints of hideous creatures lurk within the shadows. Headlights from what appears to be a haunted hearse illuminate the driveway. Within the garage-transformed laboratory, an eccentric mad scientist, vaguely resembling me, awaits his next victims, ready to reward their bravery with a handful of brightly wrapped confections. . . After this adventure fades away and the young would-be monsters have completed their adventure, this "mad scientist" retreats to the backyard bonfire to exchange ghost stories with friends and fiends. This magic meanders well into the enchanted evening.

SCARE CRED: MICHAEL GAVIN

As a fan of fear for over forty years, writing for an entertainment news site and fantasy/horror themed photography currently fuels my passion for fright filled fiendish fun. With the help of a few fiends, I created and conducted Orlando's very first haunted history tour: *Orlando Hauntings* (2000).Haunts and attractions like Terror on Church Street, Skull Kingdom, and Disney's Tower of Terror have been called "home" at one time or another. Photography and writing projects have been appeared in *Playboy, Forbes, GHOST! Magazine, Orlando Weekly, City of Orlando website, Gores Truly* and *Inside the Magic.* Images have been used to promote fan conventions, Pirates Dinner Adventure and The Shallow Grave haunted attractions.

THE WORKING DEAD

BY RICK GONZALES

POPE
U.S.

a few words from

RICK GONZALES

As a designer of horror theatre or experiences, explain your process.

I like to see how an ordinary setting and a person or animal can change in the night darkness and how it makes you not trust your senses by what you see and hear. Have you ever walked down a lovely country road in the daytime but then have to walk down the same road on a dark, moonless night? Or maybe down a darkened hallway in an old building at night? You can hear sounds all around you, and you can barely see. Weird shapes and shadows that maybe moving as you move by them? Will it reach out for me? Or see areas lit in colors that alter your depth perception. I want your mind to fill in what you can't see or hear.

When is the last time you were genuinely scared by something someone created?

Have you ever had to walk through a long spinning vortex hallway on a chain and wood planked bridge? I did. That was a fright for me. I felt that I would fall off the bridge with every shaky step I took. It didn't matter that I knew it was an illusion. It still pulled me off balance.

Tell us about your contribution to our book. What was the inspiration?

I hope to help others see how to twist a good scare into a great scare. I love seeing all the new materials and technology that is available to enhance the fright. Also. I love recreating scares from movies I grew up watching. I do enjoy making 'Zombies', Grim Reapers and Mutants. 'Val Lewton' films are a favorite. They have a lot of off camera scares.

What do you love about the genre of horror?

A good scare can make you feel so alive. The stories through history can give that 'What if?' feeling in your head. It can really be hard to shake off. It also gives many a sense of power over people. I've made up actors into monsters that won't or can't get out of character until I take their makeup off.

What is some of your favorite horror literature? Favorite Author?

Well of course all the classic stories and writers as well as Robert Bloch, Richard Matheson and Stephen King.

What are some of your influences?

Everything!!! Our world is full of dread. In nature we have creatures on land and sea that you do not want to meet. And humans can be the worst.

What is your favorite Halloween treat?

The sound of screaming victims and chocolate.

You are hosting the perfect Halloween movie marathon. What are the films you choose and why?

The Thing From Another World both old and new versions because both films had the fear of our world being taken over. *Them*, I like mutant bugs. *The Navy vs. the Night Monsters*, you can't go wrong with walking flesh eating banana trees. *Curse of the Cat People*, Hearing something stalking you but can't see what it is. And *Day of the Dead*, I love to see my zombie eat Miguel throat!

If you could continue any horror story (book or film), what would it be?

It would have been wonderful if George Romero had finished his zombie world story. Do we survive? Is a cure found? Do the Zombies regain their intelligence again and rule the world?

Describe the perfect Halloween.

The haunt and the characters all work well together. The crew and actors are into it, giving the best fright they can. I love to hear the comments of the guests being so scared and are also laughing about it. They want to do it again.

SCARE CRED: RICK GONZALES

Rick Gonzales was born in San Antonio, TX, and grew up a MonsterKid.
In the late 70's, he started working on films assisting with makeup, props and set building. He was lucky enough to be part of the Florida makeup crew on George Romero's Day of the Dead in 1984. Tom Savini was in charge of Special Effects Makeup, and Rick learned a lot in a short amount of time.
Rick eventually worked for Universal Studios Florida with fellow makeup artist Michael Davy to create makeups for their very first Fright Night events for Halloween. Rick has retired from full time production, but he still helps his friends out on special projects and teaches new artists how to create their own monsters. He is proud of giving a lot of makeup artists their first movie credit and watching their creativity grow in the haunt and film industry. He still loves the sound of their screams…

EMPTY MAN

BY NATHAN HANNEMAN

Silence filled an old and dank workplace as a begrimed old man paces around in a lab coat, looking focused, seemingly impatient, and anxious. Feelings which stem from a lengthy wait as the man is completely fixated on a nearby computer. These feelings of anxiety and impatience can only be silenced from a simple "ding." An extraordinary bit of sound which computer programmers jammed into software, alerting the impatient ones in the crowd who salivate for the moment of computeristic finalization. The finalization this old man impatiently yearned for was seemingly fixated on a file transfer. From a chipped and dirty old USB device, this man was transferring some volume of technology into a clunky pile of metal and wires that formed a mount within the corner of this messy workplace. Mixed in the mess of metal and abstract items, a shape could be seen. Human-like, but not quite. The doctor beamed with excitement, finally breaking his anxious silence. "At last, after all these years, the final piece to my creation ... I can't believe you will be complete. These command files will unlock all of your full potential!" The doctor increased his voice, and excitement as his quiet self-monologue became a roarious speech. "When these files are transferred over, my son, you will have all the knowledge in the world to help prove my life-long dream. Thanks to your amazing brain, you already have emotion and abstract thought ... but soon ... you will know so much more. Your brain was being wasted – but soon – unlimited potential! Can you imagine? If you wanted to, you could invent the world's most effective vehicles, harness energies man simply cannot comprehend and build new cities, if you choose ... imagine deciding to use an unparallelled understanding of technology to improve all aspects of life. Imagine it! A robot that could design new technologies that will allow him the capability to upgrade himself! Even better, a bobot who can think and feel, yet never be tired ... never give up! Cancer could be cursed in a matter of weeks! Hospitals will never worry about a doctor's inabilities at the workplace! And you will have the ability to make those decisions on your own. To design your own journey in making the world a better place. You, my boy, will prove that I was right. I was right ... and all the blood, sweat, and tears ... it will have been worth it! All the horrible things I have done. Things I have done to you .... but you'll see. It was for the betterment of mankind. It was for the betterment of you. You will be more important than you could have ever imagined! Maybe after you learn of your potential, you could even forgive me for what horrid acts led us to this monumental evening. But I promise you, my child. It will have been worth it." ..." KLANK! A loud sound erupts from somewhere outside of the building!

The doctor makes his way through the low-lit aisles of his workspace, to the front window of what appears to be a rundown and possibly abandoned warehouse space. Peering outside to see what could have caused such a noise, the doctor thinks to himself, 'Who dares interrupt me?' Suddenly, with a loud roar, a door on the other side of the room comes smashing open, with a violent authority that almost causes it to fall off its hinges. Before the doctor can take but five steps, a dark shadow lunges from the entrance, pushing the old man against a nearby table, almost bending his back into a horrid L shape. "You did it! You son of a bitch! It was you!" the dark intruder screams. "It took me four months, but I fuckin' found you! You sick murderin' bastard!" In a moment of extreme escalation, and as the doctor begins to beg for his life, pleading to the intruder, "You don't know what I have ..." BLAM! ... BLAM, BLAM! Gunshots echo through the dark building. The old doctor looks up in shock, holding his hand in front of his face to see blood trickling down from each finger ... the wounded man slowly slides down to the floor. The shooter, looking down in disgust, stares at the dying doctor. With tears running down his face, the stranger pulls his pistol back, pointing it right at the bloody Doctor ... life slipping from his cold, shivering body ... BLAM! ... BLAM! ... click, click, click ... The gun is out of ammo. The shooter stares blankly, as if not knowing how to proceed, now that his devilish task is complete. With a look of disgust coming over his face, the man wipes away his tears and begins to look around the mess of electronics and metal scraps that decorate the building. This rusted-out workplace littered with wire, tools, and medical-grade equipment that begins to tell a dark and sinister story. Slowly turning around, the dark stranger's eyes become filled with sadness, as he lowers his head, and utters an apology. An apology to who? ... It's very doubtful these apologies are meant for the murdered doctor laying cold on the factory floor. Tired, and content, the dark stranger turns to the door, and begins to walk ... each step taking him further into the dark, cold night ... and further away from his deadly (yet brief) encounter with the now lifeless old doctor. The dark stranger soon becomes one with the night, fading into the blackness of the outside world.

.... "FUNCTION .... CANCEL COMMAND .... FUNCTION .... CANCEL COMMAND" ...

Flashes across a computer monitor soon light up the dimly lit crime-scene, mere hours after the violent incident that had occurred. Order on the monitor continues to flash, again, and again. There is a human-like shape in the corner of the building – the same shape that had mesmerized the doctor and all of his attention earlier in the evening. "FUNCTION ... CANCEL COMMAND" ... the orders continue to flash. All of a sudden the computer monitor blinks – "FILE TRANSFER COMPLETE" ... followed by a black and blank screen. Then nothing. BOOM! Out of nowhere a sound erupts from the warehouse. Metal clashing against metal. The dormant silhouette of human-like shapes in the center of the room begins to move. Springing to life, as it were, a shriek of grinding metal fills the building with an irritating sound of static. Soon, it is very apparent that the mixture of shapes have obvious human structure, with a prominent and imposing head jittering around the body of the being. Glowing eyes appear, as the static noise increases, now obviously stemming from behind the contraption's eyes. Slowly moving to reveal limbs ... arms and legs, the being is robotic – no doubt. But moves with a painful stress upon its limbs, as if each move stems from shaking off undead rigamortis. Finally moving across the room, crashing into tables and machinery, the being monstrocity becomes visible in the buildings only overhead light, now shining onto what appears to be a robotic form ... although extremely basic in nature. A bulky torso and head, lengthy and gangly arms and legs. Hard edges, and unfinished, the being finds its way to the dead doctor, laying cold and blue on the floor. Littered with gunshot wounds, blood pooled around him in great quantity. The being kneels down, resting next to the fallen doctor. Although the basic form of the robot cannot show emotion, one would almost agree that the look of pain was visible in its demeanor. Did it want to cry? To mourn the loss of a man it may not have known? Imagine meeting your creator, but only after he had been callously murdered. Pulling up the doctor's body, the being holds the doctor close to his chest, as if hugging him. A voice begins to resonate from the static noises from within the robot. "Faaaaaaaathherrrrrr? ..... Myeeeecreeeeeeaterffffffaaaaatherr... Whooo wwwwoould .... whooo would ..." the voice slowly becomes clearer and with more confidence in each syllable. "Who would want to hurrrrt you"? ... a pause follows, as if the robot expected a response. "I did not recognize the man whooooo hurt you." .... again, silence. As if the being was slowly realizing that a response was not going to come. Holding him closer, the being continues to calmly talk to his creator. "I could not stop him. I saaaaaw him come in, and attack you ... and I could not move," the robot continues to speak through the loud static sounds emanating from its head. "I tried to overwrite the program. I tried to help, but I could not move. I could only siiiit and watch as you were .... shot? You were shot. Shot. Blood. Bloooodddd. There is blood everywhere. Dead. No. Deceased. You .... you arrrrrre. You are deceased. Expired. Killed. .... whhhhyy. ...."

As time passed, the robot sat, trying to comprehend, with his newly installed thought processors and with what seems to be ... emotions? The being may now never know or comprehend what the doctor intended from him. What his purpose was. Why or how he was created. Questions he sits and begins to ask himself ... with nobody there to answer. "Why would somebody kill my creator ... you ... are you my father"? the robot begins to question ... looking around now, contemplating what his function is. What he should do. "No logical reason explains murder. No reasons to result in death. Murder. Death. Unless death is the reason. If death was the desired goal ... logic states that the man who did this should also die." Revenge? Is that a word the robot understands? Yes. Revenge. The being begins to stand, imposing in height, the being looks around the building – this makeshift laboratory ... tools everywhere, but this ... a knife. The being zeroes in on a knife in the corner of the room. Staring intently at the blade, the robot turns and makes his way back to "Father" ... leaning over his maker, he utters, "Revenge. Your death warrants revenge. Your death warrants death. This strange man killed you. You cannot kill him. I will find him. for you. I will do for you what you cannot. You are unable to stand. Unable to hold this knife, to end this man's life. Revenge. I will do it for you." And with a swift swing of the knife, the robot strikes his maker. In a disgusting act of confusion, the being begins to cut into his "father's" face. Blood jarring and splattering onto the being's metal body as he continues to work, he soon pulls back, revealing the skinned face of his maker. He has freed the face of the doctor from his skull ... walking around the room, the nobody finds pieces of scrap to help bind the face over his own metal frame, of what you would call a "head" ... stepping into the light, having finished his goal, the robot reveals that he is adorning the old Doctor's own face ... attached to the newly reanimated being.

Using clothing from his diseased maker, the being slowly takes efforts to disguise his visage - so as to hide his true appearance to a world that he no doubt plans to enter. Vowing revenge, in the form of his fallen maker, the robot will find the murderer and bring him to "justice" ... "I will remember his face, Father. I have seen him. I will find him. I will ... murder him. I will cut him with the same blade that gave me your face. Together, Maker ... Father. We will have revenge."

Roughly 20 miles away, at a dirty little dive bar across town, the front door swings open. Amidst a cluster of downtrodden patrons scattered throughout the bar, our dark intruder ... the murderer, if you will ... finds himself a welcome table in the corner, among a seemingly familiar friend. "Did you find him"? the friend asks .... "He is done," the man sits, responding with a cold and sad look upon his face. "After months of looking, I finally found the bastard that murdered my son." ... a somber moment indeed. The friend takes a moment to follow up, "Did you find it?" he asks ... with an odd silence following ... "No. Whatever reason he stole my son's brain is pointless. My boy is dead. If he was using his brain for some half-cocked experiment, he will never finish whatever fucked up plan he had." .... the friend seems unsatisfied with the answer, but dare not push his friend. "Did you see anything that could explain why he wanted the brain"? the friend decides to prod for any information .... "No." the man fires back. "I don't care. I don't know. But I don't care. My son is dead. That's all I know. The sick son of a bitch killed him ... he took my boy, and I will never get him back. I'll never get him back. Why a sick fuck like that would want his brain, I will never know. I don't want to. And I hope to never find out." ... the two sat silently for the rest of the evening, drinking away the nightmarish events of the day. With hope that all of the death, despair, and destruction is finally behind them. ...

"I will remember his face, Father. I have seen him. I will find him. I will ... murder him. I will cut him with the same blade that gave me your face. Together, Father. We will have revenge."

a few words from

NATHAN HANNEMAN

What do you love about the genre of horror?

I love the versatility of the genre. Horror can be serious or silly. Somber or erratic. It can make you cry ... it can make you think. I have seen horror films that have seriously messed me up, from a mental standpoint. Films you can't shake. I have watched horror films that have made me legitimately nauseous and uncomfortable. A good film can cost $10 grand to produce – or $50 million. It does not matter the budget. But horror also serves as a litmus test for society. I don't trust anyone who doesn't like horror movies.

What is some of your favorite horror literature?

While I grew up on Stephen King, I believe the most enjoyment I have received from reading came from such authors as Anne Rice, William Peter Blatty, and HP Lovecraft (odd mix, maybe?). I seem to gravitate to short story format, however. Going back to Stephen King, I can't get enough of his short-form collections. Particularly *Night Shift*. "The Boogeyman" still stands as the scariest story I have ever read.

You are hosting the perfect Halloween movie marathon.

I love to invite people over to watch amazingly fun bad movies. Stuff like *The Monster Club, Green Slime*, or *Spookies*. I love playing our Halloween music tracklist and serving tacos (yep, Tacos). We do a Halloween party almost every year, and I do an elaborate taco bar. Somehow, I now connect avocados with Halloween. Odd. But I never pick movies that people will want to pay attention to. Lots of beer and costumes are mandatory. But if I am hosting an intimate movie-centric event, I always go for the mainstays. *Halloween, Trick 'r Treat, An American Werewolf in London, Creepshow*, or *Shaun of the Dead.*

What are the films you choose and why?

I gravitate to films which have a comedy backbone (or at least are a bit tongue in cheek). Halloween notwithstanding, I love colorful horror films that get crazier and crazier as the story unfolds. Anything that escalates, has humor, gore, and bright colors - most likely stemming from me being a 1980s kid, growing up with *Gremlins, Ghostbusters, Teen Wolf*, and *The Monster Squad*. I like *Chainsaw Massacre Part 2, Re-Animator, Fright Night* ... even in recent years, it's those films that have that extra "voice" that pique my interest. Films like *The Color Out of Space, The Babadook, May, The Loved Ones, You're Next.*

When is the last time you were genuinely scared by something someone created?

I get freaked out sometimes by masks and props that are on display at Mask-Fest, the annual Halloween Convention-within-a-convention that occurs at HHW events every fall. I have purchased some epic replicas of characters from *Whatever Happened to Baby Jane* or *Dead Silence* (Mary Shaw) that will sit in my house, looking back at me, and make me question my sanity for wanting to own them (both examples, sculpted wonderfully by Dan Horne).

Tell us about your contribution to our book. What was the inspiration?

I wrote a ton of short stories when I was in my early 20s, with expectations that they would one day make their way into comic-book format. I have some fun zombie stories, vampire tales, things with robots and serial killers. Most of my time writing today (now in my 40s) is spent from a historic and retrospective position. I love history. I love digging into the world of comics, film, toys, games, whatever. I also love to create art – so with my hands so full, working on conventions, magazines, articles, artwork, and merchandise concepts – I just don't create new stories anymore. So, I thought long and hard about what to contribute – and I thought that dusting off and polishing one of my older concepts was the best way to go. You get the young idealistic invention of my younger self – with the spit and polish of my older me. What can go wrong?

Describe the perfect Halloween.

The perfect Halloween to me is a night at the drive-in, enjoying an amazing double-feature of classic films. *Bride of Frankenstein* with *Creature from the Black Lagoon. Halloween* with *The Shining*. Some pizza ... a bunch of popcorn ... a cool, clear sky. That's a good night. Let alone an amazing Halloween. Because drive-ins don't run on Halloween night but a couple times every decade (it has to fall on a weekend(!)), I have only experienced this perfect Halloween a couple times in my life.

SCARE CRED: NATHAN HANNEMAN

Nathan launched HorrorHound Magazine with friends Jeremy Sheldon, Aaron Crowell, and wife Jessica. To accompany their publication, the team developed HorrorHound Weekend, which has grown into the largest horror con in North America averaging nearly 50,000 attendees annually. HorrorHound has also been the recipient of nine Rondo Hatton awards. In most recent years, HorrorHound launched a horror-themed music label, an officially licensed action figure based on their mascot (via Creatureplica Toys), and a recurring HorrorHound-branded beer. In 2019, HorrorHound unveiled their first foray into feature film production with the Ryan Merriman, Jamie Tisdale, and Heather Langenkamp-starring *Portal*. Nathan is currently working on two book projects, which he hopes to see into completion by fall of 2021.

ENCOUNTERS with the OTHER SIDE

BY TIM J. HAYS

Nestled among the rows of storefronts, a haunted attraction known as the Haunted Grimm house was located in Old Town in Kissimmee for a long time. Its Victorian-styled facade leering at the passersby's, daring only the bravest to enter for the meager price of a few dollars. Eventually, a time came when the attraction changed owners. I had the privilege to work with a group of talented artisans and veteran haunters to help reopen the attraction under a new entity - Legends: A Haunting at Old Town.

Being a makeup artist with a theater background, I had worked for a number of years in the makeup department at Universal Studios which included Halloween Horror Nights. So, I naturally fell in with the local haunter crowd in Orlando. It was during my time of working at this haunt that I was made aware of some of the inhabitants. A smattering of stories of a young boy named Jacob, who would playfully move things around or tug on clothing. In addition to him was some sort of nanny watching out to protect Jacob. Neither of whom were actually living, of course. But I just thought that they were only stories. Weren't they?

Late one night, while the interior of the building was still under construction, we had earlier filmed a promotional commercial upstairs. I was the only one left there and while packing up my makeup kit, I remembered that I had left a few items upstairs. I began ascending staircase, but before making it halfway up, my instincts screamed at me to stop. I carefully listened, but all that my ears could detect was the muffled beat of the music from the bar next door. As I dared to take another step, a heavy feeling of tension and dread manifested above me.

It slowly hovered from the wall on the right side and halted in front of me, blocking my path. Making no noise, it instead emanating a sensation very similar to the buzzing of an angry horde of bees. It couldn't see or hear it, but something was definitely there and clearly very upset!

"I'll just come back later." I quipped while carefully backing down the stairs and keeping a wary eye to the top of the steps. The next day, I explained what had occurred. Everyone nodded. "Oh, that was probably Jack."

Jack was the malevolent one. He, apparently, was a rather unpleasant fellow and extremely unwelcoming of anyone. Not much else is known about him, other than the fact that he lurks in the dark hallways...waiting. On another night, our group was immersed with each of our own projects, I was standing on a ladder, hanging LED lights. I distinctly felt a large hand on my back which then shove me, nearly trying to knock me off of the ladder. I turned to yell at whomever was messing around with me only to find that no one there. I was alone. The other two workers that were also in the room were gone, which left the mysterious phantom an opportunity to push me. Quickly climbing down from the ladder, I could feel the energy in the room was almost alive with static. The hairs on the back of my neck rose up as I retreated from the room, in search of the others to share what had just occurred.

After the haunt was in full operation, there were times when you had to be alone in sections of the buildings and you knew that Jack was always watching. But, he and I had eventually come to an understanding. I have a healthy respect for the supernatural and have had quite a bit of experience, so I am not afraid which puts Jack at a disadvantage. Using a technique that had developed over some time that I like to call: spiritual armor, I felt like I could create an energy around me that keeps any unwanted vibes away to protect myself. It seemed to work, because whenever I had to go through the halls on my own, especially Jack's dark corner, he always left me alone.

Others have had their encounters with Jack as well, but that's a different story. There were discussions to compile every bit of information about any and all encounters from within the walls of Legends. Even those that we had heard from the visitors that came out of the haunt, pale, covered in sweat and breathing heavily. Maybe one day, we actually will.

Sadly, Legends: A Haunting at Old Town had changed owners once again and has now completely morphed into a new haunt. I know that our thrill of the hunt and the memories of our time at Legends will go on.

BINGO!!

a few words from

TIM J. HAYS

As a designer of horror theatre or experiences, explain your process.

My approach is typically; How can I make this unique and interesting? Can I put a twist on it? If the design is using color, I love contrast, if it's writing, I love non-linear or a wry humor.

When is the last time you were genuinely scared by something someone created?

My first time seeing *The Exorcist*! It's been a while since I've been genuinely scared of something. When I was a little kid, my older brother told me that Frankenstein's Monster lived in my Grandmother's attic and I believed him!

Tell us about your contribution to our book. What was the inspiration?

That building that the Legends haunt used to be in definitely had a lot of paranormal activity in it. I wanted to share a little insight.

What do you love about the genre of horror?

I really love Hitchcock's type of horror. For me, personally, I feel like most of the new horror films aren't as scary as they were 20+ years ago. They're not as cerebral or don't leave much to the creativity. I'm just not into gratuitous gore and violence. Give me a good ol' monster lurking in the dark or a Norman Bates kind of killer.

What is some of your favorite horror literature? Favorite author?

I grew up reading Edgar Allen Poe. I also like a lot of Stephen King's early stuff.

What are some of your influences?

Dick Smith had a tremendous impact on me. I had taken his makeup course and was lucky enough to speak to him on the phone numerous times! Also, Rick Baker and Guillermo Del Toro, to name a few others. Another great was actually not horror-based. It is Bruce Lee. His teachings and philosophy are huge influences for me.

What is your favorite Halloween treat?

Pretty much anything with dark chocolate.

You are hosting the perfect Halloween movie marathon. What are the films you choose and why?

I'd love to mix up some classic fun Halloween themed movies like *Hocus Pocus* and *Spaced Invaders* with some classic *Universal Classic Monsters, Friday the 13th* and *Halloween* films. Also sprinkle in some schlocky ones like *Brain Dead, Plan 9 from Outer Space* and *The Lost Skeleton of Cadavera*. I know that I'm not the only one with some of those favorites, whether it's because of inspiration or even when you'd watch those films with your buddies and relive that nostalgia.

If you could continue any horror story (book or film), what would it be?

Creature from the Black Lagoon! I'd love to pick up after *Revenge of the Creature*, circumvent *The Creature Walks Among Us*, and then continue in the same vein as the originals. That sounds like a lot of fun for me.

Describe the perfect Halloween.

Building a small haunt in my backyard that's themed to be a half spooky and half dark humor mix. Just something short and fun that people go through for free and get candy at the end of it. Meanwhile, inside my house is a Halloween party with the aforementioned movie marathon playing!

SCARE CRED: TIM J. HAYS

Tim J. Hays has worked professionally as a makeup artist since 1997 and is a journeyman in IATSE Local 798 union as a makeup artist. Growing up, he loved watching monster movies, which had a profound effect on him. It had sparked his curiously as to how the monsters and makeup effects were created for those movies and he wanted to discover how to become a makeup artist. (Yes, he was that weird kid in class that loved drawing pictures of strange creatures.) Over the years, Tim has worked at places like Universal Studios Orlando and Legends A Haunting at Old Town, as well as on dozens of independent film projects. He was also a makeup instructor at Cosmix for over five years, boring the students to tears with his dad jokes. He has also had many opportunities to travel to various parts of the world, performing his craft. At the time of this writing, Tim is living in the Atlanta, GA area, still doing what he loves, working as a makeup artist on Film & TV production sets....and has since developed a sordid fear of kitchen sink sponges.

my RULES OF HAUNTED ATTRACTION DESIGN

BY ALLEN HOPPS

Allen as
"Carol Cleaver!"

1. Focus on the customer.

At every possible opportunity, put yourself in the customer's shoes. This will make every decision easier and lead to a better experience for all parties involved. We are telling a story or sharing a world. Most epic stories have a fish out of water who knows little about this new world, and that is how the audience finds things out. Harry Potter did not know about the magical world, so it had to be explained to him, Luke Skywalker did not know about life out in the galaxy or Jedi- it had to be told him. That is your customer. Make sure that you involve them through scenery and characters, so they are invested in discovering your world. Make your audience that character!

2. You must be able to explain it in 10 seconds.

Bite-sized story and scenery that can be understood with a glance. As a director, we must convey our visions (to the crew that builds the show, the actors, and the customers- The customers twice- Once to get them to come and again while they are inside). A convoluted story that spans a long time or has dozens of characters is great for a movie or show that has a ton of development time, but it will not work for a haunt setting. The ideas and concepts need to be understood immediately and be impactful. Not everything must be explained, allow yourself the ability to do some things and add some things because they are cool even if they do not 100% mesh with the storyline. The 10-second rule applies to characters, sets, costumes, backstories every aspect. Yes, there is a need for longer explanations of everything, but that is for people who want more- the 20-minute TED talk should not be necessary for them to enjoy your show.

3. Do not waste a name, sound, or surface.

You are creating a world, do not allow things to exist in it without paying their rent story and theme-wise. Need a table in a scene; it should be appropriate to the period you are set in or have a cover on it that looks period-appropriate. Have an empty wall in your haunt's kitchen? Add a calendar that has the right year for your story on it. Circle a date and write dentist's appointment on it. You have reinforced the setting with and added that extra twinge of discomfort by making it a Dentist appointment. Are they in the home of a hillbilly murder family? Make the curtains the guests pass through sewn from the victim's clothes- everything there you get to create so makes it earn its keep.

4. Engage all the senses.

Try to engage each of the five senses so that your world is experienced on many levels. Want to evoke touch? Put a cactus in baby's room; their brain will fill in what a terrible idea that is. Try an exercise where there is so much texture in a room that their eyes have to work hard to take it in. Scents are lovely but don't overdo them- Four or five in an attraction is plenty, and they don't all have to be terrible- Christmas cookie smell makes guests put their nose up and sniff, that is when an actor reaches for their throat through a hole in the wall- the smell triggered the vulnerable exposure and the actor or room took advantage and gets the scare. Sound is so important even if you don't make the sound for your show. You should play around with some sound stuff just to get an idea and to be able to express yourself through sound. Yes, sound sets a mood, but it also speeds them up and slows them down, it can make them more curious than usual- use it to your advantage and milk everything you can out of your soundtrack.

5. Be consistent in your world.

Keep the level of theming the same throughout if there is one set that is highly detailed and the rest of the show is black walls then those areas will seem lacking- spread out the design, art, sound, and talent to make the whole show good- do keep in mind the rising action principles and have a reliable exit room scare. I try to keep most of my hallways the same to establish the setting, then each room is a departure, and the halls can pull you back into the story. I do not want my guests to forget that they are in an Antebellum Mansion halfway through- I push that experience throughout with the hallways. They have scares in them as well Drop portraits, actor curtains, air cannons all of it- they just all keep the same feel. I find this to be especially important for parks that have more than one attraction. That strong hallway identity keeps each show tight to its theme.

6. Plan a scare for every space.

As a Haunt actor for over 30 years, even I hate a room that does not have a scare built-in. Listen to your descriptions and listen for how hard or easy you are making it for the actor. This is the bedroom scene, and there is an actor on the bed...and...then what? I like to give actors a distraction of some kind, a place t come from, and a place for them to go. That allows them to run a mini route that gets them back to their starting point. Distractions can be triggered by the actor or by the customer. They can be visual or audio, subtle, or more in your face. A lit fake cellphone on the ground almost guarantees someone is going to try to pick it up, and when they do, an actor's hand can reach out for theirs- it's a modern version of the quarter glued to the concrete. What is important is that it catches the guest's attention and allows the actor to hit them off guard.

7. Focus on the customer.

So Important I say it twice. We get jaded and forget to explain things visually. Sometimes, it is essential that throughout their traveling through the attraction that they are the focus. Do not allow the actors to be focused on themselves- point them at the customer. An actor is not there to amuse themselves; it should be an honest desire to influence the customer. The proper projected attitude changes the guest experience from "that was cool" to "I survived". Leave your guests feeling like they just solved a mystery, survived a horror movie, or watched the beginning of something that will spill out of your attraction and change the world.

a few words from

ALLEN HOPPS

As a designer of horror theatre or experiences, explain your process.

I am a blender. I put into the blender the finest ingredients of Character, Settings, and Situations. They are combined and distilled into something entertaining and easily digestible. Customers interact with sets and characters for very short amounts of time, so everything has to be refined and easily understandable. If you can't describe a setting, costume, or character in fifteen seconds or less then it's too complicated and might need refining. I work to keep their brain in fear receptive mode by eliminating things that will take them out of it and adding things that stimulate that area of engagement. This is true if it is a costume, a scene, or even the theme and concept of an entire attraction.

When is the last time you were genuinely scared by something someone created?

I don't usually get scared due to overexposure, which is true for many thirty-year-plus Haunters. Last Halloween, I attended a haunt tour in Atlanta at *Netherworld*. It is an overwhelming environment. I would glance at the path, then move my head around to gather details. A glance at the corridor with a turn 20ft ahead... Look at the wall section to my left that is made of coffin parts... A glance at the corridor with a turn 15ft ahead, look up at the back of animatronic gargoyle that was over the last section... Glance at the corridor with a twist now 10ft ahead... look back up at evil tree looming over the entire scene... Glance down the corridor to suddenly be nose to nose with an actor with perfect timing. If she had made a noise too early, she would have ruined it, but slipping between the gaps of my attention was impeccable. My overstimulated brain did exactly what she wanted- I got a quick start.

Tell us about your contribution to our book. What was the inspiration?

Our art is often not appreciated sufficiently by our guests. They have their heads buried in each other's backs and eyes closed to shut out the scary stuff. The process itself is done by so few that each of us comes about our process differently. By sharing our process and core design principles, we can streamline the process for others. Maybe we can all get more efficient at scaring.

What do you love about the genre of horror

I do not love horror, I love monsters. I love the bestial, the inhuman, the spectral beings that populate the dark. Designing sets is me building a doghouse for my favorite hound. Horror can be found on CNN, so I do not like to use that word. My work always has a supernatural element. I just love monsters; I love to be immersed in them. I think about how they would attack? What about them causes fear? What type of setting would give them the most advantage? Good interaction between guests and monsters can make your actor feel invincible, and your guests feel like heroic survivors, nowhere else can you find such a win-win transaction.

What is some of your favorite horror literature? Favorite Author?

My current favorite is Christopher Buehlman, I find his work is excellent and turns most of my anticipations on their ear. Jonathan Maberry has an excellent series that is a blend of monsters and science. I enjoy Brian Lumley's *Necroscope* series as well as most works by Clive Barker.

What are some of your influences?

The *Classic Universal Monsters* are huge for me as far as influences go. *Masters of the Universe* toys from the 80's also pop up into my brain and work pretty often in different ways. Some Japanese creature horror and Hammer films all play a part. I am also very influenced by nature, I think nature documentaries are scarier than horror movies. I always tell my actors that if you feel and act like a lion, the guests will feel and act like gazelle.

What is your favorite Halloween treat?

This will out me for the sugar fiend fatty that I am, but I love pumpkin shakes from Jack in the box. I have one every weekend of haunt season as a reward on the 3AM drive home. They feel clandestine because I should have so many, and most places shut their shake machine down long before I get to buy them. It tastes like a pumpkin with a side of chemicals, but I love it.

You are hosting the perfect Halloween movie marathon. What are the films you choose and why?

I'm not one for binge-watching (the monsters don't make themselves) but here is what I would do-

Halloween 3: Season of the Witch to set the mood.

Tales of Halloween to keep it fun.

Monster Squad as an homage to the greats.

13 Ghosts to showcase awesome characters.

The original *Halloween* for a real jolt.

Trick 'R Treat to finish the night.

If you could continue any horror story (book or film), what would it be?

Nightbreed by Clive Barker. I love the concept that there is a place for monsters to go, I want to build that place then live there. The director's cut is excellent and hints at so many creatures that are just out of sight, I want haunts to be like that, so you feel like you are sneaking through a sliver of a larger scary world. I would love to create a Midian themed Haunted attraction.

Describe the perfect Halloween.

I have always worked Halloween, I have not missed working a haunted attraction from the time I was 10 years old- and that is perfect for me. Typically, on Halloween weekend, I shirk my duties to my capable staff and reveal a new character. So, I arrive at the show at 3pm- help the makeup staff get everyone ready. Then I start the ritual of putting on a new character when the makeup room is quiet. I would hit the queue about the time the attraction opens. I would get to greet /scare/ interact with every customer to some degree. It carries on till closing, and the roar of the crowd is an echo in my head. We always carve a Jack-O-Lantern and keep it lit all night on Halloween it's a tradition the wife and I have kept, and it's a great way to put Halloween to bed. With my life the way it is, Halloween is my New Year's Eve, and November first is my New Year's Day.

SCARE CRED: ALLEN HOPPS

Allen Hopps started his haunted house career at ten-years old and has stuck to it with unwavering focus. Starting as a year round actor at Terror on Church st. and then Skull Kingdom (both in Orlando) he has moved on to Haunt parks in Texas and consulting for attraction across the country. From 2013 to present he has been the director of Dark Hour Haunted House in Plano TX which does 5 differently themed shows a year. Allen also operates Stiltbeast Studios a company that produces costumes and training content for haunted attractions as well as a youtube channel that is a library of haunted attraction DIY projects. Allen has a huge passion for the haunted attraction industry and does his best to help it grow and innovate.

THE CORRIDOR

BY AMY KOLE & EMMA M. OLIVER

Isozuka dabbed at his brow with a handkerchief. It was August in Osaka, and even though it was barely eight in the morning, his suit sealed in the humidity like steam in a sauna. It didn't help that it was rush hour, and most of Osaka's 2.7 million residents were making the morning commute.

Isozuka swerved through the bike path to avoid the clobbering of briefcases and swinging purses. The walking pace in the city sped up during the summer months. Everyone wanted to minimize time spent under the Osaka sun, which made even the moderately air-conditioned train stations feel like an ice bath. Isozuka quickened his pace to match the stride of the crowd.

As he came toward a crosswalk, Isozuka stopped under the shade of a tree to await the traffic signal. Out of habit, he took the long way to work, skirting along the outside of Osaka Station as he made his way through Umeda. He liked the time to himself, and with the hours he worked, it was the only exercise he got. Not to mention, he always felt funny walking through the shortcut's unavoidable Umeda Virtual Corridor.

The traffic signal switched over, illuminating the walking green salaryman. The little man's green hat usually prompted a smile from Isozuka, but just thinking about the Virtual Corridor had made the hair on the back of his neck stand up. He shuddered and crossed with the crowd to the shaded side of the street.

The Virtual Corridor was a "trick art" exhibit: one of those paintings teens and tourists could pose with to get likes on SNS. It was just realistic enough to be unnerving and quirky sufficient to intensify the sensation, with something about each subject just the slightest bit off.

Like three men carrying a billboard of what was behind the advertisement, the image cropped just three inches to the left; none of their torsos quite met their waists. Isozuka wasn't sure if this was an accident or a joke, but either way, he didn't like it. And then there was the man before the flower shop, head was thrown back in a silent maniacal laugh. Or the bride painted in the window of a dress shop, holding a glass of white wine in a toast to something unseen.

The thought gave Isozuka goosebumps, the accompanying chill a temporary relief from the heat. He reasoned that if he must venture through the corridor, this seemed as good a season as any.

Summer was the season of *Kaidan* or ghost stories. Scary tales told to evoke spine-tingling chills that brought a reprieve from the city's stifling summer climate. Primary school children put on haunted houses. Movie theaters hosted horror films. Even television channels featured spooky specials to celebrate the season. As a boy, Isozuka himself would stay up well into the night to catch after-hours shows on the supernatural that starred his favorite actors and scary stories.

He smiled at a flashback of falling asleep at his junior high school desk after a late night of horror films. He used to crave the feeling of fear brought on by a good ghost story.

Decidedly, Isozuka changed course and descended the steps into the subway. After all, it *was* just a hallway. And heat or no heat, nearing fifty, Isozuka was much too old to let his imagination run wild. As expected, the station was filled with other commuters looking to escape the sun's wrath. Isozuka gave himself a minute to cool down and wipe the sweat from his forehead. Now that he was in the subway and surrounded by so many people, he felt a little embarrassed that he had allowed the idea of the corridor to make him so nervous.

Isozuka slipped into a break in the crowd and joined the steady stream of pedestrians pulsing through the station. The sweet smells of breakfast wafted down the station's tunnels and made Isozuka's stomach grumble. Near the stairs leading to another floor of the basement, colorful advertisements covered the walls. Pamphlets broadcasting the date and time of *Kaidan* events fluttered over the curling corners of aged police posters.

The same bulletins had been plastered to this board and every other one in Osaka for as long as Isozuka could remember. In the bottom left corner, the face of a twenty-something who'd quietly gone missing in the eighties stared blankly at commuters as they passed.

Isozuka had to admit, the brief relief of air conditioning and the slower pace that accompanied the change were nice. Plus, the shortcut shaved ten minutes off the walk.

He was beginning to wonder why he didn't simply cut through the station every day when the Umeda Virtual Corridor came into view. Holding tight to his earlier bravado, Isozuka allowed the crowd to carry him into the mouth of the tunnel.

Murals on both sides of the hall formed a slice-of-life tableau. People frozen mid-moment—all Westerners—smiled vacantly at the passing pedestrians. Even the ceiling was painted: its strokes mimicked a clouded blue sky with circling birds, trapping you in the corridor's virtual world.

Isozuka had begun to slip back into the hypnosis of the commute when he was startled by a presence at his feet. He looked down to find a purring sleek, brown cat. It was a stray, judging by the scar on the creature's nose, with flat and sharp gray eyes.

Animals were not permitted in the station. The creature must-have, like him, come inside to escape the heat. Someone was bound to catch it and let it out before long, but Isozuka was in too big of a hurry to concern himself with the animal.

Isozuka nudged the cat with the toe of his shoe, and the feline took off down the corridor, getting lost in the crowd. Reaching the end of the hallway, Isozuka ascended the steps, thus ending the trial of his first encounter with the corridor.

****

Isozuka didn't think of the corridor again until the following morning. After his boss had finally left for the evening, he'd gotten drinks with men from the office and taken a taxi home, avoiding the station altogether. He hadn't given this morning's commute much thought, but when confronted with the choice, Isozuka decided it'd be safe to repeat Monday's refreshing shortcut and descended into the station.

A rush of cold air greeted him as he stepped into the fluorescent subway. His cheeks stung from the sun, and he envied the woman closing her parasol behind him.

He'd walked briskly through the corridor the day before in a deliberate attempt to avoid too much thought of his surroundings. This morning, however, with the ten minutes the shortcut saved, he elected to take his time—as much as he could in the foot traffic—and really see the corridor. This, he surmised, would illuminate the odd parts of the exhibit that so troubled him and absolve him of any prevailing discomfort. Nearing the passage, he slowed his gait.

The Umeda Virtual Corridor occupied the tunnel that connected the Midosuji Subway and Osaka Station beneath the bustling streets of Umeda. The exhibit stretched from one end of the wide hallway to the other and was designed to look like an outdoor street—an American or European avenue, Isozuka assumed, though he hadn't an inkling of which city it was meant to depict—populated by shops and cafes.

He assumed if this was the whole of the artwork, it would perturb him much less than it currently did, for the street's residents, for lack of a better term, were the part of the work that concerned Isozuka most. On either side of the corridor, over two dozen Western patrons of varying ages sat, stood, or "moved" along the avenue, unsuspectingly frozen in time.

It's not that the corridor was scary by nature or even that the artwork was poorly done; in fact, Isozuka found himself rather impressed by the execution and attention to detail. No, *unsettling* was the word he would use. And though Isozuka didn't much want to admit it, the hallway, with all its painted subjects, always made him feel simultaneously exhibitionist and as if he himself were being watched, like the eyes of the seemingly stationary forms followed him as he passed. Somehow, no one else ever seemed bothered by this, or if they did, Isozuka hadn't caught the expression of shared unease.

Lost in his thoughts, a figure in his peripheral vision startled him, and Isozuka shuddered at the image of a man on his left. The man held a bag of groceries from which several apples had escaped out a tear in the bottom and rolled further down the corridor—spotting the apples, a young painted boy points, a strange look on his face. Nothing inherently unusual, and yet something about it seemed unnatural.

Beyond the man with the apples, Isozuka continued past young painted people seated on a bench and an entire restaurant scene. It was here he stopped with surprise when he came across an unexpected character.

At the foot of one of the depicted restaurant's outdoor tables sat the image of a brown cat, its gray eyes staring at something invisible down the hallway. The gloss of the paint made his fur sleek, and a small scar sat on the cat's nose. Isozuka paused to examine the cat further, causing the unassuming businesswoman behind him to stumble as she stepped on his heels.

That wasn't there yesterday, he thought, and then chided himself. *Of course, it was.* The painting had been there for years. They wouldn't still be creating additions. But what he couldn't explain was its resemblance to the stray he'd seen in the station yesterday. No, at some point in the past, he must've noticed the cat in the mural, and having it in his mind due to the summer's first encounter with the corridor, merely *thought* yesterday's feline had gray eyes and a scar on its nose.

But now that he was thinking of it, the closer he looked at the surrounding images, the more he started to notice things he hadn't before.

Not that this was unusual. It *was* trick art, after all, crafted to gradually reveal easy-to-miss details the longer one looked at it.

And yet...with his limited knowledge of the mural, Isozuka *knew* some things were off. The image of a young boy who Isozuka was certain had once been depicted leapfrogging over a fire hydrant now lay on the sidewalk holding a ruined knee. The boy's face was twisted in agony. The sight made Isozuka nauseous. Not just because he could have sworn that it hadn't looked like this before, but because the scene itself was oddly horrific. Why would someone create something that looked so morbid?

He forced his gaze away and quickly ran his eyes over the other panels. More and more eerie details appeared, the longer he looked. Hadn't the bride in the window once been toasting out toward the street? Isozuka shook his head. He was letting his imagination run wild again. Maybe it was the heat or stress of overtime.

Isozuka swiped at the perspiration, spotting his brow. *Just stress,* he told himself. He kept his eyes carefully trained away from the empty eyes, and toothy smiles.

He hurried quickly out of the tunnel and up toward the street, only making eye contact with the young woman in the bottom left corner of the missing persons' poster. For a moment, he felt as if he'd seen that face somewhere else, but the feeling quickly passed. Isozuka shook his head and exited the station.

****

He maintained it had been stress that made his eyes play tricks on him, but he'd thought very little of the corridor before his commute home the following evening.

The workday had been long. His boss had stayed until half past midnight, which was even later than normal. Isozuka himself had run out of work to complete by seven p.m., but rather than leave; he had sat at his desk in solidarity and organized everything in sight. Papers, drawers, paperclips. He could tell by the clattering sounds around him that other salarymen were doing something similar. Finally, his boss had left, and Isozuka, dizzy with fatigue from the series of late nights and early mornings, followed.

It was Wednesday, and Isozuka was running on only five hours of sleep and fifteen hours spent hunched over his desk in the grueling sunlight from the office window. He had little confidence he wouldn't fall asleep on his feet before he made it home.

He did his best not to give the corridor a thought as he disappeared into Osaka Station.

This late at night, the station was predictably empty. The trains had stopped running, and even the foot traffic had waned to only a handful of late-night stragglers. Like him, they moved with zombie-like exhaustion.

Isozuka headed toward the entrance of the Midosuji Subway. A short flight of stairs carried him down into the train station's basement. It was even quieter here. The soft scrape of footsteps had disappeared, leaving only the dismal plodding of Isozuka's own tired feet.

He'd never seen the corridor look so empty. And yet, it didn't *feel* empty. The Umeda Virtual Corridor felt oddly charged. He'd have thought the bright lights would give him some sort of comfort; instead, he hated how exposed it made him feel. The corridor's colorful buildings and occupants appeared oversaturated under the harsh glare and made Isozuka's eyes throb.

He looked down to avoid the visual noise, but his eye caught on the shoes of the painting's closest subject, a woman dining at the restaurant. They were white women's slip-ons. His sweetheart at university had had a very similar pair back in the eighties. He glanced over. Several tables down, a man wore a pair of loafers Isozuka himself had only purchased in the nineties, the time's trendy office shoes the perfect present to himself for his first promotion.

Assessing the corresponding clothing, Isozuka noticed other discrepancies. The boy pointing at the apples wore a sweater meant for winter, while on the other side of the hallway, a man wore a pair of summer shorts, and another wore a rain jacket, both in styles from the turn of the century.

Very few of the mural's residents, it seemed, were from the same period or even time of year, as if taken from their own timelines and imprisoned together within the painting's depths. Isozuka was too mentally exhausted to wonder if this were an artistic choice or a sign of something more sinister, but just as he brushed the thought aside, determined to leave the corridor behind, his eyes trailed up to the face of the woman in the white shoes. The woman sat at one of the restaurant's tables, her brown hair twisted into a bun. For the first time, Isozuka looked at her face. He'd seen it nearly every day for most—if not all—of his working life. Only she'd gone missing in the eighties and hadn't been seen since.

The face from the bottom left corner of the police poster.

Isozuka took a step back, involuntarily raising his arms as if to shield himself from the woman. All around him, more and more faces jumped into stark clarity, their eyes seemingly trained upon him.

Were they all from the station bulletin?

Nonsense, his mind barked, *but what if*? The thought answered.

Looking back at the faces, Isozuka found it hard to believe the heat of their gaze was just a trick of his mind. Isozuka ran. He didn't dare look behind him, not that he was sure what he was expecting to see. He'd had enough of the Virtual Corridor.

****

It was no use. His trenchcoat wasn't made to withstand rain, and it was highly unlikely his shoes would dry before work in the morning if he continued his commute home in the downpour. Isozuka ducked into the station and out of the rain. He could have bought an umbrella from a *kombini* and possibly soldiered on. Still, he had so many of those transparent convenience store umbrellas around his apartment already that another would exceed embarrassing.

It was well past midnight. The rest of the city had long gone home, and the trains had stopped running, which left Osaka Station in a rare state of stillness.

Squish. Squish. Squish. His water-logged shoes sloshed across the floor and left watery footprints behind. Isozuka couldn't remember the last time he'd seen the train station look so empty, so lifeless. The silence seemed to magnify every step Isozuka took toward home, making the swish of his wet clothing deafening to his ears.

He skirted down a vacant staircase into the station's basement. He hadn't expected to see anyone else per se, but the quietness of the corridor made his heart pound. He shuddered and felt goosebumps rise along his arms. *I'm cold from being wet,* he said to himself.

But Isozuka knew that wasn't true: he found himself honestly frightened to traverse the corridor.

He wouldn't, he decided. There had to be a way around it, and with his sense of direction, he'd find it.

Isozuka hurried down the stairs. Instead of walking toward the corridor, he darted straight to his left and down the next hall. He didn't dare look up as he passed the Virtual Corridor, though he was *positive* a figure had flitted past its mouth in the corner of his eye.

All of the shops and restaurants were closed for the night. Though Isozuka had traveled through this very subway station countless times, he found it hard to navigate. He chalked it up to the foreign feel of the tunnels after closing time. It looked like an entirely different building, all locked up.

Following the signs to the street, Isozuka felt his chest loosen with relief. *Almost there,* he told himself, rounding another corner. He stopped dead in his tracks.

The Umeda Virtual Corridor stretched before him.

Stupid, he thought after a moment to digest. He'd just walked in a circle.

Isozuka turned on his heel and quickly retraced his steps back toward the street. He shortly found the problem. He'd missed a set of stairs. These would take him down before taking him back up and out, the toll of avoiding the corridor. He began to descend the steps before pausing partway down.

At the foot of the staircase, the painting of a flower shop confronted him: the other end of the Virtual Corridor. He retreated up the stairs, a little less sure of himself. At least he was on the right side of the tunnel. One of these exits had to lead to his street.

But it seemed as though, no matter how many different hallways he took, he always wound right back at the top of the corridor. He hung a left, and then a right, and then a right, and then a left again. The front windows of the restaurants—the real restaurants, he comforted himself—were shuttered and locked, leaving little visual variation to his surroundings. The station was a giant, beige maze.

It felt as though he'd spent the better part of twenty minutes trying to find his way out. His wariness mounted into nervousness, then full-fledged fear. He kept thinking that he heard a voice, maybe of an officer doing his late-night rounds, but when he followed the sounds, it only brought him back to the corridor.

He shivered in his wet clothes, anxious and frightened if he were being honest with himself, which he assumed he should be. His phone had no service, so he located an emergency phone box and lifted the receiver. He tried to ignore the trembling of his hand as he pressed the phone to his ear. Dead silence. He stabbed at the buttons but knew it was of no use.

This is absurd, he thought, even as he stuck his hands in his pockets to stop them from shaking. He just wanted to get out. And it was becoming clear that there was only one way.

Isozuka paused for one uncertain moment. He was back at the entrance of the Umeda Virtual Corridor. He would walk straight through. He didn't have to look anywhere but down.

His breath shaky, eyes trained on the tops of his wet shoes, Isozuka stepped forward.

One step. Two steps. Three steps.

The hallway felt as though it were stretching. Isozuka didn't dare look up and get lost in the faces of the people on the walls. He was afraid to see that something else was different, to find another face he thought he knew. As ridiculous as the idea was, Isozuka wouldn't lift his gaze; again, he felt painted eyes on him.

Thirteen. Fourteen. Fifteen.

He came across another pair of wet, silty footprints, and then another. It was an odd relief to know that someone else had been down here recently enough to leave footprints.

He felt his shoulders relax a bit and even allowed himself to tilt his head up. He was halfway through the corridor. Almost there.

The sight of small paw prints made him pause, then smile. With the summer heat tempting animals inside, there was nothing odd about an animal in the subway. No doubt the same stray cat from the other day. He had been ridiculous to think that, even for a moment…

The thought trailed off as Isozuka followed the delicate paw print trail with his eyes. They meandered into the gullet of the hallway and then suddenly veered right.

Don't look, the tiny voice in his head nagged. *Leave. Continue home.*

But curiosity got the better of him. Isozuka followed the prints...right to where the floor met the wall.

The paw prints went to the wall and did not come back out.

Isozuka backed up, frozen with anxiety.

He then began to notice other sets of footprints, human footprints: not the ones that wandered up and down the hall but those that wandered *across*.

Men's shoes, women's shoes, children's shoes. Unconsciously he wandered down the corridor, surveying the sheer number and fearing what they meant. When he finally stopped, the toes of his shoes aligned with a set of slender-heeled footprints. They advanced before him to where the peculiar bride stood in the window of the dress shop, stemmed glass raised in a chilling toast. The light from the stairs at the end of the hall, just feet away, illuminated her vacant expression and the presence of…

Isozuka froze, his eyes widening at the face before him. Water poured from the portrait's mascaraed eyes, leaving trails of clumpy, black ooze dripping down her face. Dizzily, Isozuka walked forward and brushed his fingertips against the tears. They smeared beneath his fingers....

The bride flicked her eyes to him.

Isozuka yelped in surprise and jumped back. She didn't move; she *hadn't* moved. *She was nothing but a painting.* Isozuka's face went hot with humiliation.

No. He would not let the corridor get the better of him.

Unfamiliar emotions flooded Isozuka: fear, shame, and rage. His hands shook.

Anguished, he screamed and clawed at the bride, his fingernails tearing through the paint of her eyes until he couldn't see her look at him. Then he went to the next figure and the next, a man looking down, the man laughing. He moved to the other side of the hall, ripping at the paint with his fingernails until his nails cracked, and his fingers bled, leaving red streaks where their eyes had been.

At last, he calmed, the pain of his hands reaching him. He stumbled back from the restaurant scene, his eyes on the girl from the police posters, now unrecognizable.

Faintly, he heard the sound of birds overhead. He looked up to see a flock circling the painted sky. The smell of decaying paint-filled Isozuka's nostrils. His grip on reality began to slip.

There was the sound of paint crackling behind him, but before he could look, stiff tendrils of pigment stretched across his eyes, dragging him backward. He screamed, and strong strings of dried paint tore open his jaw, filling his mouth. They wrapped around his arms and legs, his shoulders and torso, swallowing him.

Isozuka knew he had to be nearing the other side of the hall. But the sensation of cold drywall against his back never came. The wall behind him seemed to have disappeared, giving way to an abyss of dust and death.

Chalk-like paint flecks filled his nose and throat, stifling his screams into coughs that grew weaker and weaker as he gasped for clean air. His lungs siphoned dust.

The last thing Isozuka remembered seeing was a cat; its gray eyes narrowed into slits as Isozuka felt his gaze fade, and then...

Silence.

****

The corridor bustled with activity. *Obon,* the Buddhist festival of the deceased, was just a few days away. Spirited families prepared for the occasion, running last-minute errands and cleaning their homes in anticipation of out-of-town guests. Despite the soaring temperatures, the mood was electrifying and contagious as excitement for the festival swooped through the city. Crowds squeezed through the tunnels of the Umeda Train Station, pedestrians shoulder to shoulder as they traveled to festivities and meet-ups with friends.

The hallway of the Umeda Virtual Corridor was even more cramped with the recent addition of painters. Moving slowly, they tackled each panel one at a time, rolling pints of white paint over the images that covered the walls.

Two students marched down the corridor, their uniforms in varying stages of sloppy undress, too elated by the week of vacation ahead to concern themselves with appearances. The male student jabbed his friend in the side and indicated the painter tasked with the panel of the dress shop. The faces of the panel's bride and those around her had been vandalized. Torn strips of paint hung down from where their eyes should have been.

The students watched the man erase the bride's ruined face. Before long, it'd be just a blank wall. "I'm honestly glad they're painting that hallway," the female student confessed to her friend. "It always sort of gave me the creeps."

As they rounded the corner away from the corridor, they passed a brown cat, so still, it could have been a painting. The cat sat and surveyed the progress, fixated on the slowly disappearing portrait of a middle-aged Japanese man. As it watched with gray eyes, brown trail twitching, the once vibrant street scene vanished.

a few words from

AMY KOLE

When is the last time you were genuinely scared by something someone created?

When I went through the *Graveyard Games* house at *Halloween Horror Nights* in 2019. There's something about a good-old, haunted cemetery that will never cease to scare me—in real life or a theme park!

Tell us about your contribution to our book. What was the inspiration?

My contribution to the book was a short story called "The Corridor" which I co-wrote with my writing partner Emma Oliver. It's based on a real trick art exhibit in Osaka that was recently taken down. What struck me the most about the Umeda Virtual Corridor is that you were always noticing something new in the images, no matter how many times you'd been down the hallway. But unlike Isozuka in the story, I loved walking through the corridor!

What do you love about the genre of horror?

It's similar to comedy. It's all about setups and payoffs. I get the same rush after a good scare that I get after hearing a solid joke.

What is some of your favorite horror literature? Favorite Author?

I've always loved scary stories. I inhaled the *Goosebumps* series by R.L. Stine when I was young. I'm also a fan of Stephen King, John Saul, and Christopher Pike. *The Shining* by Stephen King has always been my favorite work of horror fiction. The scene with the miniature Overlook Hotel playhouse was so frightening when I first read the book! I couldn't even look at a McDonalds playground the same way after reading that book.

What are some of your influences?

The *Nancy Drew* books influenced me to start writing. While they aren't scary books, my favorite Nancy Drew stories always had a mystery surrounding a ghost.

What is your favorite Halloween treat?

Pillsbury Halloween cookies! I like to live life on the edge and eat those bad boys raw.

You are hosting the perfect Halloween movie marathon. What are the films you choose and why?

As a lover of both horror films and family-friendly Halloween flicks, I'd have to stagger my choices.

When Good Ghouls Go Bad - My all-time, favorite Halloween movie. It has plenty of humor to start the marathon on a high note, but enough creepy imagery to set the mood for an evening of screams. Though not a well-known movie, it stars Christopher Lloyd and was directed by Chris Columbus. Need I say more?

Nightmare on Elm Street - We've gotten all warm and cozy with our family flick, so now it's time to ease into the deep end with a classic 80's slasher. Freddy Krueger is easily one of my all-time, favorite horror movie villains.

Hocus Pocus - This movie comes next because I am a true 90's kid. Also, because we've just watched Johnny Depp get sucked into his bed and explode into a geyser of blood, so we could all probably use a singalong to "I Put a Spell on You."

Ghost Adventure Halloween Special - I know it isn't a movie, but I love *Ghost Adventures*, and their Halloween specials are always a good, scary time. Plus, we've been watching fictional tales of horror, so let's hear an argument for real-life paranormal phenomena.

The Addams Family - Let's be real: it's one thing to be ghoulish for Halloween season, but the Addams have it down 24/7/365. It's the perfect time to take pointers for next year from the true masters of the macabre.

IT 1 & 2 - This is a time and emotional commitment. It's some of the best horror I've seen in theater in years. It has a killer script, strong performances, and a whole lotta heart for a franchise built around killing children. I am in tears by the end of both of these movies, and not out of fear.

Troll 2 - Okay, the scariest part of this movie is how terrible it is, and it's become a cult classic just for that reason. I've probably just been crying for about thirty minutes thanks to *IT 2*, so it's time for a good laugh before bed.

If you could continue any horror story (book or film), what would it be?

The Blair Witch Project. Found footage, creepy urban legend, incredible marketing campaign, this movie had it all. I want to explore the legend of the Blair Witch deeper and get to know more about the tiny town of Burkittsville, MD. Plus, social media offers a plethora of opportunities to create an even scarier and more immersive marketing campaign, which is an experience in itself!

Describe the perfect Halloween.

My perfect Halloween would include trick-or-treating with my friends. I know I'm too old to trick-or-treat, but it used to be what I looked forward to most! After that, I'd hop on over to *Halloween Horror Nights* to run off all of the candy I've just eaten!

SCARE CRED: AMY KOLE

Amy Kole grew up in haunted Savannah, GA. She earned her BFA in Acting at Shenandoah Conservatory and then an MFA in Dramatic Writing at the Savannah College of Art and Design. As a show writer, Amy develops and writes the concepts and scripts for theme park experiences that range anywhere from Cinema 4-D attractions to VR coasters. When Amy isn't writing for theme parks, you can usually find her playing inside of one, especially if Halloween Horror Nights is open!

the day our HAUNTED HOUSE sank to the bottom of LAKE MICHIGAN

BY JOHN LAFLAMBOY

It was around 10 a.m., October 31st, 2014, when I received the first call: "The waves at the pier are getting pretty bad, you should come down here."

I jumped in my car and headed south on Lake Shore Drive to Chicago's Navy Pier, where our haunted house 'Zombie Containment' was sitting on top of a barge which was tied off at the Northeast corner of the pier. Once on Lake Shore Drive, I realized immediately that today would be a very bad day for the Zombie Army. I tried desperately to keep my eyes on the road, but my attention kept drifting to my left, to Lake Michigan. I didn't recognize it. It looked angry. Instead of seeing the beaches that I see every day on this drive, I saw dark churning water slamming 20' waves around where the beaches used to be. Waves were smashing the front doors of a beach-side restaurant that's usually hundreds of feet from the shore. As I approached the bend in Lake Shore Drive near the famous Drake Hotel, a large wave tore 30 feet of sidewalk away and left it a hundred feet from its original position. Still trying to focus on the road, I saw a wave break over the Lake Shore Drive retaining wall onto the northbound lane, leaving a log the size of a tree on the road. The northbound lanes now belonged to the storm.

As I exited and made my approach to Navy Pier, I made two phone calls before arriving. The first was to my camera crew ("Drop whatever you're doing and get to Navy Pier. Chicago history is being made today.") The second call was to my insurance agent, Ken Donat, "I need your help, I think I'm in some trouble here."

I was correct in both instances; I just didn't realize how bad it was about to get.

As I drove my car alongside the North parking garage lane of the pier, I suddenly felt as if I'd entered a horror movie. People were being evacuated. Geyser-like explosions of water were shooting 20' in the air through manhole covers as the waves broke under the pier. Water was shooting sideways out of the brick walls, and there didn't seem to be a safe place left.

After parking my car, I raced around the corner to see what damage the barge and haunted house had taken. I wasn't exactly prepared for what I saw. The 141' by 43' barge was behaving like a horse trying to get free of its rope while in a barn fire. The barge, flinging off its gangways, bucked and kicked against the pier. As the waves buckled the pier's concrete from below, the barge would smash it from the side. Particularly large waves would lift the barge up over the pier, smash it down on the concrete and then the barge would slowly slide back into the water, metal grinding the concrete to dust, sounding like the roar of the T-Rex in Jurassic Park. The barge was roaring at us as it tried to break free.

This went on for *hours*. The haunted house was on top of the barge.

With each crash into the pier, another container/haunted house room would break free from its welds and bolts, slide off into the water and sink to bottom of Lake Michigan. I stood there with my girlfriend and business partner, Tresa Walker, helpless as we watched each room ripped from the barge's deck.

As we glimpsed zombies, science labs, costume rooms, and pneumatic props disappearing between the gigantic waves, it was impossible not to think about all the work we'd invested, all the money we'd gambled and all of the great memories we'd shared with the crew while building this first-year attraction. We watched all our work (and all our life savings) ripped away a piece at a time, tossed around by the angry water and bucking barge before disappearing into the lake.

In the end, it took just seven hours for this freak storm to sink the haunted house that we'd invested so many hours into creating. Teresa and I stood watch until the barge stopped resisting the storm and made its final descent to the bottom of the lake. When it appeared as though the struggle was over, I turned to the fire department, coast guard, and police officers that stayed with me the entire time and said, "Gentlemen, I'm really sorry about all of this." They seemed shocked as they replied, "What are you sorry for kid? We all just watched your life savings sink, we're sorry for you." I responded, "Yeah, that's true, and in that wreckage are fifty-two lifesize zombies made of foam that will no doubt wash up on the beaches of Chicagoland for years to come, ruining beach parties, swimming events, and a lot of your days as you respond to these calls of a 'washed up body'."

I was not wrong.

Now, I've told this story many times over the years. It's not easy going over your worst day of your professional career. But I wanted to take the time to tell it today, in this book, to honor the man that stood by my side during my worst days. Earlier in the story I referred to "My second phone call being to my insurance guy, Ken Donat." Ken wasn't just my insurance guy, he was my friend. He was there for me that day, telling me that everything was going to be alright, even though it was far from alright. He assured me that he had my back, and I knew he did, because that was the kind of guy he was. Over the next few months, my insurance company denied my claim. They said that the coverage I bought to protect a haunted house (on a barge *ON Lake Michigan*) didn't cover "flood damage". Almost $400,000 at the bottom of the lake and my insurance company abandoned me.

My insurance broker Ken Donat, however, refused to abandon me. He fought them day in and day out on my behalf. And when they refused to live up to their responsibility, Ken filed a claim with his personal Errors and

Omissions policy in my name. Knowing that this move would cost him dearly in annual fees, Ken stood between Zombie Army Productions and certain bankruptcy. Ken's personal insurance paid us enough to stay in business. Just to be clear, *Ken was getting screwed by my insurance as much as I was*, and *he did not have to file a claim against himself*. He did it to save me, to save the Zombie Army.

In an industry where spectacle reigns supreme, we often speak about the great designers, builders and actors that make this Haunted House Industry successful. But I will always remember the "insurance guy" who never failed to look after us while we built our dreams, the man that cared enough to take the time to teach us why we needed certain protections, the supporter that sponsored our parties at the trade shows while he laughed in the back of the room, and the friend that would always pick up the phone when I needed him.

Ken Donat was a cornerstone during the vital years we grew into being a legitimate industry and I will never forget his impact. We lost him this year to a heart attack during the COVID-19 pandemic, and with so much happening in the world all at once, he did not get the memorial he deserved. We did not get the chance to salute him and thank him for everything he had done for us and the industry we love so much. I know you started to read this story about the day Zombie Army lost everything to a freak storm, but in the end, I wanted to tell you about a great man that saved Zombie Army from a freak storm. I kind of tricked you. So next time you see a Zombie Army show, and you wonder how we did all that we did, just know that Ken Donat had a big part in our success and we won't ever forget that!

Thank you, Ken. You were loved and you are missed.

DAY SHOWS NIGHT SHOWS
LOW SCARE
HIGH SCARE
TMS 200
STOP
NO RIGHT TURN
H110983

a few words from

JOHN LAFLAMBOY

As a designer of horror theatre or experiences, explain your process.

Everything starts with a story. I'm a firm believer that it's our responsibility to both the audience and the actors at a haunted house, that I have developed a foundation of story and concept that brings them into a new world. Once the foundation is set, I must empower my actors to not only tell that story, but they must live in a space that enables them to both scare and entertain. I approach every design in five steps: Tell a Story, Empower the Actor by designing the room around their movement and storytelling, Use all theatrical assets to create "unease" in the audience, Install spectacle props as distractions to better hide the actor, Alter materials, textures, and colors to force the audience to ask "what is that?". After those five steps are complete, I layer it all with the "science of scare" by adding two-three known phobia triggers per room.

When is the last time you were genuinely scared by something someone created?

I'm never more scared in a haunted house than when I see blatant fire safety violations.

Tell us about your contribution to our book. What was the inspiration?

I honestly had no idea what I was going to write, I was a bit frustrated. So, I sat down and just started typing. It turns out I had something to say, something I needed to say about a friend of mine. Thanks for the opportunity.

What do you love about the genre of horror?

I am a storyteller at heart. Whether I am working on the stages of Chicago theatre, on set of a movie, or in the halls of my haunted houses, it's all about telling a story. The haunted house industry enables me to create entire worlds for my audience. I am firmly against using other people's creations. You won't see Jason or Freddy at my shows. So, when I am creating something new, say a "Blood Room", I am free to create whatever I want, with no limitations. There is no one telling me that my "Blood Room" isn't accurate or legitimate. I have found creative freedom in the haunted house industry that I have found nowhere else.

What is some of your favorite horror literature? Favorite author?

I was the weird kid reading Stephen King at twelve. *Eyes of the Dragon* hooked me into a world of fantasy and fear.

What are some of your influences?

Walt Disney, Kermit the Frog, Hunter S. Thompson, Steven Spielberg.

What is your favorite Halloween treat?

Any sour candy! I cannot stop myself!

You are hosting the perfect Halloween movie marathon. What are the films you choose and why?

Jaws is the greatest horror movie ever made! No other horror movie has been so terrifying that it actually destroyed local economies, like *Jaws* did to beach towns. *Evil Dead* was the movie that made me sit up straight and say " I want to make a movie....I want to make a movie like that!" *Shaun of the Dead* was the perfect blend of comedy and horror, a true influence to all of my work. And I would round it out with my movie *The Moleman of Belmont Avenue*. Not because it can be compared to those greats, but because you can see each one of those influences of my career in the *Moleman*.

Describe the perfect Halloween.

For the last twenty years I have been very lucky to live my "perfect Halloween" each year. I get to start our haunted house each Halloween night by telling our house's origin story to the cast of 150, it's their own personal ghost story. The kids usually find some way to surprise me or punk me throughout the night, they are creatively wicked with this annual endeavor. The audience itself seems to be part of our own little party as they show up decked out in their costumes. But most importantly, I get to dress up, as I do every night, and play with the beautifully talented cast in those dark and scary halls. We are all kids playing in the dark on Halloween. I really couldn't ask for anything more.

SCARE CRED: JOHN LAFLAMBOY

John LaFlamboy, founder of Zombie Army Productions, has been producing award winning haunted houses, events, films, and theatre for the past 20 years in Chicagoland. His theatre and film background give him the foundation to create massive interactive haunted attractions that leave the audience feeling like they had just walked through a live horror film. His production of Statesville Haunted Prison has been a nationally ranked attraction and holds the distinction of being the most critically acclaimed haunted house in Chicago history. His latest creation, HellsGate Haunted House, is his dream project and the culmination of 20 years of haunted house experience. "HellsGate, it's not just a Haunted House, It's an Adventure!", says John. When he is not working in the halls of his haunted houses, he is a stage and film actor in Chicago.

THE MONSTER INSIDE

BY SHAR MAYER

a few words from

SHAR MAYER

As a designer of horror theatre or experiences, explain your process.

I am predominantly an actor and train other actors/haunters. But I also do production work for some haunts and horror shows. As for the process, first I find out what the person who I am working with wants to do, or I'll get their general ideas for what they have in mind. Then I'll fine tune their ideas and add my take on it and use my experience to bring it to life. I prefer working with others rather then on my own. I am very collaborative, and would rather work with other creative people so that we can come to a project from different angles. I believe that having everyone's strong points put forward will produce a product that will benefit from having a multi angle vision.

When is the last time you were genuinely scared by something someone created?

I love going to haunts and haunted events whenever I can, but as I work during haunt season, it's hard to find the time during season. However, in my travels I am sometimes able to find year-round haunts and once in a while I am lucky enough to get owners to let me do a lights-on tour. As long as I am in the mindset that this is a scare experience, I am always be able to get scared. It's fun because everyone likes to scare me and hear me scream. I love to scream and I am so glad I never became jaded and lost that feeling!

What are some of your infuences?

In the horror field, I get my influences mostly from art museums. You'd be amazed at the dark art that you will find in museums all over the world. And many times, that influence doesn't even have to be what is considered "dark".

Tell us about your contribution to our book. What was the inspiration?

When I travel I always visit museums, I have been to museums all over the world. On my last trip to Japan I was really moved by a sculpture I saw in a museum in Kyoto. The stone cracked opened down the center as the artist was carving it. The artist took that crack as the soul of the subject coming out of the stone. He then continued to carve the interior face right in the middle of the statue. I was fascinated by it and I couldn't leave this piece. It started to make me think of how we all have our inner self that is looking to escape. When I internalized this idea, I thought about the monster inside me that always wants to come out. The one I have to keep hidden until haunt time. This drawing talks about my own monster, the one inside me, the one which I have to keep under wrap. I plan on expanding on this idea of "The Monster Inside" and doing it as a theater piece at some point.

What do you love about the genre of horror?

I think the genre of horror allows us to explore other sides of our personality that we usually keep hidden because of our own fear of what others would say. However, for myself, I have lived on the darkside my whole life, so for me it's just a normal part of my life, and I do not have that fear. My real acting comes when I have to fit into what most people see as a "normal" day-to-day social activity.

What is your favorite Halloween treat?

I eat all candies including candy corn. As a child, I was notorious for keeping my bag of Halloween candy for the entire year. By eating a couple of pieces each week, I was able to have that sweet reminder of Halloween all year.

You are hosting the perfect Halloween movie marathon. What are the films you choose and why?

I personally love the old black and white universal horror films, like *Frankenstein, The Wolfman, Dracula.* So, I would play one from that era, then one from the last couple years like, *Midsommar*, *Heredity*, and *Us*. And then back to an older one and continue back and forth alternating between the generations of horror. I think this would be a good way to expose the movie watcher to new films as most horror fans only know the films they grew up with.

Describe the perfect Halloween.

My Halloween's ARE perfect! I spend the entire month of October, hanging out with like-minded individuals, as I scare and terrorize people who just want to share their screams with me.

SCARE CRED: SHAR MAYER

Shar Mayer is a legendary haunt actor who has worked in every aspect of the industry for over forty years. Starting in home haunts, she has worked in mazes, hayrides, large theme parks, immersive haunt experiences, horror theater shows, extreme haunts and has also monstered for film and television. She started performing on the east coast for haunts including "The Haunted Hayride NY" before moving west. She worked fifteen years for "Knotts Scary Farm", three years in Carnevil Streets and two years in the Underground maze. Shar was also featured in Jon Schitzner award winning documentary, *Haunters: The Art of The Scare*. Shar was a producer at the world's first Halloween convention "ScareLA" where she worked on the haunted mazes, horror panels and scary shows. She also worked production and scared for private haunted mazes include some for YouTube Studios. Visit her at SharMayer.com

character is a stamp of our souls

BY SHANE METHENY

The Dream Thief

Is it really there? This slender, dark figure haunts your dreams. Every attempt to wake yourself is futile as you feel its icy stare pierce your soul. Wake up...WAKE UP!!! Slowly your eyes open as you lay paralyzed from fear in your room. The shadows seem to close in upon you as you try to catch your breath. Your heart pounds in your chest as your eyes focus and adjust to dark. Something catches your eye and you turn to see it. The slender dark figure has come.

Pulled Pork

It is said that a pig can devour a human body in a matter of minutes. With his insatiable appetite, he is always on the hunt for something to nibble on. Don't allow yourself to wander into his domain, for you will never escape his clutches. But, not to worry. It will only take a few minutes.

Slits

They mocked him incessantly. No one seemed to take him seriously. How could they? After all he was quite the cut up. One day he would show them. One day they would see how serious he was. Well! It's not so funny now, is it?

Vanna T.

They say that beauty is only skin deep, but ugliness goes to the bone. But, she the perfect remedy. With a cut here and a slice there she could end her woes. No more staring in the mirror wishing that she could somehow change the reflection peering back at her. Now she had the face she'd longed for, even if it wasn't her own.

a few words from

SHANE METHENY

As a designer of horror theatre or experiences, explain your process.

First, I try to think of something that I think would give me the creeps. Then I formulate somewhat of a back story. By that I mean that I think of what the creatures thought processes would be, you know...what makes them tick. From there I usually look at a few different reference pictures to get an idea of form. After I have a basic idea of where I think the sculpture should go, I usually just dive in and start moving clay. Most times the clay leads me where to go. The forms are there. I just have to coax them out.

When is the last time you were genuinely scared by something someone created?

It's hard to say really. I would have to say when I was younger for sure. I've been into Halloween for as long as I can remember. Being in this industry I think has somewhat desensitized me.

Tell us about your contribution to our book. What was the inspiration?

I am a lover of the art of horror and all things creative. I love seeing what others create and I try and learn something other artists. This book is a great way to do just that.

What do you love about the genre of horror?

For me, it's an adrenaline rush. Though I don't really get scared, I love the anticipation of what's around the corner or what's hiding in the shadows. As for the creative side of things, mask making gives me a chance to make something other-worldly. I also love seeing other people's interpretations of what I create. I've had customers send me photos of themselves wearing a mask that they've purchased from me. Sometimes their concepts are something totally different than what I envisioned and I absolutely love that.

What is some of your favorite horror literature? Favorite Author?

I'm, oddly enough, not much of a horror literature aficionado. I have a hard time sitting still long enough to actually sit down and read. But, I do have a few favorite film directors. I really like James Wan's style. His movies recently have had a very supernatural/spiritual feel to them. I'm also a fan of Wes Craven and Tobe Hooper's work. And I can't leave out John Carpenter.

What are some of your influences?

I would say other artists are a big influence on me. I love seeing what others create. Horror movies have also influenced me. *The Texas Chainsaw Massacre* had a very profound effect on me. I love how it was gritty, and visceral, and just...disturbing. And the fact that it isn't too far-fetched makes it all the more terrifying.

What is your favorite Halloween treat?

It's a toss-up for me. If I only had Snickers or Reese's Peanut Butter Cups, I would be more than satisfied.

You are hosting the perfect Halloween movie marathon. What are the films you choose and why?

Texas Chainsaw Massacre would definitely be on the list. I would also have to include *Halloween*. In my opinion, these films changed the way horror movies are made. I would also throw in a classic or two such as *The Wolfman* or *The Mummy* simply because those movies are timeless.

If you could continue any horror story (book or film), what would it be?

I really liked the concept of *Trick 'r Treat*. I think there are several different directions this storyline could go and I would be interested to see them.

Describe the perfect Halloween.

My perfect Halloween would consist of sitting around a campfire sipping hot chocolate with my wife and family and our closest friends, spinning terrifying tales and sharing many laughs.

SCARE CRED: SHANE METHENY

Dark Illusions Mask Company was founded in early 2017 by lead artist and sculptor Shane Metheny. With a love for all things Halloween, Shane felt it was only natural to start a mask company geared towards the haunter. Dark illusions masks specialize in comfort and cutting-edge characters that are sure to send a chill up your spine. Make nightmares a reality with a Dark Illusions mask today!

HIM AND L'IL MONSTER

BY AVERY MULTER
(AGE 14)

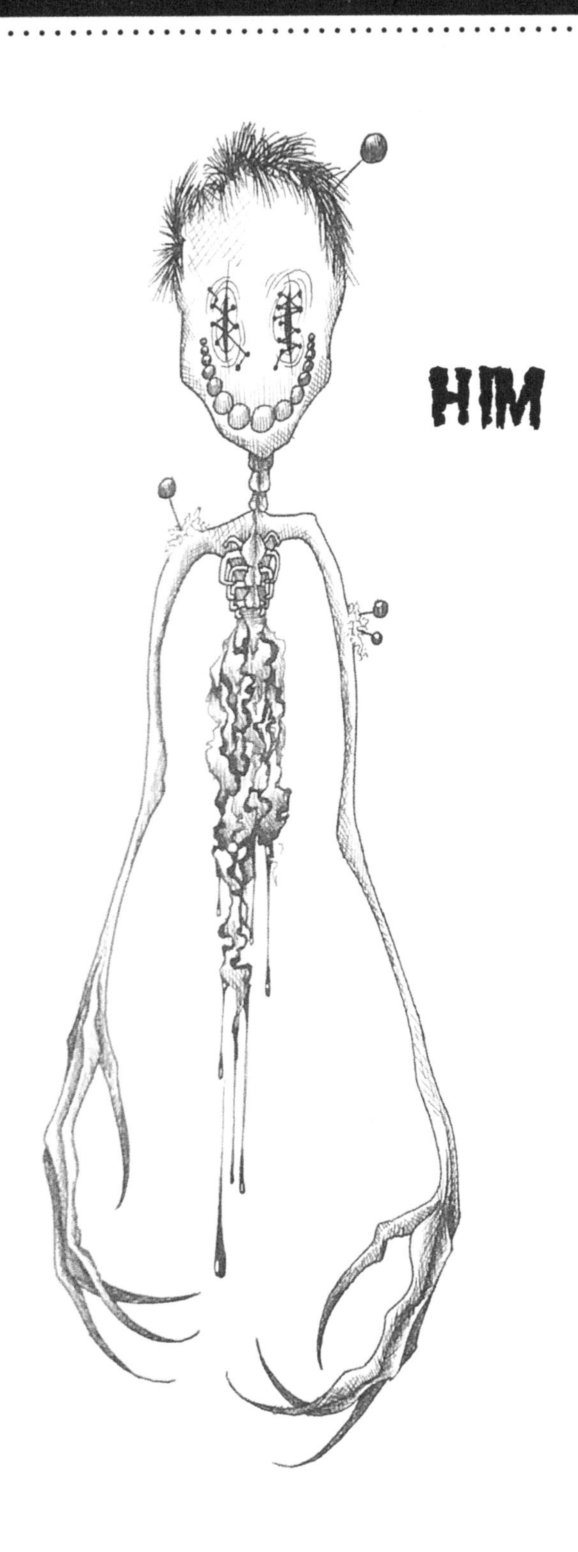

HIM

A FEW WORDS FROM
AVERY MULTER

What do you love about the genre of horror?

For me, the best kind of horror has an element of playfulness to it. It's fun to explore what scares people. I look to Tim Burton, Neil Gaiman, and the artist Shawn Coss for a whimsical adaptation of the genre. For example, I prefer fantastical horror rather than realism. If it could actually happen in real life I'm not interested. In other words: Monsters? Great! Psychos? Not so much.

Tell us about your contribution to our book. What was the inspiration?

For Him and L'il Monster, I wanted to challenge myself to create the creepiest image I could imagine. These pieces contain elements that I find the most disturbing; disembodied figures, skeletal, emaciated forms, big dead smiles, body parts sewn on, grasping hands, innards, and Voodoo dolls.

When is the last time you were genuinely scared by something someone created?

In fact, one of the scarier movie scenes I remember takes place in the Neibolt house in Stephen King's *IT*. Richie and Bill are faced with three doors labeled Scary, Very Scary, and Not Scary At All. They obviously choose Not Scary At All. Bill then opens the door and the interior is pitch black. There are a few seconds of quiet and we hear Betty Ripsom say, "Where's my shoe?" Bill turns the lights on and Betty's body is shown hanging by her arms from the ceiling, missing the lower half of her body. Chilling.

Describe the perfect Halloween.

To counter the macabre aspects of the horror genre, I like to keep my Halloweens on the lighter side. There must be an elaborate costume that takes lots of planning and effort, makeup, the whole works. I want a party with my friends, lots of candy, followed by a sleepover and Halloween treats. Horror should scare you. But it should also delight, thrill, and inspire creativity.

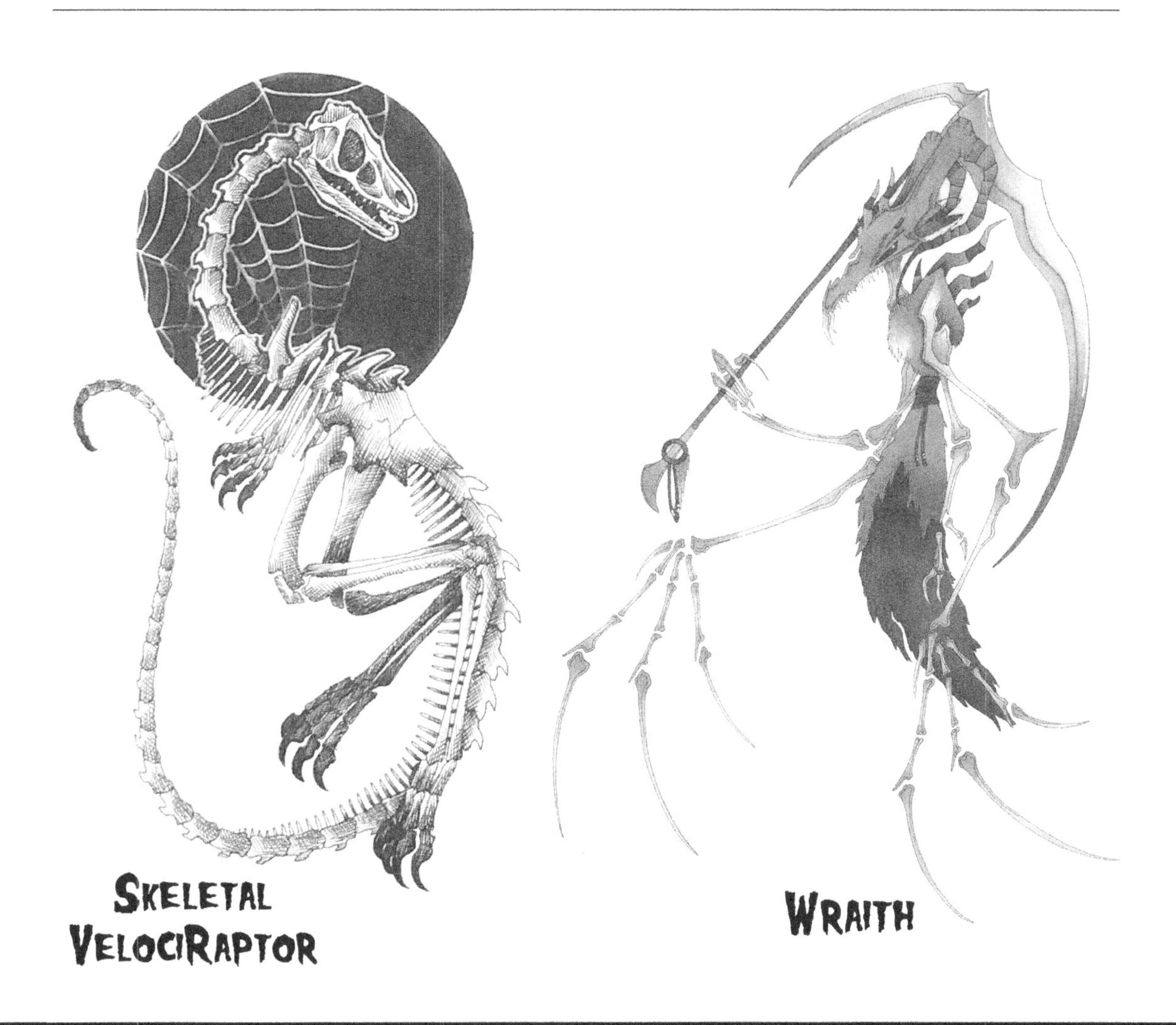

SCARE CRED: AVERY MULTER

Avery Multer is a 14-year-old Chicago-based artist. Her illustrations have been featured multiple times in *Stone Soup Magazine*, including winning the cover of the 2019/20 annual anthology. She also receives commissions for logo design, greeting cards, and other illustrations for private businesses and websites. Most recently, her artwork was featured in *Wingless Dreamer – Art From Heart* (avail. Amazon), and *Flying Ketchup Press*. She was also selected and published as a winner of the *Chicago Sun Times Imagination Project Student Art Competition*. She enjoys working with pen and ink, Copic markers, colored pencil, watercolor, as well as digital ProCreate and Adobe Animate. She hopes to pursue a career in animated character design and story development for TV and film. Avery can be followed on Instagram @hyrium26.

THE BENCH-LEG OF GOEBLE RIDGE

BY MARK MUNCY

I had heard stories of the beast that lurked near my family's lands in Kentucky. My father used to tell me the story of the creature with the dumbest name I'd ever heard that hunted the woods of Goble Ridge in Eastern Kentucky. We only lived a few hours away in Ohio so we used to spend weekends "roughing it" in Louisa and my uncle or my dad would tell us of "The Bench-Leg of Goeble Ridge." All of us kids would laugh at the name, I especially. Now I had already had some encounters with ghostly phenomena and other unexplainable experiences. For some reason I just never believed in the local legendary beast, until I saw it.

Any kid from that grew up anywhere near Isaac Church can tell you the legend of the creature. The story goes an old peddler in the late 1700s would have his cart pulled by an Ox out along what was then known as Muncy Meeks Road. He would sell pots, pans and other odds and ends to the scattered farms along the ridge. The families all knew he was coming from the sound of the old cow bell and the rattle of his wagon.

The story goes that some nefarious types figured he'd have some quick cash on him and possible gold or silver so they set up an ambush under an old tree at a bend in the road where they could hide behind the ridge. It was there they robbed the peddler. He resisted by breaking off a limb from the tree and using it as a club. Of course they overpowered him and killed him. To hide the murder they apparently butchered the cow and buried the whole mess in a shallow grave under the old tree.

As many times as I've heard the tale, up to that point it never changes. It's afterwards that everyone tells it differently, it seems to depend on which of the several family trees in the area tell the tale. Cyrus descendants say that the peddler was of gypsy heritage and a powerful curse brought forth a beast like a big cat that walks on two legs and carries the old peddler's club to take vengeance on the highwaymen. Meeks family members say the old peddler's wife was a witch that animated the bones of her husband and the cow into some odd undead creature that hunts Kentucky lands to keep away bad people. The Isaac clan generally just says it was divine vengeance that killed all the wrongdoers. My dad told it differently.

We of the Muncy family tell it a bit differently since we own most of the land the creature is said to live on. Each generation seems to have some odd encounter or tale of "The Bench-Leg." Heck, the old tree in the legend is supposed to be the creepy old tree that is right across the street from where we "rough it" in our trailer that only has fans and basic cable and no other trees will grow in the immediate area around it. The stories tend to be shared by the big fire pit where we can stay up late telling ghost stories (because basic cable sucks after 11pm). Almost every member or our family has seen the beast, including my dad, his brother, and me.

My dad told me he saw it once when he was very young while out walking his old herd of cattle in. He was walking in the holler when he saw an extra head of cattle. It seemed a little small with an odd glow about its head. My dad called to his brother and told him that one of the cows most have foaled without their knowledge. He got his bother to try and corner the "new cow" by going around one side of a small copse of trees as my dad came from the other side. They blinked in astonishment as the beast vanished in front of their eyes. My dad said just before he could have sworn it turned and looked at him with a glowing human head.

I know it's not terrifying. I know it's just odd. I also know my father never lied about a thing in his life, so I know he honestly believed every word of his story. My uncle also talks about the incident in hushed tones, which if you knew my uncle you would know that happens very rarely.

My incident came many years later. I used to drag some of my city friends with me to our land in Kentucky nearly weekly just to have someone to goof off or go hunting with. We had found and cleaned out my parent's old Airstream trailer: killed all the spiders and snakes that had nested in it: and dragged it down to the edge of an old baseball field my grandparents used to have on their land. There wasn't a ball field there anymore. It was simply a baseball diamond sized clearing in a pristine wilderness. All we really cared about was that it was about a half-mile away from where the grown-ups spent their time so we could talk about girls, school, our parents, and we could tell really scary ghost stories, not ones about a dumb named cow monster with man head and a possible wooden leg.

Anyway one night just after we had gotten to a shaky sleep after a particularly scary retelling of The Haunting of Hill House by yours truly to my friends, one of the horses that occasionally grazed in the area got real close to one of our windows and snorted… loudly. You would have thought the devil himself was at our door as the three early teenaged boys ran out of that trailer with bats and bb guns at the ready to slay whatever beast had awakened us. I seriously think we made the horses night as I imagine the sight when we all realized what fell beast had disturbed our slumber. We all laughed pretty hard.

That's when we heard the sound of more hooves. Was there a second horse out grazing that we hadn't heard about? Was this some echo from a nearby farm? We all got quiet. That's when I saw the glow through the tree line. I can still feel the hairs on the back of my neck stand on end as I type these words even now over 25 years later. The eerie green light was coming right for us and I knew exactly what it was. I was about to have my own story to add to our family's litany.

It burst forth and I could see it was about the size of a big cat. It was a deep black fur all over it and the moonlight seemed to sink into it. I would compare it to a large panther except it had no tail, I swear it had hooves and not claws, and it's head was a misshaped thing that looked like pictures I'd seen of the Elephant man. It did have the head of a man, but it was one ugly sonofabitch. I remember trying to see if it did have a wooden leg. It made a quick turn and ran into the woods just behind our little trailer.

I vaguely remember the horse bolting towards third base and the pond in that area. My friends all scattered and ran for the big trailer, I could hear them yelling for me to "get the fuck out of there." I don't remember running but I do remember being out of breath as I collapsed on the coach in the big trailer. I remember my friend PJ suddenly started yelling, "What the fuck was that?"

My dad came out of his room with mom in tow behind him. Though it had to be 2 or 3 am he had drawn his revolver and was heading for the shotgun cabinet to kill whatever had scared his boy and his friends. From our inability to articulate thanks to sheer terror and a half mile sprint he thought we had a bear or some sort of cougar loose in the area. Then our eyes made contact. He put his gun down and took a deep breath. He knew what had happened.

I don't 100% know what it was. I've never seen it since. The encounter makes zero sense, so you can tell I'm not making it up. We weren't in any apparent danger. Apart from the legends of the Bench-Leg beating up bad people and seeking revenge on the highwaymen, I don't think I've ever heard of anyone actually being hurt by the creature. I could speculate, make a story, even add to the legend I guess. All I do know is I now have a tale to add to the late night fires on Goeble Ridge.

THE LIGHT IN THE WOODS

BY MARK MUNCY

The night was dark and there was a slight crisp chill in the air as I wandered through the back hills on my family's land in Louisa, Kentucky. I had been walking along the trail in the dark for a good long while. I knew the path like the back of my hand, so the sun going down held no fear for me.

I could walk through these woods blindfolded and probably be fine. Sadly, that was unwise as we had all sorts of animals including deer, raccoons, very reclusive foxes, and even a family of black bears on the land in the old cave that once was a family coal mine. I had to be alert for the animals' sake as well as my own.

I was out and about that night for my usual stargazing ritual. We at one point had an old baseball field that my grandfather, my father and my uncles had plowed to play baseball on in the middle of this cedar and pine forest. The trees had not returned to the area and we kept it mowed frequently so it was a nice meadow.

It made the perfect place to have a great view of the stars. It was far from city lights, and just far enough away from the lights of the trailer on our property as well. It was my favorite place in the world. I would lay my blanket right about where the pitcher's mound would've been and laid down and just looked up until it either got way too cold, or I finally got sleepy enough to wander back to the trailer about a half-mile back through the woods.

I smelled the autumn aromas of the trees and feeling the wind kick up as the cold bit through my jacket. I sadly could not enjoy the autumn colors at this point as it was getting very dark very quickly. My eyes had adjusted well so I could see the path clearly; I just could not make out the colors well. On the plus the stars were coming through the trees already. I knew I was close to the old ballpark and couldn't wait for the spectacular view I was sure that was waiting for me.

The trees grew still and silent as the breeze fizzled out. I looked up to see if any of the Leonid meteors might be making an early visit in this calm, but I noticed something unusual in the trees above me.

There was a glow in the trees.

Some of the branches of the cedar just overhead had an odd illumination in them. I thought at first it might have been a light from a car from a nearby hill shining at an odd angle. Maybe it was some foxfire fungus glowing, but since there was no moon tonight that seemed unlikely, as they needed moonlight to glow properly. Maybe my folks had a misaligned floodlight way back at the trailer and it just happened to be hitting this point. It all seemed plausible.

I moved a bit to see if I could get a better angle.

The light jumped to another tree.

I swear it jumped to the tree I moved under!

It stayed right on top of me. What the hell was going on?

I figured it was some odd trick in the light of the night. I moved again. It leapt back to another tree just above me again.

I could hear this voice in my head. It was my father explaining to me to never panic in the woods at night. "Once you panic and start running, only one of two things will happen. You will run into a tree and hurt yourself, or you will trip, fall and whatever caused you to panic will get you."

I immediately thought back of so many nights sitting around the campfire. Ghost stories and our very own cryptid monster called "The Bench-Leg". Glowing things in trees seemed familiar somehow. The memory of the story or legend just was not there. My panic levels were rising.

Another step and the light followed me again. What the hell is this thing?

Now my mind raced to stories of alien abduction. More unusual things flashed in my head. Stories of a cult that killed cattle on a nearby farm flashed in my imagination. There were reports of the first wild wolf seen in years not too far from us. There were bears in a nearby abandoned coal mine. Why would I think about that? My mind was racing. Images of the movie Predator were suddenly all I could think of.

The glow was still above me. I moved again, this time practically leaping away, and the light followed me still. I moved in a quick walk and just overhead that damned glow was still there following me from tree to tree. I could not get away.

I made up my mind to make a break for it then and there. I ran like the hounds of hell were right behind me. For all I knew they were.

Every chance I could I glanced up and the light was right there: leaping from tree to tree and matching my pace. I poured my speed into my legs and felt my heart began to ache as the cold air filled my lungs with each quickening inhale of the return of the now freezing night wind.

In the dark I stirred up animals all over and as each squirrel or rabbit raced away in the dark I thought it was the glowing nearly invisible creature above leaping down to finally claim me for whatever evil purpose it had in mind as it grew tired of toying with me. I stumbled and fell on a broken branch just narrowly missing impaling my eye on another branch. The light had vanished.

I scrambled to my feet and felt the ache in my hands and knees from where I'd fallen. I took a deep breath and wiped my forehead. A few drops of blood from scrapes on my hand dabbed my face and I looked up at my hand.

The light was back.

I bolted.

I had not run much further after I had scrambled to my feet when I kicked up a deer. I do not know if you know the sound a startled deer makes in the dark. Those that do will tell you it is that it sounds like a woman being murdered. That sound combined with my imagination and fear was all it took for me to give me one more great burst of adrenaline and speed. I raced and raced.

I saw the distant floodlights of the family trailer. I had a faint sense that this thing would leap down and grab me just as I neared salvation. I would just be another story the family told by the campfire in probably less than a generation. I was doomed. But I had to keep running. I would die trying.

I reached the barb wire fence surrounding the civilized portion of our property from this forest primeval. I tore my hand further as I stumbled through the fence. I had no time to race to the gate. I had to get to my father and his numerous guns. If this thing could be hurt, I am certain he would find a way.

I reached the clearing around my farm and the light was gone. There was no longer any glow above me. Thank god.

It appeared as if the unearthly light was confined to the forest. I was now telling myself I would never set foot in that evil forest again, no matter how much I loved it. I wanted nothing to do with that alien and targeted light.

I bolted to the porch. As I reached it, I looked up and saw the glow. No longer 20 feet in the treetops, it was now just a perfect circle just above me.

It was then I remembered the flashlight I had put in my back pocket.

I had nearly died, running through freezing woods. All the while, I was simply chased by my own ass.

Years later I would insist on using remote controlled flashlights in Hellview Cemetery for our end of run "Dark Night" where we would turn off all the dramatic lighting in the attraction. I did it so our actors could blink out the guests' flashlights to enhance a scare. I had learned how scary a flashlight could be. When an object you trust to keep away the darkness fails you… Well, that is true terror.

a few words from

MARK MUNCY

As a designer of horror theatre or experiences, explain your process.

For *Hellview Cemetery* we would pick a theme for the year from our research of local urban legends and tie them into whatever the trend seemed to be in horror pop culture. We design the track work from the classic distract and scare tactic that has been used for as long as I can remember. We would then theme the room into the overall story. We always focused the most on our façade, then the first room and the finale. We learned incredibly early on that everybody would talk about the first room and the last room. The rest was always a blur.

When is the last time you were genuinely scared by something someone created?

Reading Owl Goingback's novel *Coyote Rage* gave me chills last year. I did enjoy most of the new *Haunting of Hill House* on Netflix. I am a huge fan of Shirley Jackson's original novel and the update had some great bits until the last half of the last episode. Shows you exactly like I said, "people remember the first part and the last part."

Tell us about your contribution to our book. What was the inspiration?

After Hellview was ordered closed by the City of St. Petersburg for being a bit too popular, we had all these local legends we had based the haunt on. I now write books delving into the folklore and legends. I wanted to write about a legend that was from my home and childhood and my experience with something straight out of legend.

What do you love about the genre of horror?

My earliest childhood memory is that of a strange shadowy figure reaching out for me in my childhood home's attic. My whole life, I wanted to learn more about what I might have encountered and try to understand whatever that shadow was. I was initially drawn to the paranormal and that led to folklore. It was from there I discovered a love of horror which explores those fields more than anything else.

What is some of your favorite horror literature? Favorite author?

I know it's cliché, but I love the classics. I am a huge fan of Shirley Jackson's *The Haunting of Hill House*, H. P. Lovecraft's *At the Mountains of Madness* and Bram Stoker's *Dracula*. For modern horror I am in awe of Owl Goingback's *Crota* and *Breed*. The man Is a national treasure. I am proud to call him a friend.

What are some of your influences?

Hammer Horror and Tales from the Crypt are my major Influence. I also am a big fan of horror comedies like *Army of Darkness, Shaun of the Dead* and *Cabin in the Woods*. So, we always try to throw some comedy to break up the horror, otherwise you can only get so scared.

What is your favorite Halloween treat?

I am addicted to BooBerry cereal and try to buy enough to last the year. I learned I will never survive a zombie apocalypse, I run out of BooBerry by June every year.

If you could continue any horror story (book or film), what would it be?

I'd want more Ravenloft novels. Gothic horror mixed with the fantasy elements of *Dungeons and Dragons*. So great. Truthfully, I'd really love more *Buffy, Angel, Gravity Falls, Ash Vs. Evil Dead and Stan Against Evil*. They were perfect tv shows and I wish new episodes would come out daily.

Describe the perfect Halloween.

In the morning visiting a spooky museum or haunted location to soak up the ambience while I read the last chapter of *A Night In The Lonesome October* by the late great Roger Zelazny. (I read a chapter a day of that book every year in October). Lunch would be something fall feeling. Then It would be a quick watch of one of my favorite movies hosted by a classic horror host. Following that I would watch *Hellview Cemetery* rise from the ashes. It would shape and fold itself into the maze to end all mazes with detailing to spare. All our old cast, even those no longer in this plane, would gather in the perfect places to scare the crowds once more. The night would end with my wife Kari, my partner Elizabeth, and my daughters Beth and Callie settling in for an *Evil Dead* trilogy marathon hosted by the man himself, Bruce Campbell.

SCARE CRED: MARK MUNCY

Mark Muncy is the creator of Hellview Cemetery, a charity haunted house in Central Florida so infamous it was banned by the City of St. Petersburg. An author of horror and science fiction, he has spent more than three decades collecting ghostly tales and reports of legendary beasts. His third book for The History Press, *Creepy Florida*, released in fall 2019 following up his best-selling books *Eerie Florida* and *Freaky Florida*. He is a frequent guest on *Coast to Coast AM* and *Into the Fray Radio*. He lives in St. Petersburg, Florida, on the remains of an ancient midden with his wife, Kari Schultz. Occasionally, he is visited by his daughters when they remember he is still there.

BY JACK NEIBERLEIN

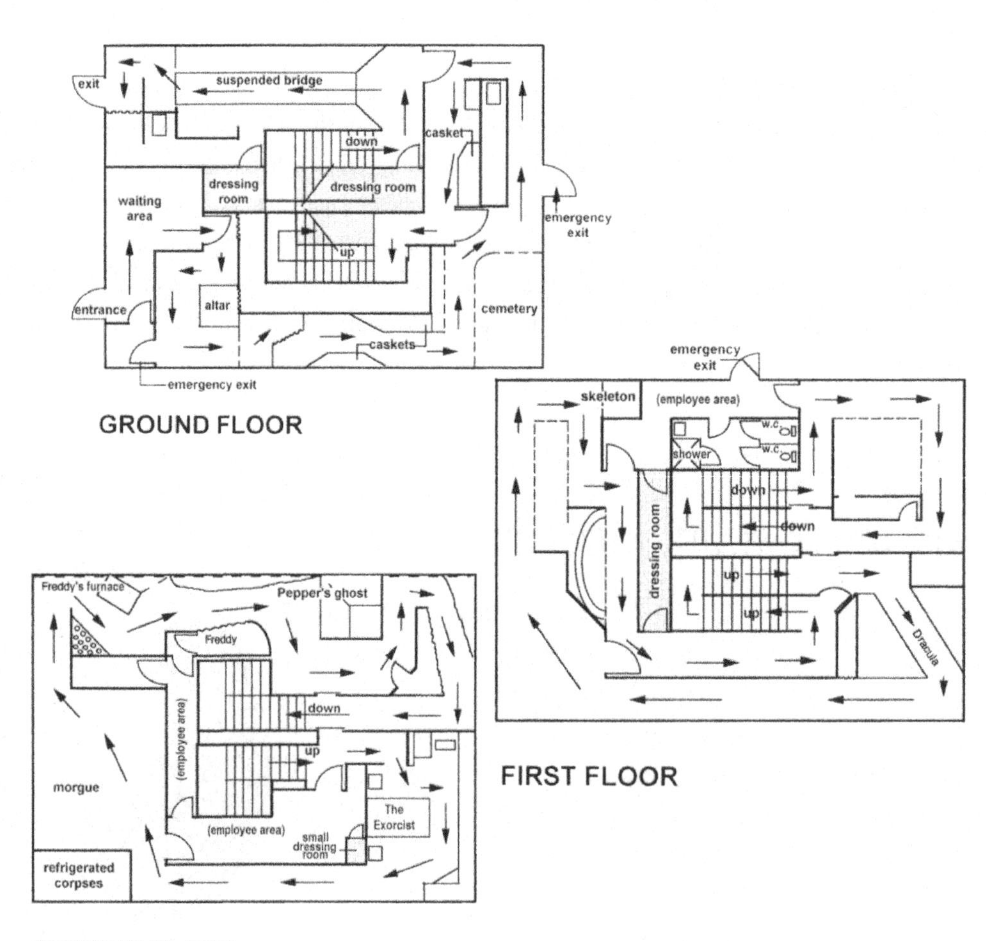

A couple of years ago, I was attending a Halloween event at an attraction in Orlando with my son, Connor, when someone stopped us and asked me my name. I confirmed that I was Jack Neiberlein, and he went on to explain to the group of friends that he was with that I had worked at *Terror on Church Street* and that he thought it was one of the best-haunted attractions ever. I told him that I was happy that he remembered and enjoyed the attraction. A few minutes later, my son said, "What was that all about?". I had mentioned to Connor my history at *Terror on Church Street,* but it was not until this moment that he understood the importance of this special place to those who attended it and to those who worked there.

Terror on Church Street was open from October of 1991 until May of 1999. Almost eight full years. I was hired as an actor about two weeks before the attraction opened and I was there the day it closed. When it closed, my title was Assistant Director of Operations. I was also responsible for most of the light design to the sets built after 1993 and all of the original audio used in the show. The attraction itself consisted of 2 floors, 23 scenes and took 20 minutes to walk through. It could be run with as few as 18 actors and often had more than 30 inside and out on weekends and peak seasons.

Why is *Terror on Church Street* still remembered twenty years after it has closed? The building itself has long been demolished, and a completely different structure exists at the corner of Orange Ave and Church Street in Downtown Orlando. I can give an insider's view of what it was like to work there. If you want to know why people who attended still remember, you will have to ask them.

The attraction itself was designed by an Artistic Team from Spain and a finance team from Spain and Argentina. Ignacio Briava was the original Director of the attraction. He brought a long resume of entertainment experience with him. I enjoyed working with Ignacio. He was a tireless and talented director who cared about the show. There was a reasonably extensive rehearsal period with Ignacio before the attraction opened. He was always open to ideas from the cast that might lead to more effective performance. He wanted to cast me as the English Bobby, the character at the start of the show, which explained the rules and leads people in. I told him that I really wanted to scare people and he immediately re-cast me in the Torture Chamber. I had a fantastic time scaring tourists and locals alike, and Ignacio appreciated my performances.

Eventually, about March or April of 1992, David Clevinger was hired as the Artistic Director of *Terror on Church Street*. David also brought a considerable resume of entertainment experience with him, including extensive theater experience and time at Disney. David's set designs were a massive improvement to the overall quality of the show. I liked that he tried to run the space like a theater. I tried to get involved in anything that was happening during the day just because I was having so much fun. In August of 1992, David asked me to be the Assistant Director of Operations. I asked David if I could design lights for one of the sets, and he agreed. The challenge was always to remember that this was a haunted house, so it had to be dark, but David's sets were so beautiful you just wanted to light them up so they could be seen and enjoyed. He was very positive after seeing my work, and he was always very encouraging. I also mentioned to David that the attraction could use some original music, and I knew some people who could compose.

Up until that time, the attraction was full of what used to be called "needle drop" audio and sound effects, sounds that had been purchased from a sound effects library. The quality varied. Some were good. Some left me scratching my head. Again, to my surprise, I was given a budget to produce music and sound effects for some new sets in the attraction. David told me what kind of atmosphere he wanted to create and left the rest to me. I got with a young composer who was a friend of a friend, and he created some new tracks. I went into a local sound studio with some actors, including Michael Roddy, and we made some custom sound effects. David was very enthusiastic about the results, and I was proud that *Terror on Church Street* had some original sound in it. This continued for a few years. David would design and build a beautiful new set, and I was allowed to light it and go into the sound studio and produce original audio. This was a dream come true for a young man who grew up loving horror films. David was very generous with his time and patience, and I was thrilled.

So why do people still remember *Terror on Church Street*? I think the strong artistic and theatrical experience of Ignacio and David was incredibly important. Both of these men brought long and varied entertainment experiences to the attraction. This was not their first time out of the gate. We also did put a lot of value on quality. We only admitted eight people at a time every 3 to 4 minutes. This was not a show with a continuous conga line of people. Each set had an actor with a directed performance. There were places in the maze with roles designed to control the flow of guests if a back up occurred. We wanted those eight people to feel "alone" in a haunted house. The mechanical effects designed by the Spanish team were brilliant. In the *Exorcist* room, an actor triggered a series of effects that made the bed jump, furniture to move around, drawers to open and close and sound and light effects to run. The guests walked into that set just like they walked into a bedroom. They were surrounded by the action, not just looking in on a set as they walked by. That is how the entire show was designed. We wanted the guests to be enveloped in the experience. The number of live actors in the show also made a huge difference. The creative team always stressed energy and follow-through in performances. We expected excellence, and we got it.

I loved *Terror on Church Street*. I knew it was special while I was there, and I savored every moment. A few days after the attraction closed, I was asked to write an article for an industry magazine about my experience. I wrote about how much fun I had and concluded by writing that when my son, who was two years old at the time, asks me what was so special about *Terror on Church Street* I would tell him that it was a place that people crossed oceans to see and talked about for years after it closed. Twenty years later, I think he now understands what I was talking about.

a few words from

JACK NEIBERLEIN

What do you love about the genre of horror?

From the beginning for me it was always about talented artists creating beautiful, thrilling work. I will never forget the first stills I ever saw of *The Creature from the Black Lagoon*. Such a beautiful, elegant design. This was not a baggy monster suit. It was carefully crafted by skilled artists who cared about the final result. The genre pieces that I admire have been made by people who took the craft very seriously. The work was never treated as just a silly horror film.

What are some of your influences?

John Carpenter, David Cronenberg, George A Romero, Tom Savini, Stanley Kubrick, Vincent Price

What is your favorite Halloween treat?

Reese's Peanut Butter anything

You are hosting the perfect Halloween movie marathon. What are the films you choose and why?

Halloween (1978)- Just to watch the beautiful photography by Dean Cundey.

The Exorcist - Has a scarier movie ever been made?

Night of The Living Dead (1968)- George Romero created a new horror genre that did not exist before this film.

An American Werewolf in London- Tons of scares, humor and Rick Baker at his best.

Bride of Frankenstein (1935)- Hard to believe James Whale created such a subversive film at a major studio. Genius.

Brides of Dracula (Hammer)- The atmosphere/photography gets me every time I watch it. Cushing's best performance.

The Masque of the Red Death---Floyd Crosby's gorgeous photography, Corman and Price at the top of their game.

Witchfinder General - Vincent Price, nothing else to say.

The Haunting (1963)- The best haunted house movie ever made.

Island of Lost Souls - Charles Laughton delivers what may be the best performance ever in a genre film. How did they make the jungle look so fake yet so creepy? Brilliant production design throughout.

Sleepy Hollow (1999)- Dripping with Halloweeney atmosphere. Great cast.

What is some of your favorite horror literature?

Cycle of the Werewolf- Stephen King, *American Psycho* - Brett Easton Ellis, *Something Wicked This Way Comes*- Ray Bradbury, *Books of Blood* - Clive Barker, *I Am Legend*- Richard Matheson.

If you could continue any horror story, what would it be?

Rosemary's Baby- The ending is so great but what happens after the baby is born and grows up? Do the witches protect him and guide him to adulthood? Does the coven of witches grow internationally as is suggested in the film? What is Satan's ultimate plan for the world? Does Rosemary love and raise the devil child to adulthood?

As a designer of horror theatre or experiences, explain your process.

I always start by trying to create an atmosphere that totally envelops the guest. Something that they actual walk through, not just look at. Once you have the guest "in the scene" you have lots of options for solid scares

When is the last time you were genuinely scared by something someone created?

Netflix's *Haunting of Hill House* had some genuine thrills and chills. I really loved all of the "hidden" ghosts and top notch acting.

Describe the perfect Halloween.

A crisp Autumn evening (50 to 60 degrees). Large speakers in the window blasting out a horror film score mix (ASCAP license paid). Tombstones and coffin in the front yard. Tons of outdoor intelligent lights to light the scene and a Grand MA-2 console to control them all. Massive fog machine...

SCARE CRED: JACK NEIBERLEIN

Jack Neiberlein was born and raised in Cleveland, Ohio and is a graduate of The Ohio State University. His professional career has included work on feature length horror films, live entertainment and attractions. He has been fortunate to work with many kind and creative people who helped to guide him through his love of the genre. Jack was the Assistant Show Director for Terror on Church Street in Orlando, Florida for eight years and loved every minute of it. He has also worked internationally bringing good fun and frights to people in Tokyo, Japan and South America. Jack is currently the Technical Director for the Flagler Auditorium, a 1,000-seat theater that hosts over 100 live events a year including a professional season of 30 touring shows.

HAUNTED INSPIRATION

BY JIM O'REAR

My fascination with haunted attractions, horror, sci-fi, and all things creepy came at a very early age. In 1971, Walt Disney World opened in Orlando, Florida, and brought The Haunted Mansion into my life. For those who haven't had the opportunity to visit Disney World and experience The Haunted Mansion, I'll try to explain. This attraction features a ride-through tour of a haunted house in Omni-mover vehicles called "Doom Buggies," preceded by a walk-through show while waiting in the queue line. The attraction showcases a number of age-old magic tricks, advanced special effects, kooky musical numbers, and spectral Audio-Animatronics. It's an immersive experience that throws the visitor into a magical and fully-realized world, completely different from our own. It is, simply, the best "live-action spook show" experience anywhere.

Even at that young age I knew I was experiencing something special. The visual effects, sets, lighting, characters, and music were all top notch and I couldn't get over the magical enchantment of it all. Suddenly, in the middle of the ride, something clicked in my young mind. A voice in my head said, "Hey! Disney is making money by fooling people with ghosts, frightening images, and magic tricks!" I'm sure the voice in my head didn't use those exact words… but that was the gist of its message. Needless to say, I was in awe.

As my parents and I exited the ride there was a small Haunted Mansion gift shop just outside. To my delight, in the storefront was a Mickey Mouse Magic Kit for children. I had to have it! I wanted to fool people with magic and illusions, too. My parents bought me the kit and I couldn't wait to learn some new magical skills. As soon as I returned to school, I did my very first magic show for my kindergarten class during Show-And-Tell using that kit. This single event started a path that led to everything that's happened to me since then. I can't imagine what I'd be doing right now if my parents hadn't taken me to Disney World and hadn't bought me that magic kit. My entire life would be different.

Around this same time in my life is when my interest in the paranormal was stoked. I had seen THE WIZARD OF OZ and was fascinated by the Wicked Witch. I could have cared less about "Dorothy" and her friends… what I wanted was more of the green bitch. I was also watching reruns of the 1969 television series H.R. PUFNSTUF… a show that featured a recurring character named "Witchypoo," a witch brilliantly played by Billie Hayes. Again, I didn't really care about "H.R. Pufnstuf" or "Jimmy" and his magical talking flute. The character that I was fascinated by was this evil, stubby woman with a long nose and pointy hat.

As in most small towns, children have urban legends and ghost stories that they like to share with each other. The little town we lived in, just outside of Nashville, was no different.

There was an old woman who used to roam the streets alone, pushing a grocery cart and constantly mumbling to herself. She was really creepy to many of us children so, naturally, it was easy to believe the stories about her being a witch were true. As legend would have it (and by "legend" I mean "bullshit story conceived by children to scare each other"), if you got near this woman and she looked at you, magical laser beams would shoot out of her eyes and kill you.

Naturally, being fascinated by the witches I watched on television and having my interests peaked in the supernatural by Disney's Haunted Mansion, I wanted to know more about this woman. She wasn't green and she didn't have a long nose and pointy hat, so something else must have made her a witch that I was unaware of.

Two of my friends and I would hide out in the bushes when she came down the street each day; 1) because we didn't want to be killed by her eye lasers and 2) because we wanted to know more about her. I, being either brave or stupid… depending on how you wanted to look at it, was the one out of the three of us who always wanted to get closer and closer to her.

One day it happened. As my friends and I were crouching behind some bushes watching this witchy woman approach, I made my move to get even closer and, clumsily, fell through the bushes and onto the sidewalk right in front of her feet. I braced for laser impact as she tilted her head down toward me and stared directly into my eyes. I knew my death was close at hand, but, to my surprise, she reached out, helped me up, and asked if I wanted some cookies.

What just happened? Why wasn't I dead? Where were the laser beams? This wasn't how I imagined things would play out, at all! What I learned from that encounter was that this "witch" was nothing more than a sweet, lonely old woman whose husband had died and whose children had moved away from home to start families of their own. She wasn't crazy. She wasn't scary. She was just lonely. From that day forward, my family got to know this woman and I continued to receive a birthday card and a Christmas card from her every year up until the day she died. She never forgot about me.

My brain connected this encounter to my experiences at Disney's Haunted Mansion and the knowledge of magic I had acquired. I learned a valuable lesson that day that made a huge impact on my young mind and permanently set me on a lifelong course in horror and paranormal entertainment. What I learned that day was that people's perceptions of reality and actual reality were often very different. What someone might perceive as a "witch" or a "ghost" or a "supernatural experience" may not be that at all. Are ghosts real? What about witches? Are there monsters or is it all entertainment? It was obvious to me that people could be fooled in many different ways… and many wanted to be fooled, especially when it came to horror entertainment.

As I grew older I began getting work in the horror entertainment field and visited haunted locations whenever possible… always hoping to experience the unexplained. It was this combined interest in horror entertainment and paranormal experiences that inspired to me to share that with others through the creation of haunted attractions and horror films, something that I've been blessed to be able to continue professionally with for over thirty years.

a few words from

JIM O'REAR

As a designer of horror theatre or experiences, explain your process.

I, first, decide if this project is going to be themed and tell a story or if it's going to be a free-for-all. I love both for different reasons. A free-for-all is much easier because all I have to do is think of random, creepy things that may unsettle people and slap those things together. It also allows me to use weird ideas that may not logically fit into a theme or story. While a themed experience is much more difficult, it can be a very satisfying experience for me as the creator and the end customer as it allows everyone to go on a journey of fear. For this, my approach is to decide on an overall theme or idea... for example, demons or animals gone wild, or crypto-creatures... then I try to create unusual scenarios that may be frightening and how I can tie those things together to take the customer on a trip that has a beginning, middle, and end.

When is the last time you were genuinely scared by something someone created?

Wow! I'm so jaded! It's been a long time. I've had so many personal paranormal experiences, since kindergarten, that nothing man-made genuinely scares me. While I do appreciate the art that goes into the scare, the scare doesn't work on me. I'm too fascinated by the process and the art of the scare.

What do you love about the genre of horror?

I think what draws me to it is the fantastical, horrific elements combined with the dark humor that almost all horror draws on. There's a fine line between horror and humor. While many a shaking in fear, I'm laughing because I can see the humorous, ridiculous elements of the terror. Maybe I'm a little twisted... I typically don't like comedies but will laugh a lot in horror films.

What is some of your favorite horror literature? Favorite author?

I read a lot of early Stephen King... before he seemed like he ran out of ideas and just started writing junk. I love the classics... *Frankenstein, Dracula, Phantom*... and liked a lot of Richard Matheson. Peter Straub's *Ghost Story* is also a favorite.

What are some of your influences?

As a creator, Disney (particularly *The Haunted Mansion*), John Carpenter, George Romero, George Lucas, Steven Spielberg, Bruce Lee, and Tom Savini.

What is your favorite Halloween treat?

I'm hypoglycemic so I can't have traditional Halloween treats.... soooooo.... tacos!

You are hosting the perfect Halloween movie marathon. What are the films you choose and why?

Halloween, Night of The Living Dead, Phantasm, The Thing, Texas Chainsaw Massacre, Reanimator, and *Trick 'r Treat*. I don't usually like anthologies, because short narrative format doesn't allow me to get invested enough in the characters to care what's going to happen, but I LOVE *Trick 'r Treat* because of the Sam character and how all of the stories tie into one larger story. It's a must anthology. The others I chose because I think that each of them was a very important part of shaping the genre. I don't think the genre would be what it is without the contributions from those films.

Describe the perfect Halloween.

Spending the entire day in Salem, MA... the Halloween capital of the world... visiting the historic witch trial sites during the day, visiting multiple haunted attractions in the early evening, and enjoying the largest Halloween party in the world at night.

SCARE CRED: JIM O'REAR

Jim O'Rear has been involved in the entertainment industry for over thirty years. Trained in New York at The American Academy Of Dramatic Arts, Jim has worked as an actor, stuntman, and special make-up effects artist on such projects as *Star Trek IV*, Stephen King's *The Boogeyman*, ABC's *Nashville*, *Lethal Weapon 3*, NBC's *Fatal Encounters, The Dead Matter, Fall Of The House Of Usher, A Christmas Carol, Mortal Kombat: Conquest*, and many more. Wanting to get some of his own ideas onto the screen, Jim successfully moved into the area of screenwriting, selling a number of horror-related screenplays. As an indie filmmaker, Jim's work as a director/producer has been seen in the award-winning hits *The Hospital, Camp Massacre, The Hospital 2*, and *Ghosts Of Tennessee*. Jim continues to write for horror publications, consult for film and Halloween/haunt projects internationally, and is the founder of Celebrity Ghost Hunters. For more information, visit JimORear.com.

SEA GREEN

BY EMMA M. OLIVER

In dusk's soft light, I welcome the night
And walk lonely among the trees,
And the song of the wren takes me to a time when
In sea green eyes she held me.

It was not long ago that I first came to know
Soft Anna in woods like these.
Oh, I could not but pine the very first time
She held me with eyes of green.
With passion I bled and for weeks devoted
To Anna all love with'n me.
But declined with soft smile, I died right there while
In sea green eyes she held me.

Like a tomb felt that night I held love unrequite,
Heart wounded to such a degree
That regrets I assigned as I took what was mine,
Fear frozen in eyes of green.
When I woke from my daze, I held her soft gaze
In hand, emeralds paired and lovely.
And myself I assure, knowing forevermore
In her sea green eyes she'll hold me.

a few words from

EMMA M. OLIVER

As a designer of horror theatre or experiences, explain your process.

With all experiences I create, I like to start with what I want my audience to feel. For my horror, the emotion I strive for is shock. Whether this be with a twist or reveal, even a line that gives me goosebumps, I find myself starting from the end to work my way backward, like setting up the edge pieces of a puzzle. Once I know the desired outcome and impact, the rest falls into place.

When is the last time you were genuinely scared by something someone created?

In 2018, Universal Studios Japan produced a horror maze inspired by Insidious. In one of the rooms, you passed through a large open space, but your path was lined with dozens of robed and hooded human figures, some statues, some live performers. The dread of knowing any one of those 50 figures could move at any moment terrified me.

Tell us about your contribution to our book. What was the inspiration?

Some of the horror stories I'm most intrigued by are those in which madness stems from romance. Inspired by Edgar Allan Poe's "Annabel Lee," my poem, "Sea Green" tells a more gruesome story of love turned deadly. "The Corridor," co-written with writing partner Amy Kole, is a short story inspired by the very real Umeda Virtual Corridor in our neighborhood in Osaka, Japan. As of Summer 2020, the mural has mysteriously been painted over...

What do you love about the genre of horror?

I think it takes a really talented creative to set up one let alone multiple earned scares. As I've delved into this genre as a writer myself, I've realized it's not only an art form but a science: you lead into a scare the same way you'd set up a joke. Like humor, so much of what we know of horror stems from human nature and our shared experience. You have to know people to scare people, and horror appeals to those fears inherent to all of us.

What is some of your favorite horror literature? Favorite Author?

As a self-confessed easy scaree, I'm fairly new to the horror scene, but I remember being terrified by W.W. Jacobs' "The Monkey's Paw." The story deeply affected me and to this day I am always meticulous with what I wish for.

What are some of your influences?

Jaws! I think the devices used throughout the book, film, and even ride are incredibly clever, from the score to the use of simultaneous visual and audio scares to catch even the bravest among us off guard. I also still find myself haunted by many of the Edgar Allan Poe works I've read, the kind of terror we inflict upon ourselves. Such psychological horror fascinates me, and as a cerebral writer, I love incorporating this as the method of my madness.

You are hosting the perfect Halloween movie marathon. What are the films you choose and why?

I'd kick off the marathon with Halloweentown to put us in the spooky spirit. Next, I'd go a little creepier with Hocus Pocus in the spot of honor at the end of Act I. We'd take an intermission for real food while fulfilling tradition with "It's the Great Pumpkin, Charlie Brown!" Then we'd transition to the Day of the Dead with Coco for something heartwarming. Once we'd passed the tissue box, I'd end the night on a good laugh with Troll 2 .

If you could continue any horror story (book or film), what would it be?

I'd continue Hitchcock's Rebecca. I feel like there's still more to that story even after the movie wraps up. I want to know if and how she haunted her lover, what Danvers' backstory is, and what became of the couple after the fire at Manderley. Think about it.

Describe the perfect Halloween.

Is there a way I can fit in the movie marathon, stop by Mickey's Not So Scary, do Halloween Horror Nights, hit up a Halloween concert for a band like Panic! at the Disco, and dress up to go out all in one night?

SCARE CRED: EMMA M. OLIVER

If you'd asked ten, fifteen, or even twenty-one year old Emma if she'd ever write horror, the answer would have been a resounding "No." Emma M. Oliver is a themed entertainment show writer - horror included - and earned Bachelors of Arts in English and Spanish from Christopher Newport University and an MFA in Dramatic Writing at the Savannah College of Art and Design. She went to her first Halloween Horror Nights (in Japan!) in 2018 and wrote for her first HHN in 2020. Her preferred forms of adrenaline are roller coasters and traveling the world, one theme park at a time.

missing her

BY NICK & BEVERLY PAPPAS

I always hate it when she's out of town. Having no children and having similar interests, we're very close. I'm going to surprise her while she's gone with a perfectly clean house when she returns. I do have to admit, I'm exhausted, and hitting the sack early tonight.

It's a moonless night; the house is pitch-black and silent. I should really sleep well tonight!

I love to sleep in total darkness and quiet.

It's almost 3 a.m…I awaken initially with a start and then a smile on my face – I can hear her laughing loudly in the back room of our house. I've always loved her laugh…until I realize - she won't be back home for another week.

HALLOWEEN, HAUNTERS, & HIJINKS

BY NICK & BEVERLY PAPPAS

Halloween...

My first clear memory of Halloween happenings was when I was around twelve. That'd be forty-seven years ago! At that time, living in Tallahassee, it was relatively safe for kids to trick or treat in small groups without parental supervision. This, in itself, leads to many more opportunities for some special memories. My younger brother and I were trick or treating, and we would always go in a two to three-block radius from our house. On the outer fringe of this range was an old widow that lived in an old house on a dark, heavily treed lot with old pine needles smothering the roof. She was known to be nice and harmless, but also kind of creepy. We all kept our distance other than to say hi if we saw her out of her house. She had a strange custom of never being home on Halloween. She'd always have a dim light on deep in her house, and she'd leave a big bowl of treats outside on a table with a sign saying, "Happy Halloween children.

"Please take only one". In the bowl, we'd always hope for candy, but, inevitably, there'd always be her hand-formed popcorn balls. We always vowed that we would never eat those popcorn balls – simply couldn't feel that they were clean or safe to eat. We would walk away disappointed but also scared a little because we were always certain that even though she was "gone," we always thought we'd see something moving around in the shadows of her front room through the curtains. We were always scared to even go up to the bowl to peer inside because we thought she'd grab us from behind while we were busy looking down into it.

There was another house that was a little past the boundary that we'd go trick or treating and it was dark on the front porch, but we could see that there were lights on deeper inside. The house was on a massive piece of treeless property, and we figured we'd chance to knock on the door for treats. We both went up and knocked, saying "Trick or Treat" louder than normal since we figured they weren't expecting us. There was no response, and we kept waiting and hoping. Just then, we heard a screen door open and slam from around the back of the house, and we heard a large dog bark and started running. Instantly, we ran and jumped on the hood of their large, old station wagon just as a German Shepherd came running around the side of their house. They had sicced their dog on us! As soon as the dog got near us, we heard a man calling him back, and thankfully he went back. That left a significant impression on us as we walked, shaking, back towards home. Oh yeah, we probably lost half of our candy too!

There was one house on our block across the street from ours that made the biggest impression on me, and I think it made me love Halloween. Every year, from when I was around twelve to sixteen years old, our neighbor would go to the local furniture shops and collect their large, empty boxes that they had saved for them. They would lay them on their sides and open the bottoms, as well as the tops, and connect them into a very long tunnel. Their front door would remain open while kids trick or treated, and the tunnel started at the front door and went deep into their house, snaking around to disorient you. It was dark and kind of low inside, and you had to crawl blindly, and while crawling through it, older teenagers on the outside of the tunnel were shaking and kicking the tunnel! You'd come to larger "rooms" that were boxes attached perpendicularly to the tunnel.

In these rooms there'd be a dim light with a person sitting on the floor and dressed in a costume that would read your palms, tell your fortune from a crystal ball or would be dressed as a witch and would have you put your hands in different bowls telling you to "feel the worms" (cold, cooked spaghetti), or "feel the eyeballs of my enemies" (wet grapes), etc. The only illumination throughout the tunnel was occasional dim lights. It was extremely fun and a little unnerving because you never knew what they were going to do to you while you were "trapped" in the tunnel until you came out the other end. Definitely, my favorite memory of Halloween!

My last memory of Halloween happened when I was sixteen. This year, after we finished trick or treating, my brother and I decided to hide in some large, dense, overgrown hedges that ran along the side of the road so we could scare kids as they walked by. It turned out we had been too greedily collecting candy for too long, and no one came by the entire time we patiently waited – at least half an hour. So, we went home, dejected. When we got back, both of us were itchy all over. I went to the bathroom to look in the mirror and saw that I had roaches in my hair and in and around my flannel shirt!! We both ran outside, freaking out, tearing our shirts off! Definitely memorable!

Haunters...

Beverly and I have hosted a Halloween party for over twenty-eight years. Over the past fifteen years, it has morphed into an eight-week-long, massive undertaking. It takes place in our house and backyard, and it's an invitation-only party for around seventy of our closest friends and family. We have friends from Louisiana, Alabama, and South Florida attend. We've converted hundreds of unsuspecting and innocent people into big-time haunters! We've found over the years that you can tell the personality of a hands-on haunt owner by experiencing their haunt. If they're outlandish and brash, you can bet the haunt will be. If they're theatrical and artistic, their actors will likely be top-notch. Finally, if the owner is only in it for the money, their actors will typically be uninspired and shallow.

Haunters are definitely a breed of their own. They are universally creative and imaginative. They're uniquely non-judgmental – exceedingly loyal and supportive of each other. Haunters love experiencing new things, no matter how extreme or different. They embrace differences in venues and people. They are a tight family. Beverly and I are proud to call ourselves haunters.

Hijinks...

Since 2010, Beverly and I have been hitting the haunt scene hard! We've attended the major Halloween and haunted attraction conventions and trade shows all over the eastern half of the U.S. Every year, we have averaged over 6,000 miles driving to these shows. In addition, in 2017, we went on a haunt tour that was from Sept. 25 through Nov. 2 and was about twenty miles short of 5,000. In 2019, we did our mega-haunt tour, which was 6,229 miles, from Sept. 20 through Oct. 29. Throughout both of these tours, we enjoyed some of the absolute best in haunted attractions that exist.

Because of all of the conventions, trade shows, and diverse haunted attractions we've attended over these years, we have cherished friends in just about every eastern state as well as countries like Australia, Ireland, Canada, and Puerto Rico to name a few. We estimate we've seen around 60 unique haunts over the years during the conventions. From our two haunt tours, probably forty-five unique haunts. Overall, including seeing haunts over the years as they've changed, combined with the unique single-time haunts we've visited, we've probably been to over two-hundred haunts in our lives. None of this would have happened without our mutual love of Halloween, haunting, haunters, and haunts. Thanks are due to all of the owners who dared to risk it all so we could be entertained, and thanks to all of the actors, builders, writers, and artists that make it all possible.

In conclusion, even though he's attended around ten of our Halloween parties, our nephew still insists that we lock the "Halloween Room" door, (storage for our props), at night when it's time for bed. I always tell him, "You know...they're all fake...they just look real." He always says: "I know, I know. But – just in case".

a few words from

NICK & BEVERLY PAPPAS

As a designer of horror theatre or experiences, explain your process.

In designing the different rooms throughout the house for our party, we enter each room and visualize a disturbing scene for it. Then we acquire the appropriate props and work on the lighting and sounds that convey the mood.

When is the last time you were genuinely scared by something someone created?

After experiencing so many different haunts over so many years, there is very little that actually frightens us. However, at the Raven's Grin Inn, in Mount Carroll, Illinois, we were both genuinely fearful to lay down on Jim Warfield's trap door in order to plunge two stories down in complete darkness to the basement of the haunt – alone!

Tell us about your contribution to our book. What was the inspiration?

Our inspiration to contribute our story to this book is our love for Halloween, the haunters we've been privileged to meet over the years and the awesome haunts we've been so fortunate to be able to attend and experience throughout those years.

What do you love about the genre of horror?

I love experiencing someone else's ideas of unknown, uncomfortable and terrifying circumstances. I love how the authors, haunts or movies have complete control of my mind – they determine what I see, feel and experience – and there is nothing I can do about it until they release me and make the experience end.

What is some of your favorite horror literature? Favorite Author?

Horror literature has been my favorite ever since I was around thirteen years old and found an old horror paperback lying by the side of the woods when I was walking home from school. That book's title was *Horror Times Ten.* Some of my favorite stories are: *The Graveyard Rats* by Henry Kuttner, *The Voice in the Night* by William Hope Hodgson, *The Monkey's Paw* by W. W. Jacobs, *His Unconquerable Enemy* by W. C. Morrow Also, anything by Edgar Allan Poe, Stephen King or H. P. Lovecraft. By the way, I still have that water-damaged, sun-faded book of horror that I found when I was 13. Its damage makes it that much scarier!

What are some of your influences?

There's no question that my first and biggest influence was Disney's *Haunted Mansion.* Our party is always a loose homage to the *Haunted Mansion.* Also, Disney's album *Chilling, Thrilling Sounds of the Haunted House*, from 1964. The well-known artist, Chad Savage, is a big influence for me. Years before I actually met him, I had unknowingly used many fonts that he had designed, and were available online, for props and signs at our party over the years. Later, when I had the opportunity to meet him and see his incredible horror related artwork, I purchased many of his pieces for use in our parties as well as for our everyday personal enjoyment.

What is your favorite Halloween treat?

Beverly's favorite treats are Smarties, Milk Duds and Reese's Peanut Butter Cups. My favorites are old-fashioned, wax paper wrapped peanut butter taffy; Almond Joys and candy corn.

Describe the perfect Halloween.

My perfect Halloween would be with Beverly on a fairly breezy, cool and clear moonlit night with lots of happy trick or treaters about. When the revelers subside, we'd watch the original Halloween movie with all of the lights off. After the movie ends, we'd go outside and walk enjoying the beautiful moonlight and breeze.

SCARE CRED: NICK & BEVERLY PAPPAS

Beverly Pappas was born and raised in Jacksonville, Florida. She majored in Mathematics and minored in Computer Science in college and owns several, non-haunt related, small businesses. The innate uniqueness and totally unknown experiences to come are what captivate her with haunts and haunters. She admires the entrepreneurial spirit and incredibly hard work of the haunt owners, artists and vendors that make the industry possible and so unique.

Nick Pappas was born in Jacksonville, Florida as well, but moved with his family within the state of Florida until he was 23, finally residing back in his beloved Jacksonville. He majored in Computer Science and minored in Architecture in college. His entire career he has been a software engineer. Nick has loved Halloween and haunts all of his life. He loves the unbridled creativity of the industry as a whole, and loves the people involved in making it all possible in particular. He enjoys the camaraderie and sincere friendships that he and Beverly have made over the years and looks forward to many more years of haunt experiences.

THE EVIL PLACE

BY JANINE PIPE

Have you ever had that feeling when you enter a building, that someone (or something) pure evil resided there? Although the place is falling down around you, it is bathed in a malevolent aura that will never diminish, even with time? I have …

When I was a teenager, I lived in a small rural village in Somerset, England called Stoford. I was a fairly normal (read nerdy) teen, aside from a distinct fascination with all things that went bump in the night. This was thanks to my father, who brought me up on ghost stories and Stephen King. Anything and everything supernatural both fascinated and terrified me, a state of limbo I identify with to this day. I had already seen at least one ghost by the time I was a teen, and would experience more during these formative years. However, the day I visited the remains of Barwick House AKA the "school for naughty boys", is a time I will never forget.

I was around thirteen, foolhardy and ready for adventure. Buoyed with confidence by having a mate with me, it was decided we would go and visit what remained of the once majestic manor house. I had heard the rumours after moving to the village aged twelve. That the house had been turned into a reformatory for boys who had been expelled from mainstream schooling. There were whispers of abuse, of the masters beating the boys. But no one in the village really knew. *Something* had happened, and the school had been closed. Abandoned was more like it. Tales from other village teens told of classrooms still filled with books. Of paper still on desks, as if, the pupils and teachers, had just upped and left … or vanished. The anticipation of that we might discover was too much for a thirteen-year-old, who thought herself more of a Hardy Boy than Nancy Drew, to ignore.

Now you need to remember, this was the early 1990's in a country village in the United Kingdom. There were no security cameras or electric fences. Hell, it wasn't even properly boarded up. I found a way in through the rusted gates quite easily, and the building was so dilapidated through lack of care, it was easy to break into. Having to be very cautious, as the walls looked ready to fall down around us at any given moment and the floorboards were most precarious, we explored in silence. And it was, completely and utterly, silent. Not even the scampering feet of a rat was to be heard. There were no birds overhead, no chittering insects or buzzing flies – nothing. I can quite honestly say that I was petrified.

The building had been abandoned some years before, but it looked more like decades. There was mould and rot, filth and debris where the walls had crumbled and been exposed to the elements. There was evidence of nosey wildlife and quite probably, tramps. It smelt revolting. Like, death.

Yet far worse than the sights and smells, was the emotion the place emitted. Pure, unadulterated evil. We tried to be brave. My mate wasn't as into the supernatural as me, and I think she was more concerned about either being caught somewhere we ought not to be, or hurting ourselves. But I could sense it. The undiluted wickedness radiating from the walls. It doesn't take a genius to work out if it was supposed to be a sanctuary where children who were deemed too 'naughty' for a regular education were placed, then there inevitably would have been some bad vibes. However, this felt way, way worse than the sins of children. This place oozed degeneracy.

We left soon after. The sight of pencils still on desks, books still open as if lessons had just ended seemed unnatural, especially since the school had been abandoned for years. Feeling dirty both physically and metaphorically, we never returned.

Many years later, now a horror writer, I was doing some research into the town I grew up in. I stumbled across the name Barwick House in a Google search along with the headings – scandal, abuse, murder … It transpires, that those feelings of unease were founded. I began to dig up more and more stories and allegations of sadistic abuse that the boys suffered at the hands of the masters, the people who's care they had been entrusted with. As it was still being investigated, and many of the alleged offenders were now dead (most of this appeared to have taken place in the late 1970's-early 1980's), it was difficult to find any hard facts. But the stories that have made it onto the web, told me all I needed to know. Ritual abuse, beatings. Bullying which went ignored, or worse, was encouraged.

Perhaps the most chilling, were the ones that recalled the Cold Room. A corner of the basement where they would be stripped naked and left, freezing for hours as retribution. Although corporal punishment was not officially banned in schools until 1986, this was not a ruler across the knuckles. This was torture. There were tales of suicide, how some boys went on to continue the spiral of abuse on their own families. The ones who ended up in Borstal, then prison, unable to cope with what had happened.

A lot of their tormentors were now dead, but one, was serving a life sentence for murder. I couldn't validate this or whether it was related to the school or an entirely separate offence, but it summed up the calibre of person 'teaching' these children. It is no wonder I could feel the evil permeating the building. No wonder I have never ever forgotten the feeling of torment and anguish that was imprinted on those walls.

It truly was, a place of pure evil …

a few words from

JANINE PIPE

As a designer of horror theatre or experiences, explain your process.

Well, I am a horror writer, so my process is creating a story, characters and setting and then finding the time to get it down on paper.

When is the last time you were genuinely scared by something someone created?

Just a few days ago. I watched the movie *Host* on Shudder. I haven't been that scared since 1992 when I watched *Ghostwatch*. It's no coincidence that the creators of *Host* were influenced by *Ghostwatch*.

Tell us about your contribution to our book. What was the inspiration?

It is a true story from my youth. It was a genuinely freaky place and I often find my mind wandering back there when looking for inspiration for my writing. The place exuded pure evil.

What do you love about the genre of horror?

It is in the main, a flight of fantasy. Something to lose yourself in. And it often surprises you. As a writer, you are always trying to second guess what is going to happen, especially if you know the author and their usual style. I like it when they defy my expectations and I'm left thinking, well, I did not expect that to happen!

What is some of your favorite horror literature? Favorite author?

Favourite author hands down is Glenn Rolfe. His werewolf book *Blood and Rain* is one of my all-time favourite books. Much like King, he lives in Maine and often refers to things I love like Boston and the Red Sox. His characters are believable, settings beautiful and stories in which you feel fully invested.

What are some of your influences?

Stephen King of course, I don't think there are many of us out there who don't have a shelf full of his books. Glenn too is a major influence and I am very lucky to call him a friend. Not many people can say that the author they enjoy the most is also someone they can talk to about their own writing. Someone else who I would cite as in influence is

R L Stine. Whilst I love creature features and sometimes write baring on the extreme, I also love YA and even middle grade stories, and will often read some Goosebumps or Point Horror if I am in a slump.

What is your favorite Halloween treat?

Being in the UK, Halloween is growing in popularity every year but still no where near as big as in the US. My favourite treat would be Pumpkin Spice Latte though which I ADORE and we need way more PSL stuff in Britain.

You are hosting the perfect Halloween movie marathon. What are the films you choose and why?

Dog Soldiers - all-time favourite horror movie ever with some of the best lines

The Lost Boys - best vamp movie with awesome soundtrack

Halloween - the original of course, you just have to watch this

Final Destination - love the concept of this and it has some amazing death scenes

Host - super new and super scary. Best watched on a laptop and in the dark.

If you could continue any horror story (book or film), what would it be?

That is super hard as I wouldn't want to presume that I could carry on anyone's work. Maybe I'd like to write an episode of *Supernatural* and make Sam and Dean come over to the UK ... and of course, I'd need to meet with Jensen and Jared to make sure they got their lines right.

Describe the perfect Halloween.

Carving a Jack O Lantern with my daughter and then Trick or Treating with her and her friends. Next, a not too scary party with lots of yummy treats and friends. Then once she is in bed asleep, watching something like *Creepshow*

SCARE CRED: JANINE PIPE

Janine Pipe has been enjoying writing scary tales with a twist for many years, since discovering Stephen King at the tender age of nine. She cites Glenn Rolfe and Jonathan Janz amongst her influences and greatest inspiration. You can find just some of her work at Kandisha Press, Diabolica Britannia, Iron Faerie Publishing and Black Hare Press. She has also featured on several podcasts and is a regular for *Ghost Stories - The Podcast*. Her biggest cheerleaders are her husband and daughter.

DARK WOODS ALLURE

BY ERIN PYNE

The Woods. Dark. Twisting. Dead and colorless in the winter. Where hungry eyes watch, and hapless souls are lost into darkness. An ominous place, but not for me. I've lived here for so many years, traveling back and forth from my cluttered and comfortable study. Tonight, I sit in my chair, tablet in my lap, tea cooling, my mind lost between worlds. A lifetime of stories in my head for inspiration, from books and movies of horror, some funny, some sad, some terrifying and some disturbing. I remember my fascination with the dangers of the dark began as a child reading stories by flashlight under the sheets.

There! Among the trees! A splash of red on a young girl's cloak, a knotted weave of lengthy flaxen locks, and seven cursed ravens waiting for release. A poisoned apple, a towering beanstalk, a tempting house of bread and sugar: a world without order, a world without sense. I became lost in the dark stories and characters of legend and fable, where endings were not happily ever after.

Behind every gnarled tree, I see a girl and boy abandoned in the woods, a family suffering poverty, a maiden grieving for her mother, a prince longing for love, a queen yearning for youth, a giant falling hard. A thread of loss binds them all.

Now I write new worlds, sometimes recreating well-known characters and settings, sometimes creating my own domains of terror. I am no longer in my seat. I become lost in the woods, lost in the depths of darkness, fathoms beneath the surface. I do not want to rise. Hold me down.

The cold air is quiet underneath the shadowy canopy. I remember to breathe and exhale a warm fog that disappears into the night. The ground crackles as I take a step forward, the dew frozen beneath my feet. Every step leaves me spellbound by struggle, fear, and misfortune as monsters within begin to rise.

Plunging into the mind of darkness, I swim through, delight swelling as my next victim comes into view. Knowing the next moment I will cause the racing of a heart, a scream choking out with a gasp, the stopping of breath. My timing must be just right so that the shock causes muscles to fail and the body to freeze or drop to the ground as all thought is lost and overwhelming fear takes over rational sense.

There she is. Walking this way, foolishly through the dark woods, not a care in the world. Never thinking for a moment that her world is about to end. Everything she has worked for, everything she has ever cared about, those plans for the future, that half-written memoir, that trip she has tickets for, those people she expects to see tomorrow… none of it matters. For she is going to experience something different now. She is prey and her life is only worth my next meal. I will feast upon her fear, her screams, and her pitiful attempts at escape. The thrill of the hunt consumes me and I'll even let her go for a while, hurt, let her run, let her think about all the things that will be lost if she dies. She'll run along the path I have set for her and I'll give her hope as she sees a light in the darkness. Then shock her again as she realizes she has run straight into my trap so that dread fills her very soul. Her eyes will darken as the inevitable sets in. She'll either panic, flail, writhe, and scream until death, or she will harden her jaw, finding strength and bravery she never knew she had, ready to accept her fate, unwilling to give me any satisfaction in the kill. But then the pain comes with a flash of razor-sharp metal. Neither panic nor grit can stop that.

And then I feel it, that joy. That surge of pure glee that comes with the scent and bright red of fresh blood. I move close so that I will feel the heat of the last gasp and see the light as it leaves the wide eyes to see nevermore. My chest feels like a balloon is swelling up inside. The emptiness, sadness, and pain of the past disappear. My head clears. I smile. I laugh. My skin tingles. I savor it. I let it wash over me. I let out a long breath of blissful relief. And then it fades. And I'm left with the cleanup. It goes quickly as I had it all planned out. They will never find her. The woods hide all secrets. They will search and every news story and article will captivate me. The neighbors will chat about how such a horrible thing could happen. People will dissect her life looking for answers. Family members will distrust each other as suspicions grow. All fun.

But eventually, the memory of the joy will fade, and I will start to crave it once again. It will begin to consume my every thought and I will imagine the death of every person I see… until I find the one. The one that I know will bring me the taste of joy. And I start to plan. And the darkness of the woods overtakes me again.

* * *

I look up from my screen and look around. I had forgotten where I was, in my house, my kids sleeping peacefully nearby. My mind comes out of the woods and I take a break from writing looking around my library of books and catch a glimpse of an old Grimm Fairytales collection.

Those stories speak to me, from the vault of time, orally passed from parent to child, teacher to student. Stories nearly lost to the age, unwritten, almost forgotten but resurrected with a new breath of life from writers willing to spend a life harvesting rumors, anecdotes, yarns by the fireside, and tittle-tattle from the kitchen table; for preservation, for immortality.

I turn again to my keyboard, safe in my own cozy home. Never believing anything could disrupt my world or that the eyes of darkness could be upon me. I glance at my window anyways. Nothing there. The blue light of my screen illuminates my face as I lean in, take a breath, and re-enter the mind of darkness. Once again, I become lost in the woods, lost in the depths of darkness. The silence presses me in. I am bound.

The house is dead quiet. I stand still, wondering if the pressure from the mountain altitude has clogged my ears. I wiggle my jaw and pull on my ear lobes trying to get my ears to pop. But still, I cannot hear a thing. Surely there should be some sound. The creaking of the old house settling, a bird chirping outside in the snowy evening, the furnace in the cellar grumbling. But there is nothing. I stand still on the spot, wondering briefly how long I have been standing there, just waiting. I walk over to the spot in the room with the squeaky wooden plank and step on it. It squeaks. So my hearing is fine. But everything else is eerily silent. How long have I been standing here, waiting? I check my watch. 7:30 pm. That is strange. How did the time move so fast? Sam should have been here by now. Perhaps the snow was slowing the drive up the mountain.

I call Sam's cell phone. No answer. I hear a creak upstairs and look up. Old house. Just settling. I send a text. 30 seconds later, still no reply. A door creaks and then slams. I sigh. Just a draft. God, I have a headache. It is starting to feel cold in the house and I realize that the furnace has probably gone out. Why did Sam invite me to come up to his crummy inherited house in the middle of the woods to stay for the weekend? His way of trying to apologize or give us one last try before finally giving up? Or did I know somewhere down deep that it was already over? Inevitable. Like everything that is going to happen has already happened, leading to the same end no matter how long I try to drag it out.

I shiver. I have to check on the furnace or I would freeze up here. The cellar. Dark, dank, and stale. My fingers find the switch and the hanging bulb clicks to life. Down the iron staircase to the dusty cement floor littered with tools, wood, and bags of salt. I trip over some boxes and unlabeled canisters. I stand before the black iron furnace clueless on how to start it. It has some dials and looks like a gas furnace, so I experiment and attempt to start the pilot light. I hear clicking, but nothing happens. Sigh. I am not going to wait here in the cold for someone who is two hours late. Why am I even here? I never should have agreed to this, after what he did. I always thought of myself as a strong woman, and yet here I was, meeting again for a weekend away, even after I found out about her.

I go outside to my car, determined to leave these woods and get back to civilization, even if it means driving in the dark. But my car is blocked in. Sam's car? It has a layer of snow, so he has been here for some time. I look in the windows and see his bag in there. The car is unlocked. Nothing in the backseat except his hunting rifle case laid across on the floorboard.

A door slams somewhere in the house and I spin around. "Sam?" I call out. Silence. The snow is coming down. But I can see indents in the snow of old footprints. Sam's boots. He's wearing those same damn boots! Those ones he was wearing when I saw him with her. The prints led around to the back of the house and up into the kitchen.

"Sam?"

The door is unlocked and I enter, a tinge of fear flashing for a moment. Why isn't he answering me? How long has he been here? Inside the kitchen all is silent. But his beer cooler is on the floor and I see a wet washcloth hanging on the sink. Inside the sink are two large knives, wet, clean, and sharp. Why are they here? Who used them? Who washed them?

"Sam? Where are you? What are you doing?"

I grab one of the knives as the hairs on my arms and neck go up. A door slams upstairs and the kitchen door behind me slams. Damn drafty house! I am freaked out now. Everything seems strange. Like a cloud on my brain is keeping me from thinking straight. Nothing is making sense. My head aches. Where is Sam?

Knife in hand I walk through the house. Dead silence and cold wrap me. Something upstairs creaks.

"Sam?"

I go to the stairs and walk up slowly, looking up as I go, but seeing nothing. I go inside the only bedroom to see the bed is not made. The blankets and sheets are disheveled. Tousled like children had been jumping around on it. Or like there had been a struggle.

Then I see the blood. On the bedpost at the right head of the bed. A round metal post with a pointy knob on the top. Dark blood, drying but still shiny, covered the point and had dripped down the round post.

"Sam?" I call out loudly. My voice cracking the still, cold air. I quickly back out the room and, turning, discover the bathroom door ahead is shut.

"Sam, are you okay? Are you hurt?"

Taking a step forward I raise my hand to the knob and realize I am holding the knife. I reach out with my other hand and knock on the door. "You in there?"

No answer. I turn the knob and open the door, peeking inside. It is empty. Just the sink, toilet and tub. Nothing else. Not even towels. Not even a shower curtain. I look closer. Some shower hooks are still there, and bits of ripped plastic vinyl. The tub is wet inside as if someone had recently drained it. My confusion grows as I wonder when all this occurred and then I hear a creaking of the floorboards below. I tighten my grip on the knife. Looking at it, I see a warped reflection in the shining metal. Why had there been clean knives in the sink?

I suddenly have an overwhelming drive to leave. Not quite a panic attack but my chest feels heavy and all my muscles tense and then ache as if I have been working them out hard. Everything in my head tells me to get out of here. That things aren't right. I move quietly down the stairs, tiptoe across the wooden living room floor but then my foot hits the creaky floorboard and the sound seems louder than fireworks. I freeze in place. I can feel something in the back of mind telling me there is something I need to do before I leave, but my entire body is telling me to go! I near sprint to the front door, throw it open and run out into the dark snow. Sam's car is still blocking mine in the narrow unpaved drive. I jump into his car and shut and lock the door. Frantically, I search everywhere for his keys but cannot find them! I turn to the back seat and there is the rife case on the floorboard. I stare at it for a minute. I never did like him going hunting. Poor innocent deer, never did anything but live peacefully. And here comes a random monster from the woods with a power no creature could escape. A predator but with a more sinister goal than needing his next meal. It is a trophy. Something to hang on the wall. Something to show off to others that you were the monster in the woods.

I open the case. The gun is gone. Suddenly something familiar courses through me. A feeling of a memory that I have seen this or done this before. Déjà vu. I get out of the car. The dark night is still and cold. The only movement is the air when I breathe. Sam is missing. His gun is missing. A shower curtain is missing, there is blood on the bedpost. There were wet knives in the sink. Nothing makes sense.

I get in my car and start the engine. The roar sounds like a volcanic eruption. I try to move around Sam's car but there is no space between his car and the trees of the woods or between his car and the house. I cannot get out. Behind my car are more trees and a storage shed. My eyes double-take in the rear-view mirror at the shed.

There is a faint light coming from the inside. I sit in my car, numbly, for a few moments and then begin weighing my options. I cannot leave, so I need to find Sam. I get out, knife in hand and head towards the shed.

"Sam?"

There is no answer. I peek inside and a lone flashlight on the ground is shining the light towards the door. I walk inside and pick up the light. Shining it around the shed, I see the hunting rifle laying in the dirt where it dropped along with scattered bullets as if someone was trying to quickly load it but never finished. Somewhere in the back of my mind I feel that I had seen this too. Like a dream you wake up from too quickly, and you can't see it anymore, but you can still feel it. The details disappear but the impression lingers.

I turn and shine the flashlight upon the house. There is the ground-level window to the cellar directly ahead. It's slightly open. I walk to the window and wipe away the snow that had crusted against it. Shining the flashlight down, I see a blob on the floor. A plastic blob. A shower curtain wrapped around something blob.

I stumble back, slip on the icy ground, and fall into the snow. Breathing quick and shallow, clutching the flashlight and the knife, a vision flashes of a shower curtain falling down upon a body lying in snow. A stirring of the air, a shifting of the light. Warm water vapor creates a cloud of haze as I breathe slowly out into the cold night.

It all came back, like a rush. A moment where time seems to stop as every detail floods in from the past hour in only a second. I had arrived early, to prepare. He arrived, came straight into the kitchen and unpacked his cooler, putting the beer in the fridge. He then wanted to go straight to the bedroom, of course. I let him place his things on the side table and watched as he kicked off his boots and socks and pulled off his sweater and shirt. He laid against the pillows and I crawled up beside him. I kissed him and he kissed me back pulling seductively at my shirt and jeans. But I knew he was full of lies. Deceit, betrayal, mockery. He was laughing at me with every smile. Laughing that I had been such an easy, witless, dupe. He had brought her here, to this house, and most likely had her here on this bed. I took his head in my hands, his hair running through my fingers, his body relaxed and loose. And I grasped his hair tightly, lifted and smashed his head into the sharp- pointed bedpost. His eyes were so shocked as pain ran through him. I had expected him to die but he just stared at me with wide eyes, his mouth opening in a silent scream. I stared back in a weird kind of staring contest. I blinked. Then he pushed me off the bed hard and he got up, running down the stairs. I started after him and watched as he stumbled getting out the front door. I turned and went to the kitchen. I opened the knife drawer and grabbed two knives then headed for the shed.

He was in his car, realizing his keys were still upstairs along with his phone on the side table. He leaned around to his back seat and got out his hunting rifle. Only his bullets weren't in the car. While he had been in the kitchen putting away his beer, I had opened his rifle case and removed the bullet boxes. Extra bullets were in the shed where he kept all his other hunting equipment. He staggered over to the shed, flashlight and rifle in hand, and in his haste did not realize that it was already unlocked. He was freezing and he stamped the cold off his bare feet on the dirt floor. From the dark corner, I watched as he fumbled with the bullets, wiping his blurry eyes a couple of times. I could see the bloody gash in the back of his skull, bleeding profusely onto his shoulders and back. He was doubled over, loading bullets into the rifle when I stepped out of the shadow and plunged a knife into his left side. He cried out and stumbled towards the shed door, but only dropped the rifle when I stabbed him again in his right side. I pushed him out of the shed and he landed hard on the icy ground. I pulled the knives out and waited, watching over him until his breath no longer created little puffs of clouds.

I washed the knives and my hands in the sink, and I went upstairs. I ripped down the shower curtain in the bathroom and soaked a towel in the tub. Back outside I rolled the lifeless Sam into the shower curtain just as it began to snow. I opened the small cellar window at the base of the house and somehow managed to slide him across the icy ground and through the window. I heard a thump as he hit the ground. I used the wet towel to wipe up the pool of blood spilled on the icy ground, but it was more than I had anticipated. I turned on the hose and sprayed water onto the blood, washing it away from the ice and into the dirt. The snow was falling faster now covering whatever might have been left. I tossed the wet towel through the window as well. All that was left to do was to clean up the bedroom, get his keys, move his car, and then complete the plan.

I turned too quickly and where I had sprayed the ground with water, a new layer of ice had formed. I slipped backward and hit the ground hard. My head smacked the ice-hard ground and I stumbled back to the house, blinking to keep my eyes in focus. And there in the living room is where I remember standing, waiting for Sam to arrive. But I had only been stunned. Momentarily blocking out what had just happened.

Still sitting in the snow, I reach around to the back of my head and feel the tenderness. My headache returns full force. I sit in shock, realizing I am the murderer that I have been running from. I laugh. My laugh turns into the fog that floats upwards into the dark canopy. Time to finish.

I scoop up the bullets into the boxes and pick up the gun. I wipe it all down and put it back in the case in his car. I go upstairs and grab his things then make the bed. I wipe the bedpost with toilet paper and flush it away. I place his boots by the door and go outside to his car with the keys this time. I move his car around the side of the house and leave the keys inside. I go down to the cellar. I open the canisters and pour the gasoline meant for the generator all over the floor and the shower curtain blob. I turn some dials on the gas furnace and smell rotten eggs. I go to the kitchen and turn on the stove pilot before running out to my car and pulling away. I make it perhaps a half-mile away and then see a tremendous blaze erupt in my rearview.

I smile. I glance into the rear-view to watch the flames devour the house in the woods. I see my own eyes and can't look away. It's like a strange staring contest. Then I see his eyes. Sam's cold, angry, betrayed eyes staring straight at me. My head is in his hands. I am laying in the bed, my phone and keys on the side table, and I feel hot blood trickling down my neck. I lay there, paralyzed, my head smashed against the bedpost. He blinks. I keep staring, unblinking.

* * *

I look up with a start. I've stayed up far too late writing again. I've got to force myself to sleep. But when I close my eyes what will I see? My fingers touch the keyboard again. I'm lost in the woods, lost in the depths of darkness. I cannot reach the surface. Let me drown.

a few words from

ERIN PYNE

As a designer of horror theatre or experiences, explain your process.

I immerse myself in the subject matter, If I am working with a well known Intellectual property I'll watch the movies, read the books, go on fan pages and find out as much as I can about what people love the most about it before creating an experience. If It Is an original story, I get in the mood by reading or watching something creepy or frightening so my emotions are in the right place when I begin writing. I collect lots of flavor images to convey the style I am after to assist the artists in developing the look of the space. As always, every project is a huge collaboration that will go through many changes.

Tell us about your contribution to our book. What was the inspiration?

Trying to decide what to write about, I decided to just begin typing out what was going on in my brain as I was conjuring up something dark and creepy. This led to me creating the final story, but I decided to keep my initial ramblings, keeping the character of the writer, to show how we can get lost in our own minds and that is where our darkness lives. The difference between the writer and the murderer is that we can look up, breathe, and go about our day without the darkness reaching our hearts.

What do you love about the genre of horror?

I love the inventiveness and creativity involved in developing something that will scare someone. Even something you would think is simple, like a man in a mask with a knife, is perfect in its simplicity because most terror revolves around simple chaos. Not understanding why someone is doing something, not knowing what will happen next, not being able to predict the next move. Lack of control. There is no reasoning with the killer, no bribery, no inducing guilt or empathy. Just the relentless pursuit. The dread of having no control anymore. Horror invents new ways to create that chaos. Wrapping it in different stories and settings. Creating new looks for the killer or even backstory for the killer so that the audience feels empathy for the murderer. But for me, it is the unpredictability of the victim's death that causes fear.

Driving a car has a much higher death rate than being attacked by a shark. But we control the car. Driving doesn't frighten us. However, the idea that death can come unseen, anytime, violently, without reason or predictability scares us. And we are wary to swim in the ocean.

What is some of your favorite horror literature? Favorite author?

I recently was handed a murder mystery by Agatha Christie- And then there were none- where ten people are picked off one at a time based on a nursery rhyme. The terror came knowing someone was going to die and having a bit of a clue, but not knowing who would be next or who among them was the killer. It was really fun as there were to be no survivors (the title told us this) and after everyone was dead I still didn't know who the killer was. The reveal and explanation in the last chapter was a peek into the mind of a murderer and really well done.

What are some of your influences?

All the classic horrors of the eighties (which I still don't understand how I was ever allowed to watch any it), along with my obsession with Mystery Science Theater 3000 which showed some absolutely terrible yet amazing horror films. As a kid, I loved curling up on the bed with a flashlight to read *Scary Stories to Tell in the Dark*, with those haunting illustrations that wouldn't let you close your eyes for fear the image would return. My ten-year-old self would read the stories and, shaking ask why on Earth am I reading this in the dark, alone, scaring myself to death?

Describe the perfect Halloween.

Up north where the leaves change colors, the air is chilly, and night falls early. We visit a pumpkin patch in the early afternoon and carve pumpkins to decorate the front porch with glowing Jack O' Lanterns. At dusk, we dress up and the kids go trick or treating through a neighborhood where every house is decorated. We all come home and after sorting our candy we stuff ourselves while watching *The Nightmare Before Christmas* or *The Great Pumpkin Charlie Brown*. We play some games like candy checkers (the candies are the game pieces and you win other people's candy), then read a few funny ghost stories before bed. As much as I enjoy horror, I love children's Halloween!

SCARE CRED: ERIN PYNE

Erin Pyne is an award-winning freelance Creative Producer and Show Writer who has worked professionally in the industry for over a decade beginning with the Wizarding World of Harry Potter in 2008.

She is the author of several books including The Secret Garden of Zombies, The Doll House Murders, A Curiouser and Curiouser Series and The Ultimate Guide to the Harry Potter Fandom. She has written scripts for or produced Halloween haunts and events for Hallowscream at Busch Gardens, Halloween Horror Nights at Universal Studios Resorts, Carnival Cruises, and Dark Passage in Philadelphia. Erin is also a science writer and exhibit producer for zoos, aquariums, and museums around the world who worked in the zoological industry for over 15 years with a variety of species, most extensively as a dolphin trainer at Discovery Cove. Other species she has worked with include penguins, sea lions, manatees, big cats, birds, reef fish, sea turtles, and horses.

HOME HAUNT

BY DR. BILL RAMSAY

I have received a few questions from friends and others regarding my interest in Halloween. Maybe I opened a can of worms by even mentioning it, but, oh well, here goes, I'll be candid...

As far as the Halloween "thing" goes, here's my best explanation: It all started innocently enough. When I was 14 (1974) I put my innate creative abilities to work by crafting and hanging an 8'x8' black visqueen "room" (floor, ceiling and walls) in the foyer of my parent's home in the Villas. It was a dark, "foreboding" room with thin black ribbons of plastic dangling in the doorway. I artfully -- as much as a 14-year-old could be -- hand-painted "spooky" (read as "cheesy") skeletons, eyeballs, tombstones, ghosts, and other assorted Halloween figures with fluorescent paint throughout my scary little domain. I then grabbed my new 18" blacklight out of my bedroom (oh, you should have seen the great fluorescent posters I had back then – hey, it was 1974, what do you expect?!!) and hid it ever so cleverly just above the doorway.

Later, I stuffed newspapers into clothing to make a "terrifying" scarecrow to reside on the wooden bench outside our front door. Disney's *Haunted Mansion* had nothing on me! I was THE prop master (well, at least in my mind, anyway). On Halloween night, I sat within the confines of my "room of terror" eagerly awaiting my first evening of innocent victims. Now, if I would have just thought first about our barking miniature Poodle and the blaring TV in the background ruining the scary atmosphere, things might have not been so amateur.

Well, throughout that night I experienced the thrill of having an emotional effect on TOTs (trick-or-treaters for the layperson). I found that the groups had their brave individual who always cautiously peeked in with trepidation, and I then would jump out from my secret vantage point and get my reward – that spontaneous and reflexive "agh!", "whoa!" or "eeek!". Ah, the sweet sound of success! Following my ritual of fright, I would produce my treasured selection of delicate, sweet morsels to reward the brave souls who had survived their face-to-face encounter with sheer and utter terror. Those lucky few who made it out alive ran to tell their quivering friends of their near-death encounter with all that is evil.

Yup, it was fun even coaxing in the littlest kids that would approach no closer than ten feet away from what surely the gates of Hell itself. Surely, I had found my calling...it's to instill terror into other kids each Halloween. It seems it wasn't too hard to do since they each had infused themselves with anticipation of the evening; all I had to do was push their mental button. Later that night, I found I enjoyed showing the older kids how I had made my own world of horror. Some were duly impressed.

Since that time, I have celebrated the season to varying degrees. I enjoy it now more than ever. I enjoy eliciting unrestrained emotion from my "prey", be it shock, fear (including, of course, the elusive sudden-loss-of-bladder-control), curiosity, terror, awe, or even just a plain-old smile. I have the same zeal and grin-evoking thoughts each Halloween season as I relive my fondest Halloween memories...as "Dr. TerrorEyes."

To answer some questions I seem to be asked by folks: No, I'm not into "Gothic" stuff; no, I don't have props set up at the house 365 days per year -- only 30 ;-) ; no, I don't have cauldrons of dead chickens in the kitchen ('cause they're in the bathtub!!...okay, that was just a joke folks); no, my kids aren't "into" the Halloween season I am, but they help out; no, I don't have goat sacrifices (only virgins, but that has been a rare occurrence seeing as they are so hard to find these past few years); no, the pool isn't filled with blood (because I use a red light instead); and no, I don't want to stop because I have a significant artistic flair and the stuff I make is releasing my "inner artist"...and for stress release, I guess. Now, just because I fill up our barn does that make me goofy? I don't know, you decide.

I'll just keep having fun hosting my yearly Halloween parties. I do it all for fun and I enjoy sharing my enthusiasm with people. Of course, we are always open for "business" on Halloween night for friends and victims!!

a few words from

DR. BILL RAMSAY

As a designer of horror theatre or experiences, explain your process.

I originally performed as a home haunter (since 1974) but became involved a decade ago with helping a friend created a commercial haunt. I helped him create scenes and used my creative skills to insert my self-made creations into the 5,000 square-foot haunt's appropriate areas.

When is the last time you were genuinely scared by something someone created?

A few years ago, I toured some local haunts while at a Halloween convention. One area of darkness had subtle voices over my shoulder. *That* was creepy because it was not palpable and yet, I saw nobody.

Tell us about your contribution to our book. What was the inspiration?

To share my journey these past forty-six years as I moved from a home haunter to a commercial haunter to Halloween convention producer.

What do you love about the genre of horror?

I don't like gore so much as I like suspense -- like in the original 1980s movie *Alien*. That movie had me enthralled the entire time.

What is some of your favorite horror literature? Favorite author?

Who doesn't like Edgar Allan Poe and horror?

What are some of your influences?

The Outer Limits TV shows, Dr. Paul Bearer (the original), works by Edgar Allan Poe, seasonal carnival dark rides, and Stephen King.

What is your favorite Halloween treat?

Candy corn, of course!! (And it *has* to be Brach's brand.)

You are hosting the perfect Halloween movie marathon. What are the films you choose and why?

Beetlejuice -- Creepy enough and fun

Halloween (1978) -- It's just THAT creepy!

The Exorcist -- Nothing scarier!

Ghostbusters (1984) -- Ghosts, humor and Sigourney!

The Nightmare Before Christmas -- A must-see every year. Fun and creative!

Describe the perfect Halloween.

Just after sunset on a cool night and walking with kids ages six to thirteen around a neighborhood that embraces Halloween as a time to decorate, dress-up, act a bit creepy, and pass out candy. It's also fun to stay at home and instill just enough fright and fun to make them muster up a partial scream, but not run away before they receive their candy reward.

SCARE CRED: DR. BILL RAMSAY

I could never have imagined that after forty-plus years of home haunting, in 2014, I could find support from ten Halloween product manufacturers that would enable me to go to present courses at: Canadian Haunted Attractions Conference, TransWorld, National Haunters Convention, HauntX, West Coast Haunters Convention, and Midwest Haunters Convention. I had already presented at some of those in previous years, but 2014 was a fun and extensive year of travel -- all thanks to my numerous generous and supportive sponsors. I was able to share my experience, skills, knowledge, and Halloween zeal all over the USA and into Canada. Whether teaching a prop building seminar, performing a "How-To" course or advising a standing-room-only lecture hall full of fellow haunters about the many supportive internet sites which could propel their Halloween love forward, I truly enjoy helping haunters reach the next level for their home or commercial haunt.

APPLEDORE

BY CHRISTOPHER RIPLEY

It was in the winter of 2010, and we had been commissioned to refurbish this vast old farmhouse near Pluckley by the Crown Estates, which is the property company that the Queen owns. Through time the Crown Estates has inherited or purchased vast old estates who fell on hard times, and this appeared to be one of them. The house was over three floors, which is unusual, and it was built in the Victorian era in the gothic tradition - proper creepy old house style – something Scooby and the gang would love. Anyway, the house was huge with 7 or 8 bedrooms plus lots of other rooms, a big attic, and a basement - all of which is not typical for this part of the country (plus outbuildings and a big garden). It was cobwebby, overgrown with weeds, damp, cold, and hella spooky!

It had been previously rented by a CEO of a large investment bank who had mysteriously been offered a job in Asia and had up-sticks and left very abruptly, leaving a signed note with the Estate that any possessions left could be sold on or trashed. He had left lots of gym equipment, loads of clothes, a drum set, a string guitar, pinball machine, loads of old books (though these may have been there before him), and just some general house bric-a-brac. The Estate said we could take away what we wanted and trash the rest as per the instructions, in fact, in the end, the new tenants (a family of 4) they signed a contract to rent the place before we started and they said they would be glad to inherit them, which they eventually did. It was just bizarre that these relatively new and expensive items and lots of clothes were left behind - anyhow. To make things weirder, he had been living between 2 or 3 rooms and that most of the house had just been vacated. Why did a single man need such a large house in the middle of no-where?

We started on-site, and after about four days, we starting painting in the rooms, replacing the kitchen cupboards and trying to get this ancient and antiquated boiler to work. The paint wasn't drying, and the temperatures were dropping, the workers were complaining, etc., so we decided to stay late with this boiler expert to try and get the boiler working. The engineer finally got it working at around 7 pm that evening, and then he and I locked the house and was leaving. As we turned the key in the door, it started to heavy snow, and by the time we had walked to our cars, backed them out, and then drove down the long tree-lined drive, the snow was lying all around and was pristine, excluding our tire marks.

The next day, as I had the key, I had to be on-site for 8 am to open up. It had snowed all night and was quite thick underfoot, I set out early and more or less at 8 am I arrived, and the grounds were all heavily blanketed with thick heavy snow, and my car was the first to arrive. I pulled up out the front and checked my cell phone with 5 mins later, another vehicle arrived for my site manager. He and I chatted briefly, and we unlocked the house together, we walked inside and found a whole host of creepy things. The dust sheets we were using had been thrown around the ground floor; they were initially on the 2nd floor. The banker's guitar had been placed on a downstairs table. Some paint tins we were using had been moved from the rooms they were left in and placed in the hallway. Two pairs of curtains had been pulled down and placed on another table. Books that were neatly stacked by a large bay window had been moved and neatly stacked in another room. Tools we had been using to fit together the kitchen cupboards had been taken out of their box and placed neatly on the floor and then finally, a piggy bank which contained around £50 in coins had been removed from a shelf, smashed and the money placed in neat piles on the table, in random piles (as in just random coins on top of each other with no sense to them). Nothing had been taken, and no damage had been done, other than the smashed piggy bank.

We were dumbfounded as to why someone had done this, so we quickly checked all windows, and they were all fixed shut, most weren't even operable. We searched all floors and the basement, and then we walked outside, and there were no footprints in the snow whatsoever around the whole building—no signs of forced entry and no footprints - very weird. The snow around the entire house was perfectly laid and undisturbed.

We didn't report it to police as no real harm was done, but we were left confused as to why this happened and who would've done this. Was the banker still in the house? Did kids get in somehow without making footprints? Where did the kids come from as this house was in the middle of nowhere? Did the new family get in and mess with our stuff without leaving footprints? We did ask the family, and they said they knew nothing about it but weren't surprised by the weird goings-on as it was near Pluckley (the most haunted place in the world). The banker nobody got hold of as his deposit was due to be paid to him, and they never found him, such was his haste, to pay the man his money. After this, we carried on working and nothing else weird occurred. That is except the strange basement.

The building had a basement which is not very common for this part of the world. The basement was also tiny, and it had one staircase and two lightwell windows, one large and one smaller. We didn't need to do any work in this basement, so we never really ventured down there, that was until the last day of the project. On the handover day of the house after the works were completed, I opted to stay behind and meet the new tenants at 6 pm. It was winter, and it was pitch black by about 4 pm. The last person left at around 5 pm, and I had an hour to myself in this weird old house. Thinking I'd probably go and sit in my car with the heater on and read my Kindle, I picked-up my things and headed for the front door, that was when I passed the door to the basement, which was locked but was now open. Strange, I thought, and without putting too much conscious thought into it, I opted to go down into the basement and make sure no one else was in there before I locked it.

I crept down the creaky wooden steps, flinging a few ancient cobwebs as I entered down. I stood in the small lonely basement looking at the furthest and smallest lightwell as a small pane of glass was missing, and a vine of ivy had grown into the basement via it. I contemplated removing it but thought better against it. It was then I noticed something quite bizarre. The basement wasn't actually small; it was huge. You see, running along the flank of the stairs was a large newly constructed brick wall that cut the lightwell window in half, thus making it appear to be smaller than the other window. Why would anyone construct a wall to reduce the size of the basement? That's when it occurred to me: you would only do this if you were trying to hide something!

a few words from

CHRISTOPHER RIPLEY

As a designer of horror theatre or experiences, explain your process.

For me, it all comes down to planning. I have many ideas and ideas are great but you need to work on them before you start planning. My technique is to keep a small book and that's near me morning, noon and night, so whenever as idea strikes I quickly write it down and then promptly forget it. It sounds strange I know, but the best ideas are the ones I can't forget, these are the ones I start to plan and take forward.

When is the last time you were genuinely scared by something someone created?

The real world scares me more than the created world. As my old Grandfather used to say, "it's not the dead that'll kill you, it's the living." If you can take enough reality to a project that doesn't ruin it then you can usually create something very scary.

Tell us about your contribution to our book. What was the inspiration?

It's an excerpt from my actual diary. It accounts for the time I once worked inside a real haunted house that was owned by the Queen. My inspiration was that I added to the story to make it more of a narrative and then we our co-host, our Ghost Host – The Spooky Voice Guy, read it on our podcast – *The Halloween Half Hour*.

What do you love about the genre of horror?

I think for me, the genre has so many possibilities. You're only constrained by either your imagination or your budget (often both for me!). Whereas other genres are constrained by their conventions or can be fairly formulaic, horror can have so many possibilities. It also has the ability to showcase not just the best in humanity but the best we can do as a society.

What is some of your favorite horror literature? Favorite Author?

I'm always so busy and hardly get any time to read, and if I do it's usually for research purposes for a project or it's a non-fiction text. My favorite writer growing up was Terry Deary (he of *Horrible Histories* fame). Long before he did educational history he used to write these incredible books by the Osborne company that were so beautifully illustrated. They blurred the line between fiction and non-fiction and were usually always about famous mysteries or horror folklore. I could never put them down!

What are some of your influences?

I am a lifelong Alfred Hitchcock fan. Of all artists, it is his work that has had the most profound and lasting influence on what I do. Happy fun fact, which I have never revealed before, he features in every one of my published books in some way. I call it his continued cameos from the dead!

What is your favorite Halloween treat?

Anything pumpkin spiced!

You are hosting the perfect Halloween movie marathon. What are the films you choose and why?

I have an annual tradition of watching *Trick r' Treat* every year on Halloween. If not, I usually stick to the classics. Start off with some *Psycho*, maybe a *JAWS,* and end the night with something more modern like the new *Halloween* movie.

If you could continue any horror story (Book or Film), what would it be?

Did I mention my ideas book? If legal and budget were no issue, I would have to make another *JAWS*. I have the perfect idea for one too, but if I told you what it was I'd have to kill you, unless your surname was Spielberg of course...

Describe the perfect Halloween.

I live in a big creepy house in the middle of nowhere. I would invite all my friends and family over and hold the single greatest Halloween party ever. There would be special effects, a pretend murder, costumes galore, loads of treats, and lots of music.

SCARE CRED: CHRISTOPHER RIPLEY

Christopher Ripley was born in the UK but has been travelling to and living in the US for many years. He authored his first book in 2015, *Halloween Horror Nights: The Unofficial Story & Guide*, which went on to become a bestseller and was awarded at the Reader's Favorite Awards at the International Book Fair in Miami and at the Halloween Book Festival. Since then he has setup the wildly popular *HHN Blog* (*HHNunofficial.com*) become a co-presenter of the Rondo Award-nominated *Halloween Half Hour Podcast* and *Dis After Dark* (the Europe/UK's number one downloaded themed entertainment podcast). He has also ghost written or co-authored a further fifteen books on architectural history, themed entertainment, and hollywood history.

FULL TIME

BY J. MICHAEL RODDY

EXT. HORROR HOUSE - NIGHT

Langmore Street. A large, industrial building in a barren part of town, it should be abandoned, but next to it is a parking lot full of cars. Several GUESTS move towards the building with excitement. THE CAMERA moves closer. Red lighting across the building creates an ominous aura. The windows are decorated with unusual and horrific items. Skeletons, coffins, pumpkins, flashing yellow eyes. Across the front is a banner in fun, spooky lettering - HORROR HOUSE.

There is loud music pumping through speakers keeping the LONG LINE that extends from the entrance around the corner; People of all ages charged and excited, wait for their turn to enter. Fog seeps out of the entrance a CARETAKER, dressed in a victorian style appears and takes tickets. The Group enters into the darkness.

The HOST, a large man in his thirties, with well-done white face makeup and glowing yellow contact lenses. He is an homage straight out of London After Midnight, complete with a tall, beaver hat. He is presenting the fun to be had inside, performing to the crowd in true campy fashion.

HOST

Do you dare enter the Horror House?

INT. HORROR HOUSE MONTAGE

CUT TO:

Quick cuts of the interior experience. Classic scenes of horror and mayhem from pop culture's most frightening fiends play out, jumping and terrorizing a Group of TOURISTS. A VAMPIRE bares his fangs at helpless, screaming GIRLS... A WOLFMAN swipes at a group of TEENAGERS who run away... A ZOMBIE pops up from behind a styrofoam gravestone, black make-up streaming from his mouth...

HOST

Witness Vampires, Ghouls, Ghosts, Zombies and all manner of things that go bump in the night. Horror House, the world's oldest spook-show and maze, now open! (MORE)

FADE IN:

HOST (CONT'D)

Can you survive? Who knows?

The voice ends with a loud, ghoulish cackle.

EXT. HORROR HOUSE - NIGHT

CUT BACK TO: The Camera PANS across the building and we see a sign - Help Wanted. The Help is scratched out and written in red lettering above is the word "Bodies". ETHAN, just turned seventeen years-old, excitedly walks up to the building. His hair is unkempt, and he is dressed in a T- shirt featuring the commanding image of the CREATURE FROM THE BLACK LAGOON along with ripped jeans and converse sneakers. He smiles at the setting. This is his world. The Host is staring at him. They lock eyes.

Three GIRLS try to move past the Host. Ethan sees them and motions with his eyes to the Host who smiles and turns, lunging at them with a growl.

HOST

I see you!

They scream and run. Ethan laughs. The Host moves to Ethan, and bows in a most theatrical way. He rises and smiles, his teeth cracked with black make-up.

HOST (CONT'D)

Good evening my boy, welcome to the Horror House!

ETHAN

Good evening good sir.

HOST

Now, I can see by your choice of t-shirt that you might just be a believer.

ETHAN

I am. Creature from the black lagoon. 1955. The last of the classic monsters.

HOST

And a dear friend. They are all inside waiting.

Ethan motions to the “Bodies Wanted” placard in the window.

ETHAN

I see you need some bodies?

HOST

We are always looking for fresh...
help.

ETHAN

Perfect. Where can I get an
application?

HOST

Right inside. But before you do,
can I tell you a secret about our House?

Ethan shakes his head in approval.

HOST (CONT’D)

Now, do you promise you won’t tell
anyone?

Ethan shakes his head again.

HOST (CONT’D)

Not a soul, living or dead?

Ethan nods, smiling, wondering what will happen next.

HOST (CONT'D)

Say I promise...

ETHAN

I promise.

HOST

Listen very carefully...

Ethan brings his head in closer. The Host moves in to whisper and then bellows a loud...

HOST (CONT'D)

BOO!

Ethan jumps back smiling. The Host erupts in a deep bass laugh.

ETHAN

Awesomeness...

Ethan turns and walks into the gift shop.

INT. GIFT SHOP -NIGHT

Ethan walks through rows and rows of movie memorabilia and costumes. He is like a kid in a candy store. This is the Captain Company on steroids. Things that were only seen in the back of the pages of Famous Monsters of Filmland are on display here. He spies an issue - number 93 featuring "Tales From The Crypt" on the cover. He looks at the price - $19.99. He takes the magazine and walks to the cashier counter where we find CREEP, an actor in his early-thirties dressed in a long brown robe and face made up to look recently dead with gray skin and black around his eyes. He is chewing on something.As the conversation progresses we see that it is a roach, rubber and black. It makes a disgusting sound as he gnaws it between his teeth. He looks at Ethan.

CREEP

What do you want?

ETHAN

I'd like to buy this.

CREEP

Of course you would.

Ethan hands him a credit card. Creep takes it and rings in the sale.

ETHAN

I'd also like an application.

The Creep rolls his eyes and pulls an application from under the counter. He hands it to Ethan along with a pen.

CREEP

Here, fill this out... if you can write.

(He spits the roach at Ethan) Ethan ducks to one side, the chewed black rubber roach missing him by inches. Ethan laughs. This is the coolest place on earth.

CUT TO:

EXT. SUBURBAN HOUSE - NIGHT

A "typical suburban home," with landscaped lawn. The phone rings. PASTOR DENNINGS, comes into the room. He is in his early-forties, a stern man with a stern manner. He moves to the phone.

PASTOR DENNINGS

Hello? Hi Al. Yes. Of course. I can meet you. Bring your bible and meet me at the fellowship office.

Pastor Dennings hangs up the phone. His wife, ESTHER DENNINGS walks in. She is in her late-thirties, with slight silvery hair, a little plump and placid. Together they represent the picture-perfect conservative couple.

ESTHER DENNINGS

Do you have to go out?

PASTOR DENNINGS

I'm afraid so. That was Al. He is having some tests this week and he needs me to come sit with him for a while.

Pastor Dennings picks up his briefcase and his bible and moves to get his coat nearby.

PASTOR DENNINGS (CONT'D)

Where's Ethan?

MRS. DENNINGS

He’s in his room, studying.

INT. ETHAN’S BEDROOM

CUT TO:

This is a Monsterkid’s room. All kinds of monster items, Aurora model kits, a poster of King Kong. All this is mixed with the relief of some things “normal” teenagers would have in their rooms. Ethan has his issues of Famous Monsters magazines out. He is studying, thumbing through the issues and memorizing every image. We hear the sound of a ringtone. It is the unmistakeable voice of Colin Clive as Dr. Henry Frankenstein proclaiming “It’s alive! Alive!” Ethan pulls the phone out of his pocket and looks at the screen. The number comes up as unavailable. Ethan clicks to answer it.

ETHAN

Hello? Yeah, I’m Ethan Dennings. Tomorrow night? Sure. That would be great! Yeah! I will be there. Thank you Mr. Marlowe.

He hangs up the phone, excited. The CAMERA moves and settles on the gazing, leering face of Christopher Lee as Dracula.

DISSOLVE TO:

EXT. HORROR HOUSE - THE NEXT NIGHT

Ethan enters the gift shop. Creep appears from behind a row of old style makeup. He is still chewing a rubber roach.

CREEP

You again?

ETHAN

Yeah. I have an appointment with
Mr. Marlowe.

Creep looks him up and down.

CREEP

Master.

ETHAN

What?

CREEP

We call him Master.

Creep turns and picks up the phone. Looking around again Ethan notices a series of gruesome masks next to a door that states "NO ADMITTANCE". Drawn by the masks he looks at the sign.

ETHAN

What's in here?

At that moment the door explodes open as a group of FRIGHTENED TEENAGERS plows right over Ethan. They are being chased by a MANIAC holding a chainsaw. He REVS the motor and waves the saw above his head in victory before slowly stepping back into the darkness. The door SLAMS shut. Ethan is sprawled out across the floor. He starts to get up when a towering figures shadow comes across him.

MR. MARLOWE

You alright?

He is MAXIMILLIAN MARLOWE, a towering man from a different time, aged somewhere in his fifties. Vincent Price/Christopher Lee. Jet black hair, perfectly pulled back across his head. He is dressed in an impeccably-tailored black suit, but could easily look sophisticated in anything. He helps Ethan up with one hand and stands almost a full foot taller than Ethan.

ETHAN

Yeah. Just a little trampled. I wasn't expecting a group of people being chased by a chainsaw wielding maniac to come at me.

MARLOWE

No one ever does, it's all part of the show.

CREEP

Watch out for this one, he drools.

ETHAN

Thanks , I'll be mindful..

CREEP

I was talking to him sir.

MARLOWE Come on in the office.

Marlowe walks towards the office. Ethan gives Creep one last look just in time to see him spitting a wet, sloppy, rubber roach at a WOMAN. The woman screams and races out of the shop. Ethan laughs, and walks into the office.

INT. MARLOWE'S OFFICE -

Marlowe and Ethan walk into the office.

MARLOWE (CONT'D)

Welcome to my office.

ETHAN

May I enter?

MARLOWE

What's that?

ETHAN

I can't come in unless I'm invited...

CUT TO:

Marlowe stares at him for a second. Then cracks a knowing smile.

MARLOWE

Perfect. Yes, you may come in...
unless you are a vampire that is.

Ethan enters, pleased that Marlowe knows the lore of the vampire. He looks around. The office is still in a state of being unpacked, but impressive. Opened shipping boxes spill out with more memorabilia.

Laying against the walls are framed photos and posters from the history of horror. In the corner of the room is a beautiful, ornate full-sized coffin . Ethan is transfixed.

ETHAN

What's the coffin for?

MARLOWE

I never said I wasn't a vampire...

(a beat) There is silence.

MARLOWE (CONT'D)

We use it for promotional pieces.

ETHAN

Ha. Right.

Marlowe sits behind his desk and moves stacks of old monster magazines and books.

MARLOWE

Alright let's see where's your application? No... no... no..

ETHAN

You've had a lot of applications?

MARLOWE

Oh, yes my boy. But, this job opportunity isn't just for anyone.

The turnover rate is extremely
high. People come and go when they
realize it is more than just
jumping out and saying boo.

ETHAN

You're kidding?

Marlowe is still plowing through an incredible stack of applications. He looks up at Ethan's last comment.

ETHAN (CONT'D)

I'm not just saying this to get the
job, but really I just love horror
movies so much and I would think
this would be such a great job!
For me, maybe I'm biased but working
here would be a trip!

MARLOWE

Yes...

Marlowe continues looking through his papers. Ethan feels as if he may have blown his chances.

MARLOWE (CONT'D)

As I was saying, it's not for
everyone, but then that's why
out of all these applications...

Marlowe pulls out Ethan's application.

MARLOWE (CONT'D) I called you.

They both smile.

MARLOWE (CONT'D)

Now, are you interested in full or part-time employment.

ETHAN

Full. Definitely.

MARLOWE

Are you sure. A full-time commitment means just that. Full time.

ETHAN

I'm sure. I really would like to grow with the company. I have loved horror since I can remember, my whole life. I mean I could really see this as a career for me.

MARLOWE laughs to himself.

MARLOWE

Your enthusiasm and sincerity are appreciated Ethan. (MORE)

MARLOWE (CONT'D)

But, I'm not sure if we have any
full-time positions open right now.

Ethan is disappointed.

ETHAN

Mr. Marlowe, can I tell you why I
want this job so bad?

Marlowe is taken by the question. He sits back in his chair, and folds his fingers together.

ETHAN (CONT'D)

I have always been in the wrong
place. Not just now, but my whole
life. I am different than other
kids, I am different from my
parents. I have always been drawn
to the dark, and the creatures and
characters that I find there. I
come here, and for the first time I
feel like I belong. I belong here.

MARLOWE

You are also 17. I will need your
parent's permission.

ETHAN

Why?

MARLOWE

We are open until late on several nights, and your state's labor laws say I need their permission until you turn 18.

Ethan knows this won't happen. So does Marlowe. He smiles, suggesting an alternate form of approval

MARLOWE (CONT'D)

It's a simple form they need to sign. I can send it with you.

Ethan smiles.

MARLOWE (CONT'D)

If you do that, you're hired, but I want you to be sure, before you make this your life. Come in tomorrow around four, and I'll show you where everything goes.

Ethan is beaming. Marlowe stands and extends his hand.

MARLOWE (CONT'D)

Congratulations, oh and also you might want to wear something dark... we wouldn't want any fake blood to stain your good clothes.

ETHAN

Thanks Mr. Marlowe...

MARLOWE

Don't thank me yet Ethan. See how you like it first.

ETHAN

O.K. Mr. Marlowe, see you tomorrow.

MARLOWE

Good night Ethan and as we like to say, we'll be lurking for you...

He laughs in the best Vincent Price style.

MARLOWE (CONT'D)

See you soon.

Ethan leaves as Marlowe closes the door behind him. We hear SCREAMS and the distant WHIRRING of a chainsaw. Ethan smiles and leaves.

DISSOLVE TO:

EXT. SUBURBAN HOUSE - NIGHT

A thunderstorm is brewing. We hear the SOUND of rumbling thunder, and lightning flashes.

PASTOR DENNINGS

I absolutely forbid it. You will not be working there.

INT. HOUSE - NIGHT

CUT TO: The living room. Pastor Dennings and his wife, Esther are sitting in a pair of matching leather chairs. Ethan is standing in front of them. This is the end of a conversation that is going badly. Ethan is almost in pain, pleading with them.

ETHAN

Dad... Father, please. You said you wanted me to get a job. This is exactly what I want.

PASTOR DENNINGS

Do you know what this place is? It's a festering abomination. It celebrates the occult and lures us into complacency.

ETHAN

It's not that at all...

PASTOR DENNINGS

Sex, loose morality, and temptation. That place is filled with scenes of mutilation, violence, and populated with creatures born from the most evil sources. You believe this is acceptable?

ETHAN

It's not satanic... it's just fantasy. It's fun, like a roller coaster.

PASTOR DENNINGS

If we could we would have shut it down, but the council believes it is good for the economy. It is a filthy, wretched place aimed at warping young minds. What would my congregation think, our friends think if they knew my son was playing a role in this attack against our morality.

ETHAN

We don't have to tell anyone. Father, it's just harmless. None of these things are real... I know that. It's fantasy.

ESTHER DENNINGS

Ethan, listen to your father.

PASTOR DENNINGS

Fantasy is the deceiver of the mind to allow darkness in.

ETHAN

You don't understand. You have never understood.

ESTHER DENNINGS

What do you mean? We let you have the magazines, toys, watch the movies within reason.

PASTOR DENNINGS

And look where it has led. Now, he
wants to go out and act on these dark impulses.

ETHAN

I am not going to go out and have
sex, or drink or do drugs, or harm
anyone. You don't see how important
this is. Did you know I have no friends,
I have no life. I like what I like. And
every step, I had to fight for who I was,
and who I am. If you just took the time
to see what I liked about it...

PASTOR DENNINGS

Son, you will listen to me. This is
temptation pure and simple. It is a test.
A test for you and a test for me. Your
infatuation with the grotesque is an
embarrassment to this family. I will not
have my son be a part of what I have
dedicated my life to protecting my sheep
from. We are done here. You will not work there.

Pastor Dennings rises as an act of resolution. Ethan's anger is seething, ready to blow. They stare at each other, a defining moment between son and father.

ESTHER DENNINGS

Ethan, this is because we love you.

ETHAN

Love? Fuck you! You have never loved me because I'm different.

Pastor Dennings slaps him across the face. Ethan turns and flings the front door wide open. He disappears into the approaching storm. Mrs. Dennings follows and stands at the door frame looking out.

A rumble of THUNDER echoes.

DISSOLVE TO:

EXT. HORROR HOUSE - LATER

The Horror House parking lot is empty except for a an old but polished black Cadillac and a beat-up pickup truck parked some distance away from each other. The building is dark. The SOUND of the wind is rising. Marlowe appears from the behind the building and walks to one the Cadillac. Lightning illuminates the lot. He spies the other car and smirks. He opens his car and slowly gets in.

He starts the car and drives away. As his car passes, three figures appear, rising up in the truck's cab from their crouched position. Two men, and one girl get out. DAVE, GIL and IRENE (18), three rougher, redneck kids get out.

HOWIE

He's gone. Time for some fun.

IRENE

Yeah!

Dave pulls a crowbar from the bed of the truck. He opens a cooler and pulls out a twelve-pack and a bottle of Jack Daniels.

DAVE

Grab the Flashlights.

IRENE

And the sheets.

Howie grabs two flashlights and a dirty sheet from the bed of the truck. They quietly move toward the building.

EXT. HORROR HOUSE BACK DOOR - CONTINUOUS

CUT TO:

Dave forces the crowbar into the groove between door and frame and easily cracks it open. The door creaks open. Inside is pitch black. Irene is carrying the sheets and beer. Howie takes a swig from the Jack. A crack of lightning illuminates the inner wall revealing the image of the Jack Davis six-foot poster of the Frankenstein Monster. Irene screams. Howie clicks on a flashlight. Dave does the same. Two Beams pierce the darkness inside. Dave rips down the poster and the trio enter. The door closes behind them.

CUT TO:

EXT. SUBURBAN STREET - NIGHT

Ethan is standing under the arc of an overhead sodium streetlight. Tears stream down his face. The wind ripples his clothes madly. In his hand he holds the crumpled permission slip. He stares at it.

We HEAR the sound of the "Frankenstein" ringtone. Ethan pulls the phone out of his pocket and looks at the screen. It reads "Mom". He denies the call and puts it back in his back pocket. He is done with that life. SOUND: a louder crack of lightning.

CUT TO:

INT. HORROR HOUSE - MASK ROOM

A flashlight beam runs across several beautifully detailed masks hanging in a row. Costumes hang from racks around the room. Irene and Howie rush in. Howie takes one of the masks down and puts it on.

HOWIE

Ever been eaten by a zombie, Irene?

IRENE

That is so hot.

The lights suddenly come on revealing tons of props and other costume pieces. Irene screams. Dave rushes in.

DAVE

Are you gonna keep screaming?

Irene gives him a seductive smile.

IRENE

Maybe.

Dave opens a beer and downs it. He discards the can on the floor.

DAVE

Let's go.

They move into the hallway and open a door that leads them into...

INT. FRANKENSTEIN'S LAB SCENE

A recreation of the classic Frankenstein laboratory. Jacob's ladders buzz with electricity. A mannequin of a hunchback recoils in terror. Another mannequin represents the Doctor, his hands outstretched in victory. A beautifully sculpted piece of machinery points at a form on a lab table. Here, in beautiful lighting is the Monster. Dave grabs Irene and starts to growl.

DAVE

Hmmmmm, good.

She giggles. He takes the bottle of Jack and gives the Monster a drink. Brown liquid spills out across the grayish-green features.

DAVE (CONT'D)

No?

He pulls the Monster mannequin off the table and it falls to the floor with a crash. Irene grabs the sheet and rushes to the table.

IRENE

Oh Doctor?

She stretches out on the table. Howie is the third wheel.

HOWIE

I'll see you guys later. I'm gonna
go find a lonesome witch or... corpse.

He exits as Dave downs another beer. He drops it and it scatters across the floor, hitting the discarded Monster.He Crawls onto the lab table and kisses Irene.

CLOSE ON MONSTER'S EYES It stares blankly.

CUT TO:

INT. BOILER ROOM

A recreation of a dark, bloody boiler room. Claw marks are etched across the walls. A dim, orange light flickers from the boiler, casting shadows. Howie moves through the space. He runs his hands across the railing and pulls it back. Blood. He wipes it off and continues deeper into the building.

CUT TO:

INT. DRACULA'S BRIDES CHAMBER

Howie emerges in a castle chamber. Three beautiful Vampire Bride Mannequins are posed under a shaft of blue light. Howie smiles. He slowly scans each one.

HOWIE

Eeeny, meeny...

Then he sees his prize. A mannequin with a deep, plunging neckline reminiscent of Madeline Smith from Taste the Blood of Dracula. Her eyes are striking and lustful. They call to Howie. His rampant hormones pulsing. He moves closer, her eyes reflecting in the flashlight beam. He cups the body of the mannequin and slowly kisses her. He pulls his head back. It's not real, is it? He kisses her again.

CUT TO BLACK.

EXT. SUBURBAN HOUSE - THE NEXT MORNING

Sprinklers shower the lawn. A garbage truck roars past.

CUT TO:

INT. SUBURBAN HOUSE - MORNING

Pastor Dennings is sitting in his chair, studying his bible. Esther comes in, dressed in a nightgown and robe. She has not slept.

ESTHER DENNINGS

Ethan hasn't come home.

PASTOR DENNINGS

He did. I heard the garage open later. He slept in a sleeping bag.

ESTHER DENNINGS

Maybe we were too rough on him. You didn't have to...

PASTOR DENNINGS

Hit him? Do you know what they show in that place? Murder, evil representations of Godless creatures...

ESTHER DENNINGS

That place scares you?

PASTOR DENNINGS

Yes, and with good reason. But, what scares me even more is that...

He pauses. His steely sermonizing replaced by tenderness.

PASTOR DENNINGS (CONT'D)
What scares me is I lost my temper
and reacted with violence. When he
was cursing you, I was afraid. I feel
like he is slipping out of our control.
I am losing my son.

ESTHER DENNINGS
He is his own person. He always has
been. But, you are his father.

PASTOR DENNINGS
When he gets home from school, I
will talk with him. Now, let me get my coffee.

The phone rings. Pastor Dennings gets up and answers.

PASTOR DENNINGS (CONT'D)
Hello? Oh, hi Al...

Esther sits, worried.

CUT TO BLACK. FADE IN:

EXT. HORROR HOUSE - LATER
It is the same building as before, but now it is desolate and deserted. Paper bags and refuse litter the street. The daylight takes away all mystery.

Ethan walks along the building excitedly yet somewhat disappointed as the electricity of the previous evening is gone. He is dressed in a different horror-themed shirt, carrying a backpack. He peers in the front door, into the gift shop. It is dark. Ethan looks out into the parking lot. There in the distance is Marlowe's Cadillac. He moves around to the side of the building, past a series of dumpsters. Peering out from the corner is the torn Frankenstein poster.

Suddenly, a STREET BUM appears from behind the dumpster. He is terrified. Ethan is startled and jumps back as the bum shirt and stares past him, dead into space. white from blindness.

STREET BUM

I hear things at night here. Evil whispering things...

ETHAN

Listen mister, I don't have any spare change...

STREET BUM (terrified)

Listen, can't you hear the evil?

ETHAN

Mister, c'mon please!

Paranoia sets in as the bum runs away, brushing invisible demons from his body. He mumbles as he hurries out of sight. Ethan continues walking around the building to the back door and finds the door buzzer. The damage from the night before has been repaired.

He buzzes and waits... and waits... and waits... Then he buzzes again. Marlowe's voice comes over the speaker.

MARLOWE O.S.

Is that you Ethan?

ETHAN

Yes sir, Mr. Marlowe.

MARLOWE O.S.

I'll be right there.

Ethan smiles and leans against one of the building's columns. He then notices the Bum across the street. The Bum is staring right at him, then bows his head and genuflects the sign of the cross. Ethan turns right into Marlowe standing right there. He is dressed in another beautiful black suit and wearing dark sunglasses.

MARLOWE

Vagrants, I call the authorities on them all the time. I used to buy them fast food and feed them scraps at the back door, until one night one of them attacked me with a straight razor.

ETHAN

What happened?

MARLOWE

I got stitches.

Marlowe extends his arm and we see a long jagged scar running down his forearm.

MARLOWE (CONT'D)

I guess it's a good thing it was somewhat dull. Ethan, wait in the hallway, right around the corner. I am going to turn on everything and take you for a tour.

Ethan walks into the darkened hallway. Ethan begins to look around as he waits for Marlowe. He is admiring the scenic design and finds his eyes and curiosity carrying him through the hall. He notices a doorway and opens it. He looks behind as if to ask then shrugs and lets his curiosity continue to carry him through the doorway. Theatrical Lighting comes on, along with the SOUND of all of the effects and screams throughout the building. He is uneasy for a moment but then starts to enjoy himself. He continues forward into a atmospheric sub chamber.

CUT TO:

INT. DRACULA MAUSOLEUM

A beautiful theatrical set. A large, gothic window shows a brilliantly-painted faux full moon. Lighting casts an eerie blue tint. The SOUND of baying wolves mixed with Tchaikovsky's "Swan Lake" underscore the scene. In the center of the room is an ornate coffin lying on a stone base. On the lid is the crest of Dracula. Ethan looks at it and it almost calls to him. He looks around as if things are whispering to him. He pulls himself closer to the coffin takes one more quick look around and then laughs to himself.

He knocks on the front of the coffin.

ETHAN

Hello, in there?

He continues to giggle then opens it. There in the coffin lies a well-dressed mannequin of a Vampire.

MARLOWE

Beware the bite of the vampire.

Ethan jumps, startled by MArlowe's baritone voice.

ETHAN

Whoa, these things look so real.

MARLOWE

That is the point. It's all part of the show.

Marlowe closes the coffin lid.

MARLOWE (CONT'D)

But now, the vampire sleeps.

Ethan laughs.

MARLOWE (CONT'D)

How was school?

ETHAN

It really sucked. I would rather be here.

MARLOWE

Education is important Ethan.
Remember that.

Marlowe looks around the Mausoleum.

MARLOWE (CONT'D)

This is one of my favorite rooms.
The Vampire legends are so humorous.

ETHAN

I think they are cool.

MARLOWE

But so much has been done and they
are now a joke. The Vampire is the
King of it's kind.

Marlowe sighs.

MARLOWE (CONT'D)

I love the genre of fear and horror.
The characters are all so rich. You
know their names, their motivations,
their stories of creation. And so many
get it wrong nowadays. Give me the classics.
My first film was Frankenstein Meets the Wolfman,

and then... I was hooked. They were
all so charming. It set me on a path
to collect and then create. Each one
of my scenes have been designed to really
portray these great titans of terror in
an immersive, interactive setting. I don't
want to just startle my guests, I want to
scare them, sending them home with the
promise of sleepless, nightmare-filled nights.

Marlowe slowly walks ahead, Ethan following... mesmerized. They turn the corner and enter the next chamber.

CUT TO:

INT. DRACULA'S BRIDE'S CHAMBER

Marlowe and Ethan enter the chamber. THE CAMERA tracks them, but we don't fully see the scene.

MARLOWE

Each one of these costumes and
replicas has been tailored from years of study.
Did you know, I even visited
Forrest J. Ackerman in the Ackermansion once.

ETHAN

You did?

MARLOWE

He was a great fan as well. I wish
he could have seen where we have come.

I am always looking to perfect the
scene, adding new scares and details.
Take this scene for example, I just
added this tiny detail.

THE CAMERA pulls around revealing the entire scene. It is the same scene as before, with one major change.

ETHAN

Look at that!

Howie is now a victim, the Vampire Bride has turned the tables, biting deep and jagged into his neck. His face is frozen, petrified in pain and terror. Blood gushing down his neck. Marlowe smiles.

MARLOWE

My dear boy, it appears you have
the same appreciation for our displays
as I do. You know, maybe one day you
will join me and let me mentor you in
my designs.

ETHAN

That would be a great honor.

MARLOWE

But first things first. You have to
start like all my eternal dwellers...
at the bottom. You work hard, and
You will move up. Speaking of which,

did you get the permission slip? The minute
I have it in my hands, you can start scaring.

Ethan smiles.

ETHAN

I will.

MARLOWE

That's my boy. Now, let me show you
out. I have a few more preparations
to finish before tonight.

INT. ETHAN'S BEDROOM - LATER

CUT TO:

Ethan is sitting on his bed. On his lap is a sketch pad. THE CAMERA shows that he is designing a new haunted house experience. He has talent. A knock at the door. Esther Dennings peeks her head inside.

ESTHER DENNINGS

Ethan? Can I come in?

ETHAN

You may enter... unless you're a
vampire.

She forces a smile, not understanding the reference.

ESTHER DENNINGS

How was school?

ETHAN

Fine.

ESTHER DENNINGS

I heard you slept in the garage.

ETHAN

Then I snuck up early and took a
shower and went to school.

The conversation is awkward, but Esther still pushes.

ESTHER DENNINGS

I want to talk with you. Your
Father is at Al Reiners right now,
but when he gets home. Can we?

ETHAN

Yeah, ok. But I'm leaving to work soon.

ESTHER DENNINGS

It is that important to you?

She moves into the room.

ESTHER DENNINGS (CONT'D)

You really want this.

ETHAN

Yes.

ESTHER DENNINGS

Ethan, I have loved your Father
most of my life. He is a good man,
and he does love you. I wish you two
could really talk and understand each other.

ETHAN

I don't want to be an embarrassment
to you, but I like this stuff. It fascinates
me. It doesn't mean I worship at the feet
of the great deceiver.

ESTHER DENNINGS

But, I also know that you are a good
son, and I have never been embarrassed
by you. I will try to talk with your
Father as well. Just please try to
understand, he wants to protect you.

ETHAN

Mom, I am sorry about what I said to you.

Esther is happy to hear those words. She sits on the bed next to Ethan. She looks at his drawings.

ESTHER DENNINGS

What monster is this?

ETHAN

That is a ghoul. It robs graves,

feeds on humans... you know, like
Father says, the satanic stuff.

ESTHER DENNINGS

Oh, Ethan, Can you at least try to
talk to your Father when he gets home?
We have to put this behind us.

ETHAN

Ok, mom. I will try. For you. And I
really am sorry that I said those things to you.

ESTHER DENNINGS

I love you Ethan.

She leaves as Ethan continues to draw. She closes the door.

ETHAN

I love you too.

EXT. HORROR HOUSE - LATER

CUT TO:

The afternoon light is slowly changing to the promise of night. Ethan approaches the building. He looks up at the dark windows and sees movement. Something is staring at us, something horrible and rotten and grinning with a kind of lunatic glee. Ethan squints. Is it a new decoration? Behind him, in the distance Marlowe's Cadillac comes into the parking lot. It pulls up next to Ethan. Marlowe, impeccably- dressed in a different black suit and sunglasses, shuts off the motor and steps out.

MARLOWE

Ethan! Good evening.

ETHAN

Hi Mr. Marlowe. I love that new decoration.

MARLOWE

What decoration?

ETHAN

In the window above the sign...

Ethan points and now there is nothing there.

MARLOWE

No, but not a bad idea.

Marlowe starts to walk towards the building. Ethan follows.

CUT TO:

INT. GIFT SHOP - TWILIGHT

Marlowe opens the door and walks inside. Ethan follows. The store is eerie, with the light bleeding in across the masks and memorabilia. The masks look as if they are hiding from the remnants of the sun. Ethan looks around.

ETHAN

Am I too early?

MARLOWE

Oh no, your timing is perfect.

Everyone else should be showing up anytime.
Did you get the permission slip signed?

Ethan pulls the slip out of his pocket. It is signed. Marlowe looks at the signature with satisfaction.

MARLOWE (CONT'D)

You know, your Father came to see me earlier today. He was very polite. I showed him around and we talked a lot about what this place represents to me and what it represents to him. Eventually, he was very understanding. He even offered to come and bless it... Isn't that funny?

ETHAN

Hilarious.

Ethan knows he is caught in his deception.

MARLOWE

So, I am glad he decided to let you be a part of our family. You are sure this
(He holds up the forged paper)
That this is what you want?

ETHAN

I am. I want this more than anything.

Marlowe extends his hand.

MARLOWE

Ethan, welcome to my house.

Ethan shakes his hand with happiness, his dreams are coming true.

MARLOWE (CONT'D)

Now, I am going to turn on the lights
and sounds. Wait for me in the Mausoleum.

Ethan smiles, and walks towards the door into the hallway. Marlowe watches him, proud and beaming.

CUT TO:

INT. DRACULA MAUSOLEUM

Ethan walks into the Mausoleum set, confident in what is inside. He sees the coffin and again seems drawn to it. He opens it. There, in the darkness is the Vampire mannequin, only it looks more realistic without the show lighting.

ETHAN

Hi. I'm your new co-worker.

He pokes the corpse squarely in the cheek. He is surprised as his finger indents into the fleshy, hollow cheek.

ETHAN (CONT'D)

Feels gross.

The VAMPIRE opens it's eyes awakening from a human touch. It sees Ethan and hisses, opening it's mouth wide to display a set of fangs.

Ethan screams and the lid slams down hard as he reels backwards into the other coffins. His footing slips and he falls onto the floor. Ethan is stunned. Over his shoulder we see what he sees... the coffin is slowly opening as a ringed-hand grasps the outside wood slowly pushing upwards. Ethan has seen this before in countless movies, read about it in countless books. He is in amazement at what he is witnessing. Then suddenly the coffin flies open and the Vampire, like Nosferatu, moves straight up into a vertical position.

It scans the room with glowing white eyes and sees Ethan. It rears it's head back and lets out a violent hiss, then with a ferocity of an wild animal attacks... almost flying across the space between them. It grabs him, lifting him upwards and exposing his bare neck. The Vampire then rears back sprawling backwards trying to catch himself. Ethan doesn't understand then looks down to see his crucifix. Ethan looks back at the Vampire then back to the crucifix.

The Vampire attacks again. Ethan grasps for the crucifix but watches as the tiny symbol is flung from his hand. It clatters to the floor as the Vampire throws Ethan. He hits another wall. Part of the scenic falls away. Pieces of wood and debris covering Ethan's head and shoulders. Clearing his head from the swipe, he sees the Vampire from across the hall making what he is certain is the last attack. The Vampire hisses and attacks. Ethan scrambles across the floor reaching for some weapon. He sees two pieces of broken wood from the wall. He lunges and grabs them and puts them together.

The Vampire lunges and is met face to face with the makeshift crucifix. He screams, his face burning with holy steam and falls backwards. Ethan seizes his opportunity and runs. The Vampire has now lifted himself up as we see Ethan running in the background.

The Vampire feels the wound where the crucifix rested upon his face. It is foaming. We see anger and pain well up within the Vampire as he lets loose with a bellowing SCREAM that echoes throughout the hallways and rooms.

CUT TO:

INT. DRACULA'S BRIDE'S CHAMBER

Ethan runs through the chamber. It is the same scene as before, but now the Brides are slowly coming alive.The Lights and SOUND come alive, plunging the area into a disorienting scene of horror. The VAMPIRE BRIDE is ripping out Howie's neck in a ravenous attack. His screams are silent, his vocal chords severed. Blood gushing down his neck. The other two BRIDES turn and see Ethan. Their eyes lock onto him and they start to move towards him. He rushes out of the scene.

CUT TO:

INT. FRANKENSTEIN'S LAB SCENE

Blinding flashes of lightning from an unseen lighting source. Electrical equipment arching. Ethan rushes past the mannequins. Irene has replaced the Monster on the Lab table as a new recreation of the Bride. She is wrapped in head to toe in bandages. Her face exposed, her mouth frozen open in a perpetual scream. The Frankenstein Monster watches over the proceedings with anticipation, awaiting his new bride. He turns and sneers at Ethan.

CUT TO:

INT. CHAINSAW SHED

Ethan continues running. He enters a rural shed scene. Flashing strobes cause disorientation. In the flashes we see the horrors on display. Rusty meat hooks with hunks of bloody flesh hang from above... glass jars filled with viscous fluid... Bones of varying shapes and sizes. The SOUND of the musical underscore is piercing. A sign reads "Country's Best Bar-b-que". Dave is stretched across a butcher's table. His legs have been sawed off. His hands stretched tight above his head. Red blood and intestines spilling out in a frozen tableau. A CHAINSAW MANIAC is slowly cutting through a section of his torso. Dave SCREAMS. Ethan is losing his mind. The Maniac raises the bloody chainsaw above his head and dances in excitement. He REVS the saw and moves towards Ethan. Ethan grabs a discarded 2 x 4 board and swipes at the maniac. The board connects, sending the maniac backward and down. The saw lands on top of him and he SCREAMS in agony. Flesh and blood spray across Ethan. He backs away and turns, fleeing from the scene.

CUT TO:

INT. GRAVEYARD CEMETARY - NIGHT

Ethan runs into the graveyard. It is scenically painted to be black and white... stark and foreboding. He looks over his shoulder and all around, sweat dripping from his brow along with a small trace of blood. The lightning effect is tripped blinding Ethan's eyes as they are already focused for the dark., He rubs his eyes when he hears a scraping sound. He follows the sound with his eyes and spots the cause. Rising from the floor from the fog and smoke and concrete is a ZOMBIE. It is well decayed and spots Ethan immediately. It grabs his leg and pulls Ethan down... teeth gnashing . Ethan is being drug down and closer to those carnivorous teeth. He uses a standing tomb for support, grabs hold and with his free leg kicks the Zombie repeatedly in the head.

ETHAN

Here! Eat this!!!

Ethan makes one final hard kick and the Zombie's head flies backwards and off, trailing bits of decomposed flesh and bone. ETHAN is up and moving when he sees several other Zombies rising and lurking out from behind scenic crypts and tombstones. Ethan sees a red EXIT sign emanating from a doorway behind one of the Zombies. He moves quickly hitting the Zombie running full force. The Zombie crumples as Ethan falls through the door into...

CUT TO:

INT. SNACK MACHINE HALLWAY - NIGHT

A break space for the building's employees. He slams the door shut behind him as he falls over empty water bottles and rests against a snack machine. He breaths hard not knowing what has happened or what is really going on. There are distant GROANS as the building seems to be coming alive. He looks over and sees the dead body of the BUM. The body of the Bum rests against the snack machine, two large holes in his neck, and blood flowing down his body. Ethan screams and backs into Marlowe. Ethan screams again and backs against the opposite wall.

ETHAN

Mr. Marlowe?

MARLOWE

Oh, there you are my dear boy, I was beginning to worry where..

He then sees, illuminated from the light of the snack machine Marlowe's face. His mouth is covered in blood as it drips down his chin. He smiles at Ethan.

ETHAN

What the fuck is going on here?
What is this?

Marlowe smiles wide displaying a set of sharp teeth covered in blood and flesh. We hear clawing now at the door. Marlowe smiles and picks up the bum's body with little effort opens the door and throws the body to the creatures waiting on the other side. They rip the bum apart as Marlowe smiles, shuts the door and pulls Ethan's application from his pocket.

MARLOWE

It's what you wanted Ethan...

Ethan is now petrified as tears and blood stream down his face.

MARLOWE (CONT'D)

You're hired ... FULL TIME!

Ethan screams as Marlowe attacks. Ethan in a last burst of panic and energy escapes running through another door. Marlowe stands laughing.

MARLOWE (CONT'D)

It's a great job...isn't that what you said?

INT. STAIRWAY - NIGHT

CUT TO:

Ethan runs up the stairways screaming. He reaches the top landing and peers over the landing and sees Marlowe and Zombies staring upwards at him, grinning.

MARLOWE (CONT'D)

FULL TIME! Ethan... FULL TIME!!!

Ethan runs into the adjoining room. He is now berserk with fear.

CUT TO:

INT. POSSESSED GIRL BEDROOM -

Ethan rushes into a full blown exorcism scene. On a bed is a young, POSSESSED GIRL (11), her face a twisted mask of pain. She opens her mouth and spews green bile towards her tormentor. Ethan turns and finds his father, Pastor Denning. He is resolute in his mission.

PASTOR DENNINGS

The power of Christ compels you!

The power of Christ compels you!

He screams at his Father.

ETHAN

Dad! Dad, help me!

The possessed girl starts laughing mischievously.

POSSESSESED GIRL

He's ours now.

The Pastor seems to be taken over by an invisible force. He claws at his eyes.

PASTOR DENNINGS

Help me!

Ethan screams.

ETHAN

Dad!

A force hits the Pastor, pushing him back and into the scenic wall causing a large dent in the plaster. He lifts his head, revealing HE IS NOW POSSESSED. The Pastor turns to Ethan. His eyes are now ghastly white orbs. He reaches out at Ethan.

ETHAN

No!

He kicks out at his father, sending him reeling.

INT. MORGUE - NIGHT

Ethan runs into the rooms and stops dead center, horrified by what he see... Bodies hanging from the ceiling wrapped in plastic. Across the room he sees a doorway he starts for it... and stops as he sees several CREATURES and ZOMBIES crawling in. He backs away and turns...right into Marlowe. Behind him are the rest of the cast of Horror House... Dracula, The Bride, the Frankenstein Monster, the possessed girl and his FATHER.

MARLOWE

YOU'RE HIRED...FULL TIME!!!

Marlowe laughs, Ethan screams, and the cast's hands reach up surrounding him.

MARLOWE (CONT'D)

It's more than just saying BOO!!! Join us.

ETHAN

No!

Ethan is covered by clawing hands as he continues to scream. THE CAMERA dollies right into his screaming mouth until it is out of focus. We then pull out of the same mouth covered in plastic cellophane. Pulling back we see Ethan is now hanging in one of the bags along with the rest of the bodies, presumably all past applicants. He squirms to free himself as the lights flicker on and off. We hear Marlowe's laughter as a group of people walk in screaming. They are customers and TOURISTS.

TOURIST

Man, these things look so real!

Ethan has now become a permanent addition to the attraction. He has his wish...he is employed full-time. The camera pans along with the group as we pan we find the Host who has been witnessing the "onboarding". He turns to the camera and shrugs.

HOST

Looks like Ethan got his wish, He's employed full-time. I don't think he'll last though, it's only his first day, and he's already bagging it.

The Host laughs as we see the bodies dangling in the background.

FADE OUT:

AN INCIDENT AT JOE'S TAVERN

BY J. MICHAEL RODDY

INT. JOKER'S BAR - NIGHT

A smoky, overdecorated cocktail lounge and nightclub. On the jukebox is Dean Martin singing about the birds and the bees. PAULIE GIMBALLI, a 40-year-old gangster is holding court at the bar. Silver haired and sharply-dressed, this man has seen a lot of bad things. Several MEN and WOMEN surround him. Everyone has been having a good time. A well-dressed HOOD walks in with his statuesque GIRLFRIEND.

HOOD

You're a legend Paulie! You're a frickin' legend!

PAULIE

Five years! Don't let this evening end.

Paulie smiles. He is the man of the hour. Drinks all around. Two MEN enter. BILLY BURKE and JIMMY SGAMBETERRA. Both are in their late-twenties. They are like sharks. Paulie looks up to see Jimmy. There is history between them.

PAULIE (CONT'D)

Look who's here! Little Jimmy Sgambeterra.
You grew up fast Scampy.

JIMMY

Hey Paulie, good to see you.

PAULIE

That's it? Come here Scamp!

Jimmy walks over and Paulie grabs him, messing up his hair and squeezing his cheek. Jimmy doesn't like it.

JIMMY

Hey Paulie, watch the hair.

PAULIE

What the fuck? Are you kidding me? You ain't seen me in five years and that's what I get? I gave you your first taste you little fuck.

Billy steps in, seeing the situation is getting tense.

BILLY

Hey Paulie-

PAULIE

What the fuck are you, his bodyguard? I knew both of you when you were both stealing cigarettes. Now, your too good for me?

JIMMY

We just grew up a little since you've
been gone. No one calls me scamp anymore.

PAULIE

We're only kidding. Relax you two.
I'm celebrating. Jimmy calms a little.

PAULIE (CONT'D)

Now why don't you sit and drink
your soda while the men have drinks?
That okay with you scamp?

Everyone erupts in laughter, except for Jimmy. He fumes. Paulie turns his back to him. Jimmy starts towards him and Billy steps in.

BILLY

Come on, Jimmy. He's had too much
to drink. He's celebrating.

Jimmy stares at Paulie, but then coldly turns and exits.

LATER - The Bar is now almost empty. Paulie sits with Billy. Jimmy enters. He locks the door behind him. The BARTENDER slowly exits somewhere in the back of the Tavern. Paulie is continuing, not noticing Jimmy slowly and deliberately moving in behind him.

PAULIE

Respect is important. You have to
show respect, that is how we all survive...

Paulie turns and sees Jimmy.

PAULIE (CONT'D)

Hey kid...

Paulie looks down and sees that Jimmy has a gun in his hand. Billy grabs his arms and we see Jimmy smash the gun into the side of Paulie's head. WHAM! WHAM! WHAM! Paulie goes limp. Billy holds him up and Jimmy smashes it one last time. Blood splatters. Paulie drops to the floor with a thud. Jimmy smiles, blood splatter on his face. He pulls off a tablecloth from a table.

BILLY

Fuck. I think you killed him.

Jimmy grabs a set of keys from his jacket.

JIMMY Bring the car around.

BILLY

Jimmy, this is bad. He's a made guy.

JIMMY

I know a place they'll never find him. Get the car.

EXT. BACK DOOR - JOKER'S BAR - NIGHT

Darkness. The open trunk of Jimmy's silver Cadillac. Jimmy and Billy are wrestling with the lifeless body, now wrapped in a tablecloth. The body lands on a shovel.

CUT TO:

EXT. COUNTRY ROAD - NIGHT

A desolate road in the middle of nowhere. No cars, no lights. Snow lightly falls. Jimmy's Cadillac pulls into view, speeding along.

INT. JIMMY'S CAR - NIGHT

Billy is driving. Jimmy is in the passenger seat, his head against the window, sleeping. The sleepy HUMMING of WHEELS. Billy lights a cigarette. Smoke trails around him as his eyes slowly close for a second. He shakes awake.

BILLY

Oh God!

FRONT WINDOW

The headlights illuminate a form in the center of the road about the size and shape of a small child. Billy slams the brake pedal down. The car skids along the road. The child-sized form starts to run but the car clips it and sends it rolling up into the air. It heads the road with a sickening THUMP. The car continues to brake, sliding off the road an onto the loose gravel of the shoulder. It finally stops sending Billy and Jimmy forward.

INTERIOR

Jimmy's head hits the dash, slamming his nose.

JIMMY

Ah, my fucking nose!

Jimmy pulls out a handkerchief from is jacket and holds it to his bleeding nose. Billy is shaken, breathing hard and terrified at what just happened.

BILLY

Jimmy...

JIMMY

I shouldn't have let you drive. I think you broke my nose.

BILLY

Jimmy!

Jimmy turns to Billy. He has never seen his friend this shaken.

BILLY (CONT'D)

I think I hit a kid.

Both men get out of the car.

JIMMY

What would a kid be doing out here. You hit a deer.

Jimmy moves to the front to inspect the damage. One of the headlights is pointing straight up.

JIMMY (CONT'D)

Shit. This is gonna set me back.

Jimmy sees blood splatter across the front of the Cadillac, and a ripped piece of bloody fur.

JIMMY (CONT'D)

See, you hit a deer...

They turn back to the road. The taillights cast and eerie red glow across the road. There in the center of the road is a furry clump. It is motionless.

BILLY

There it is.

JIMMY

Let's get the fuck outta here. We still have an issue in the trunk. I'll drive.

Billy moves towards the clump.

BILLY

I want to make sure it's not in misery.

JIMMY

You what?

He moves closer to the clump. The closer he gets, the more he realize this isn't a deer. He kicks at it with his foot. It doesn't move. He goes to turn it over. Suddenly it springs up, standing on two legs. It is humanoid and child-sized but covered from head to toe in dark-brown fur.

It YELPS in fear and pain, and lurches towards the tree-line. Jimmy pulls his revolver and SHOOTS. The creature is hit three times in the back and falls down an embankment.

JIMMY (CONT'D)

What was that? What the fuck was that?

The two men move toward the embankment. They look down and see nothing but trees and darkness. Nothing moves.

JIMMY (CONT'D)

Let's get out of here.

They get back into the car.

TREELINE

In the darkness we can make out the shape of something... large.

INT. CAR

Jimmy is now driving, still holding a handkerchief to his checks it and the blood has stopped flowing, so he it to the floor. Billy is sitting quietly. Jimmy slows the car down.

CUT TO:

BAR

In the distance is a small roadside bar. The parking lot is almost empty except a Station Wagon, a beat-up Ford pickup and a motorcycle.

INTERIOR

Jimmy checks his watch. It is half-past 1AM.

JIMMY

I need a drink. How about you?

BILLY

Yeah. Sure. I need something.

The car pulls into the parking lot. Across the parking lot are large brown and black boulders. Too heavy to move. They are scattered across the parking lot in various shapes and sizes.

INT. JOE'S TAVERN - NIGHT

A small, roadside bar. The place is dark, musty and sporadically populated. There is a pool table, some booths, an old-fashioned jukebox, and a long, wooden bar. Behind the bar is CLU, a man in his late sixties, thinning hair, a lifetime of struggle chiseled into his face. Sitting across from him is CHET, an old biker with ponytail, and earring. Chet finishes his shot of Jack and gets up. He pulls on his leather jacket and reaches for his wallet.

CLU

Ready to close out?

Chet shakes his head and grunts. Clu moves to the register. At the pool table are Two MEN playing a game. BYRON and NATE, both in the early twenties, dressed in contemporary clothing. Watching them is DIANE and CYNDY, both pretty and collegiate. All college students.

Byron aims up his pool cue for a final shot and shoots. The ball misses, bounding off the side of the green.

BYRON

I suck at this.

The door opens. Jimmy and Billy enter. The entire place stares. There aren't many strangers at this time of the morning in this bar.

JIMMY

You still open?

CLU

Last call is at 1:45. What can I get you?

JIMMY

I'll have a Cutty and water.

BILLY

Shot of gin.

The two men move to a table and sit. Clu returns to Chet and hands him his bill. Chet pulls out a wad of cash and leaves Clu a twenty.

CHET

Interesting.

CLU

What's that?

Chet motions to Jimmy and Billy.

CHET

The shorter one has blood on his shirt. You want me to stick around?

CLU

I see. I think I can handle any problems.

Clu motions under the bar.

UNDER THE BAR

A double-barrel shotgun.

BACK TO BAR

Chet nods and zips up his jacket.

CHET

Heading out.

CLU

Be safe out there.

Chet turns to leave.

CRACK!

Across the room Nate breaks in a new game of pool. Billy jumps, his nerves are shot. Clu brings over the two men's drinks.

CLU (CONT'D)

Here you go. Let me know if you need anything else.

JIMMY

You Joe?

Clu stares at him.

CLU

What's that?

JIMMY

This is Joe's Tavern. Are you Joe?

Clu laughs.

CLU

No.

He turns and walks away.

JIMMY

Real friendly folks up here.

BILLY

Can we just finish this, and take care of Paulie and then get back. We have to figure out what we say when we get asked if we know anything.

JIMMY

Relax. We had no beef with Paulie.
No one is going to suspect us.

BILLY

Jesus, he just got out of prison and he
disappears? Someone will remember...
he's a made guy.

JIMMY

Look, I said relax. You are shook
up. You hit a deer and you are all freaked...

BILLY

It wasn't a fucking deer!

Everyone looks over at he outburst. Jimmy smiles.

JIMMY

Sorry. We had a small accident and we hit
a... an animal... My pal is just a little raw.

Everyone returns to normal.

JIMMY (CONT'D)

Look Billy, you need to calm down.

BILLY

You saw it. It fucking walked on
two legs. What was that thing?

JIMMY

A bear? Who knows. It's dead and I need you to be solid right now. We have shit to do. We are gonna take care of the problem in the trunk and then get back to the city. Now stop being a jerkass.

Jimmy downs his Cutty and looks at Billy, who downs his shot of Gin.

JIMMY (CONT'D)

Hey! Not Joe! Another round.

EXT. JOE'S TAVERN - NIGHT

CUT TO:

Chet is walking to his bike, a beautiful custom chopper. He mounts the bike, ready to turn on the ignition when he hears a low GROWL sound. He stops. He dismounts and looks around. He scans the tree-line just past the lot. Darkness. Nothing is moving.

CUT TO:

INT. JOE'S TAVERN

Nate is winning. Clu brings over another round for Jimmy and Brian. Jimmy hands him two twenty-dollar bills.

JIMMY

Keep the change, not Joe.

CLU

Thanks.

JIMMY

How far are we from the main highway?

CLU

About 5 miles. Closer to Horlicks University. That's where those kids are from. Between here and there it's just us and a Gas station about a mile north.

The moment is shattered by the sound of a SCREAM. Clu turns.

CLU (CONT'D)

That's Chet!

Jimmy stands, his hand moves instinctively inside his jacket. Clu grabs his shotgun and opens the door.

PARKING LOT

Clu stops.

Chet's motorcycle is turned on its side. Chet is nowhere to be found. Clu steps out.

CLU (CONT'D)

Chet! What's up? Where you at?

Silence. The four college kids are staring out. Jimmy and Billy step out into the parking lot. Clu slowly walks to the bike.

CLU (CONT'D)

He loves this bike. This ain't right.

Jimmy and Billy scan the lot. Nothing but the large rocks. Suddenly, one of the rocks springs up and moves. It's two-legged and hairy - A BIGFOOT! The Girls SCREAM from inside the bar. Jimmy and Billy pull their guns. It makes a run for the tree-line. It's big and fast.

CLU (CONT'D)

Holy...

Jimmy fires at the creature. He misses and the creature leaps into the woods and disappears.

BILLY

What was that?

CLU

We need to get back inside.

The sound of an unearthly HOWL rises in the air.

JIMMY

We are getting outta here.

Another HOWL from the opposite side of the parking lot makes Jimmy and Brian turn. Clu moves forward.

CLU

You won't get far.

Jimmy pulls back the slide re-cocking his pistol.

JIMMY

Watch us.

Jimmy moves to the Cadillac. Billy follows. The sound of THUMPING is heard, like something fell from the sky. THUMP! THUMP! THUMP! Billy is hit with a large rock. Several more rocks hit the ground. Jimmy grabs Billy. The Cadillac is pelted with rocks, shattering the windshield and causing great dents on the roof and the hood. Jimmy is hit across the back with a large stone. He turns and shoots blindly. Billy is trying to move to the entrance of the tavern. Rocks hit the front of the building. A neon light shatters, sending sparks across the front. Jimmy grabs Billy and throws him inside. He turns, emptying his gun blindly before jumping into the open doorway.

CUT TO:

INT. JOE'S TAVERN

Clu slams the door and locks it. Several more rocks hit the building.

DIANE

What is happening?

Cyndy is covering her ears. Nate and Byron are holding pool cues in defensive posturing. The sound of the ROCKS slowly stops. Silence. Then the sound of HOLWLING is heard. It stops. Jimmy looks at Billy's head. There is a large gash across the forehead from where the rock hit. Blood streaming down his face. Jimmy reloads his pistol. Clu moves to the phone.

CLU

Gotta get the Sheriff out here.

JIMMY

Hold on that old man.

Clu continues dialing.

CLU

Hello?

JIMMY

Put that fucking phone down.

Jimmy is pointing his pistol at Clu.

BYRON

What the hell?

Nate and Byron make a move towards Jimmy. Billy stands, and points his gun at them.

BILLY

Stop!

Diane holds onto Cyndy as the two men stop. Jimmy cocks the pistol.

JIMMY

I'll drop you where you stand.

Clu hangs up the phone.

JIMMY (CONT'D)

Smart move not Joe. Move over there with the others.

Clu looks at the shotgun on the bar and moves to the College Kids.

JIMMY (CONT'D)

No cops.

Billy collapses in a chair, his head is pounding.

JIMMY (CONT'D)

You ok Pally?

BILLY

What are those things?

JIMMY

Take it easy. You are bleeding bad. (To Clu) You got a first aid kit or something around here.

CLU

Behind the bar.

Jimmy turns, the gun still at the ready.

JIMMY

You. (pointing at Diane)
Go get it.

Diane moves behind the bar and finds a small, white first aid box. She brings it over to Jimmy. Nate moves forward. Jimmy looks at him.

NATE

I'm pre-med.

Jimmy motions him over. Nate opens the box and surveys the supplies. He pulls out some bandages.

JIMMY

Everyone just stay cool. Anyone have any idea what just happened? Nate starts to clean the wound on Billy's gash.

NATE

You need a hospital man.

JIMMY

Just do your best right now.

BILLY

Jimmy, those were more of that thing I hit on the road.

JIMMY

You hit a deer-

BILLY

I DIDN'T HIT A DEER! I hit one of
those things. You shot it. Now, they want me!

Billy passes out. Nate cradles his head and lays him on the floor.

NATE

Dude, your boy needs a Hospital. He might have a concussion. He definitely needs more than I can do with bandaids and rubbing alcohol.

The sound of a HOWL is heard in the distance.

BYRON

That sounds farther away.

DIANE

Maybe they're leaving.

CLU

They aren't leaving.

JIMMY

No? How do you know that?

CLU

If you're friend is telling the

truth, and you killed one of them,
they aren't leaving without you.

JIMMY

You seem to know what these things
are. Start talking.

CLU

You heard of 'em. They hide in
plain sight. Every so often, a
Hunter or some hiker will see one.
They live in the woods. All over. Not
just here, out west, down south.

BYRON

Are you talking about Bigfoot?

CLU

Some call 'em that. Some call 'em
Sasquatch. All I know is that you made 'em
angry. For them to attack us? I only heard
of that happening once before.

CYNDY

They don't really exist. They're
like a myth -

JIMMY

You are outta your fucking minds
out here.

CLU

You asked.

JIMMY

Yeah. Now I'm asking if you got any
other weapons in here but that shotgun.

CLU

That's all I ever needed before, so no.

Nate slowly approaches Jimmy.

NATE

Sir, I know that you don't want us
calling the cops, but your friend is
in bad shape, and something attacked us.
I don't know what trouble you or your
friend is in, but we never saw you. I
promise. Just let us go.

BYRON

Or you guys can leave.

NATE

We will not tell anyone you were here.

JIMMY

Just give me a minute. I need to think.

Billy slowly starts to come around.

BILLY

Jimmy?

Jimmy moves to him.

JIMMY

Hey there, Pally. You scared me for a second.

BILLY

Take me home.

Jimmy stands and looks at Byron and Nate, sizing them up.

JIMMY

Which one of you is faster?

NATE

I am.

Cyndy grabs at his arm.

CYNDY

No, don't do it.

Nate hugs her.

JIMMY

Ok, you and me are gonna make a run for my car.

Jimmy points at Byron.

JIMMY (CONT'D)

Doc, I will pull up to this door
and you will help my friend get inside.
Then we are out of here. Once we're gone
you can call anyone you want.

NATE

Alright.

The two men head for the door. Cyndy hugs Nate one more time.

NATE (CONT'D)

Look baby, we get these guys outta
here and on their way, then we can
call the cops.

Jimmy takes the shotgun.

NATE

I'll be right back.

Byron pulls Billy up. Diane helps him.

BILLY

You be careful out there.
JIMMY Yeah. Real careful.
He cocks the shotgun.

JIMMY (CONT'D)

Open her up!

Clu opens the door. Standing there, filling the door frame is a BIGFOOT. Massive, strong and piercing yellow eyes. A mouth full of sharp teeth. Cyndy screams. The Creature swings his arm at Jimmy, sending him into Byron and Billy and stumbling backwards. The Creature grabs Nate and yanks him out.

CYNDY

Nate!

Jimmy rushes forward and fires the shotgun point blank into the Creature, blowing a huge chunk out of it's hairy shoulder. The Creature howls in pain and then in defiance, rips Nate in half.

CYNDY (CONT'D)

NO!

Jimmy reloads the shotgun and fires squarely into the creature. It takes the full impact of the shotgun and drops to one knee.
Jimmy doesn't hesitate but reloads the shotgun and fires again at the creature's head. It explodes apart in bits of fur and skull. The body FLOPS to the ground. Jimmy runs for the car. In the distance an angry HOWL. Jimmy reaches the car. The windshield is shattered. He opens the door and starts the ignition in one "getaway" move. He slams on the accelerator and the car lurches forward. He pulls up to the door. He pushes the horn signaling several HONKS. Byron is holding Billy up. He moves with him to open the rear passenger's door. Two Massive Arms reach down and grab Billy, yanking him up. Byron falls to the ground as Billy is pulled away. Jimmy opens the door and looks up to see a BIGFOOT silhouetted in the moonlight. The creature holds Billy up over his head and breaks him, bones CRUNCHING. Billy chokes as blood rains down, splattering Byron.

JIMMY

No!

Jimmy fires. The Creature drops Billy's broken body on the hood of the Cadillac. Jimmy slams the accelerator. The car spins wildly across the gravel and slams into the rocks. Steam and smoke burst up from the collision. Byron turns to run, but another BIGFOOT appears from the side of the building. It moves towards him like a locomotive, all muscle and fur. It sweeps him up without stopping and disappears around the corner. SCREAMS echo O.S. Jimmy pulls himself out of the car, dazed. He shakes it off quickly and starts towards the Tavern. His jog becomes a sprint as his head clears. He leaps into the doorway, landing hard on the floor. Clu slams it shut.

INSIDE

Clu picks up the shotgun. He aims it squarely at Jimmy.

CLU

You stay right there.

Jimmy doesn't argue.

CLU (CONT'D)

Girls, one of you get on that phone and
get the Sheriff out here with everything he's got.

Both Girls are in shock.

CLU (CONT'D)

Move!

Diane runs over to the bar and slides behind it. She picks up the phone and starts to dial.

DIANE

We need help...

The wall behind Diane EXPLODES in wood and glass bottles. Two HAIRY ARMS tear through grasping at her. One hand connects, pulling her hair. She screams as she is inched closer to several jagged wood shards. Cyndy runs to her, grabbing her arm and trying to pull her to safety. A piece of wall breaks away revealing the face of the creature. It is frothing at the mouth, filled with anger. The attacking Beast's mouth opens to feed on Diane. Cyndy frantically grabs at splintered piece of the broken wall and buries it into the Bigfoot's right eye. It HOLWS in pain. Clu runs to help. Jimmy stands and stares. Clu drops the shotgun on the bar, using both hands to pull at Dianne. Jimmy grabs the gun. Clu sees him.

CLU

Help us!

Jimmy turns and heads for the back exit. He rushes out as the Bigfoot takes Dianne's head into his open mouth and bites. Jimmy has slipped out and makes a run for the tree-line. The sound of SCREAMS echo behind him. Jimmy runs through the dark forest, breaking branches in his way. Moonlight shafts light the darkness. He continues to run. Out of the corner of his eye Jimmy sees three Men kneeling with bright flash lights. TIM, CAL and GEOFF, dressed in full camouflage including make- up and lots of night-vision gear. They're pouring what looks to be Plaster of Paris onto the ground. They jump up as Jimmy rushes in.

TIM

Jumped up palomino!

JIMMY

What the fuck are you guys doing out here?

CAL

We're Squatchers.

JIMMY

What?

TIM

We study Cryptozoology. There have been countless sightings in this area since the 1930's-

JIMMY

Go that way.

Jimmy points behind him and then runs off.

TIM

You sure you're ok?

CAL

That was weird.

TIM

Definitely.

The three men continue with their pouring of plaster. A giant BIGFOOT rushes through knocking all three of them back.

ON PLASTER

The creature's mammoth foot splashes the plaster leaving a much bigger footprint. The light shatters apart.

ON SQUATCHERS

They stand, scanning the area with their flashlight beams.

CUT TO:

EXT. ROAD - NIGHT

Jimmy clears the tree-line and steps out into an empty road. A sign read HORLICKS UNIVERSITY - 5 miles. In the distance, a flashing red and blue light appears. It is moving fast. As the Cop Car comes closer. Jimmy steps out, trying to wave the officer down. As the car approaches, Jimmy is grabbed by a blur of fur. The Cop Car continues on its way. Silence.

JIMMY'S POV

The world is spinning fast, deftly moving through the night forest. Jimmy's eyes close and he passes out.

CUT TO BLACK.

EXT. - WOODS - NIGHT

Jimmy wakes up. He is in a small clearing. The moon lights the area. He hears a sound of CRUNCHING twigs. He turns, reaching for his gun. It is gone. Jimmy turns and sees a towering Bigfoot. It stares at him, breathing hard, eyes glowing. It drops the body of the child Bigfoot.

JIMMY

I'm sorry.

It makes three sharp guttural BARKS. Jimmy starts to back away. The trees move behind him, branches SNAPPING. He turns and sees three small Bigfoot BABBIES. They move slowly toward him. They GROWL, showing tiny, razor sharp teeth.

JIMMY (CONT'D)

Oh no.

They all rush him, ripping and tearing. He SCREAMS as the baby creatures tear him apart.

CUT TO:

EXT. DAWN

The cold blue light of the rising sun bathes Joe's Tavern. Morning fog is creeping through the trees. The parking lot is busy with activity. Several Cop Cars and an Ambulance are parked around the entrance. PATROLMEN stand around. SHERIFF HUNT, graying and out-of-shape, moves to a PATROLMEN

SHERIFF HUNT

Anyone?

PATROLMEN

We got a ton of blood, but no bodies. We are running plates now. The place has been trashed.

SHERIFF HUNT

I want these woods searched as soon as it gets more light -

We hear a dull THUMPING sound. We move closer Cadillac. The Thump is coming from the trunk. THUMP! Silence.

The trunk springs open and Paulie rises from the compartment, the blood-stained sheet still covering him. He climbs out. His face is swollen, and a large series of bruised gashes and dried blood cover his face. He looks around, confused.

PAULIE

Where am I?

Two PATROLMEN rush over.

CUT TO BLACK.

a few words from

J. MICHAEL RODDY

What do you love about the genre of horror?

The horror genre is a blend of three elements… fear, anxiety and relief. The sense of foreboding that sets you up, then the impact that the nightmare is potentially real, followed by the resolution and then calm. I love that feeling, that unnerving, slow approach of creepiness that crawls up your neck and then the exposure, the dark veil lifted… BOOM! Do you fight or succumb? Regardless of the outcome, it ends. But, the calm is what is really the echo of it all. All is back to normal, but the memory of the horror can creep back time and again.

What is some of your favorite horror literature?

Stephen King, Ray Bradbury, Robert McCammon, Peter Straub and Richard Matheson.

What are some of your influences?

John Carpenter, Steven Spielberg, Houdini, Tom Savini, Greg Nicotero.

What is your favorite Halloween treat?

Halloween M & M's and Almond Joy bars.

If you could continue any horror story, what would it be?

I have always wanted to continue the story of John Carpenter's *The Fog*. I have a pretty solid concept that had Blake and his crew returning to Antonio Bay 30 years after the events of the first film. I also have a lot of pieces to a sequel to *Frankenstein* that would continue the creature's journey, but there has been so much already. I have always wanted to try my hand at a revision of *The Most Dangerous Game* as well.

As a designer of horror theatre or experiences, explain your process.

My process starts with connection. What role are we asking the Guest to play in the experience? I believe that mazes and haunted houses are moments in a bigger story. If I had no restriction on time, I would create an entire story presented as moments of theatre, but usually, you only have so much space, time and budget, so I create an immense backstory that I can explain through video, sound and setting, and then put the Guest into that story as an active participant at a specific time.

When is the last time you were genuinely scared by something someone created?

From a movie standpoint, the following films have done a pretty effective job at scaring me. Hereditary disturbed me greatly. *The Host* on Netflix. Mike Flannagan is becoming one of my favorite new filmmakers. *The House on Haunted Hill, Doctor Sleep, Hush, Gerald's Game…* I would love to spend a few minutes chatting with him.

Tell us about your contribution to our book. What was the inspiration?

I have included a few different pieces that show different aspects of my fascination with the genre. I have included two horror scripts that I want to produce as part of an anthology project, as well as a look at producing filmed media for horror events. I also added some photography that defines my love for one panel storytelling.

Describe the perfect Halloween.

If I could have my Mom back for one more Halloween, and let her see how her sacrifice and love inspired me to do the same. The perfect Halloween would involve friends, food and fear. There would be a cold chill in the air, and the smell of crispness. There would be giggles and screams, and a bit of creeping foreboding to the sun setting. There would be a bright full moon, and the promise of the supernatural.

Halloween seems to be changing from what was so special for me… the feel, the chill, the senses. It has become somewhat melancholy, as I keep looking backward into the autumns or my youth. It seems the innocence of allowing yourself to be scared by folklore and traditions has been replaced by cynicism. I hope that we can get that back for future generations.

SCARE CRED: J. MICHAEL RODDY

J. Michael Roddy began his entertainment career as an actor. His encyclopedic knowledge of pop culture brought him opportunities to write and direct. He has created experiences as a prevalent member of the design team for Universal's Halloween Horror Nights at Universal Studios. During his time there he created and implemented over 100 Haunted attractions and scarzones. He has also created successful shows and attractions for Walt Disney Creative Entertainment including *Star Wars, Frozen, Pixar, Marvel,* and Disney Cruise Line. He is also a Producer of 2011's award-winning documentary – *The Shark is Still Working: The Impact & Legacy of Jaws* and 2017's award-winning *Monsterkids.* In 2018, he won a Rondo Hatton Award for Best Documentary. He recently formed Roddy Creative LLC where he provides creative writing and directing for live shows, attractions, exhibits and marquee events. He is also the creator of *Monsterkids* - a podcast that delves into the positive influence of horror genre on culture. He lives in Central Florida with his wife, two kids, three dogs, and two cats.

IN THE HALLWAYS BELOW

BY EMILY LOUISE RUA

Mom says that we shouldn't play in the abandoned train station, but if we listened to her we'd never have any fun. Sure, there's a big ol' fence surrounding the place with "Do Not Enter" signs in bold red letters hung every few yards, but they're for the adults. If we don't look up, we won't see them. If we don't see them, we don't need to follow the rules – we honestly won't *see* that we are breaking any rules. Besides, if the place really was off limits, they would've patched up the kid-sized hole in the fence long ago. I bet that even my mom fit through the hole once. Maybe she tells us we can't play here because she's mad that she can't go in here anymore.

The jagged end of the fence catches my pants as I squirm under. A little rip and a tear before I wiggle my lower half all the way through. Soon I might be too big to get in. Maybe then I'll side with my mom and yell at all the younger kids to stay away too.

Lindsay and Chad are already bolting towards the side door with the broken window. I'll wait a few more seconds for Phil, Maggie, and Gail, but if they don't hurry up, I'll leave 'em in the dust. Lindsay and Chad always cheat – exploring ahead and finding all the good hiding places first so there's nowhere left when we actually start playing.

Phil and Maggie are through now, we're all just waiting on Gail. No one even wanted to ask her to come along, but her dad makes really cool lanterns. They look way better than normal ol' flashlights – especially for exploring the abandoned train station. We agreed to let her come only if she brought some lanterns. Stupidly, she only brought three. She said that it was all she could carry, so we made her carry 'em the whole way here herself.

She's taking forever – setting each lantern down through the fence, then making sure her dress doesn't get caught on the jagged metal. Who wears a dress while exploring? I finally pull her up and yell at her to get moving. Her dress gets a little dirty in the process, but she seems to want to hang out with us more than cry over the dress, so she follows us as we run to catch up with the rest of the group.

As hard as it is to sneak onto the grounds, getting into the building is super easy. You stick your arm through the broken window – making sure not to nick yourself on the few remaining shards of glass – reach the handle, and open the door. This side door leads into a small dusty hallway the engineers and workers used to get into the building. It isn't nearly as fancy as the grand entrance the passengers came in through, but those heavy doors are always sealed shut on the outside. We tried to open 'em tons of times over the summer, but it's pretty much impossible.

"Do you want me to light the lanterns?" Gail asks eagerly, already reaching for the book of matches in the pocket of her dress.

"No, not yet," Phil snaps, "You'd be wasting everything up here where we can see. Wait for us to go in the basement. With the creepy ghosts!" Phil makes an eerie moan and wiggles his fingers to mimic the ghost he says he saw last summer. Maggie, Chad, Lindsay, and I don't really believe him though. What does he think we are? Five year-olds? Nothing down in that basement scares me. Gail seems scared, though. She would be; she's pretty much a big ol baby.

The hallway is pretty well lit from sunlight peeking through the cracks in the boarded up windows. All you have to be careful of is the shadows on the floor, because they can hide the debris and junk from the decaying building. Last week I tripped on a broken chair leg and cut myself up pretty bad. Mom yelled at me the whole night for getting blood on my new jeans Dad worked so hard to pay for. I had to lie through my teeth and tell her we were playing tag in the park. If she knew I got it here, I'd never be allowed outside again.

We finally make it to the main station entrance. Chad and Lindsay are already there, sitting cross-legged on the floor. Lindsay starts to tsk, "Took you long enough!"

She always has such a snotty attitude. I snap back, "We had to wait for Gail!" I turn to glare at Gail, only half trying to tease her. She lowers her head, more than half ashamed.

"Who cares?" interrupts Chad, "Let's get the game started. Hide and seek. Today we have the lanterns so we are going to go into the basement to play. Since we only have three, we'll split into pairs. Besides, this way Phil will have someone to save him from the ghost!" Phil sticks out his tongue at Chad, unamused.

"Anyways," Chad continues, "Lindsay and I will go together, Maggie will go with..." I cross my fingers. Please be me, please be me, please be me. Chad looks around, drawing out the process, before finally deciding, "... Phil. That leaves Barb with Gail".

Shoot.

Gail smiles and grabs my arm to show everyone that we are now best buddies. I push her away. "Hey," I whine to the others, "if I can't be with one of you, I at least want us to be It first. Okay?" The rest all say, "fine", although it's clear that they're a little grumpy about it.

We make our way to the darkened stairwell that leads down to the lower level. Spider webs and dust line the walls for as far as we can see – which isn't very far, because unlike the upper floors, the basement gets no light from windows. Down there it's as black as a night without the moon. From somewhere down below we hear a loud squeak, much louder than a mouse would make.

Next to me Gail lets out a short shriek, "Rats!" She steps away from the doorway. It figures that I would be paired up with the wimp, but since I'm stuck with her, I try to console her, "Oh come on. Rats are just big mice. You're still way bigger than them. And they're probably scareder of you than you are of them." She presses her lips together as she thinks about what I said, but stays a yard away from the top of the stairs. "Come on, if you don't want to play, that's fine. I'll go down alone". I grab at the lantern, but she pulls it away from my reach.

"No," she murmurs, "I'll go down there. I want to play with you guys." Her hand shakes as she lights the three lanterns and hands the two off to the other pairs. Chad has a sly smile. I bet that he came here yesterday and explored down in the basement on his own. He'll hide somewhere great and we'll never be able to find him. I hate losing to a cheater.

Gail and I turn our backs and begin the count to one hundred. "One, two, three, four..." Behind me I hear the gang's footsteps rush down the stairs. Their giggling gets farther away as they run further into the train station's catacombs. As much as I try, I can't figure out which hallways they might be turning into down there.

"...Sixty-five, Sixty six, sixty seven..." I can hardly hear any scurrying now. Well, except for the rats. They've probably picked their rooms and settled down in one spot. We'll have to search everywhere to find them. Hopefully Gail doesn't chicken out. She's not all bad - she's great at helping with projects at school or building blanket forts in the house, but she's too much of a girly-girl to do the really fun things like this. I bet she'll scream if she sees a bug.

"...Ninety eight, ninety nine, one hundred! Ready or not, here we come!" It's finally time to go down the stairs. I grab the lantern and step down first. Gail puts her hand on my shoulder and follows me into the darkness. The lantern doesn't provide nearly as much light as I thought it would. The tiny flame barely lights the area a foot in front of me. "Can you even see me in front of you with this thing?" I ask Gail.

"Not really," she replies, "You are mostly all dark like a shadow. I've never really played with my father's lanterns before. I didn't exactly tell him that I took these either. This is just our secret, okay?"

"Sure," I say and shrug; it doesn't really make much of a difference to me. We aren't going to break the things, and even if we did, it doesn't matter to me if she gets grounded. We never *forced* her to sneak these things to us – we just said that if she didn't bring them, she couldn't play with us. In the dark I can't see her face, but from her squeal of delight, I bet she's smiling. She gets so excited when she feels like she's one of our group.

There are three different hallways to choose from at the bottom of the stairs. Since I can't see past a yard in front of me, they all look the same. I eeny meeny miny moe and pick the left hallway.

This area is far worse off than upstairs. Big ol' chunks of wall are gone in places, some of the rooms have lost their doors, and rat droppings line the hallway along both sides – it's pretty gross. Gail clings to me, scared of the bugs and critters that may be hiding in every crack or hole in the wall. I peek into one of the rooms and listen for a moment. There's only a bare desk and a couple of wooden chairs in here – no real spaces for two kids to hide. I can't hear any movement or giggles – the room is probably empty.

It's the same with the next room and the next. The fourth room we try is a bit bigger than the rest. It's hard to make out everything with the stupid little lantern. "We gotta go inside," I whisper to Gail. We stop a moment before going in. I'm not scared, but for Gail's sake I'll go nice and slow. It's not normal to go so long in the darkness without seeing or hearing anyone else. Not scary, of course, just weird.

Stepping into the room, I can see an old wooden desk with a chair, rusty filing cabinets, and a dusty blackboard. It must've been someone's office back when the station was up and running. There's a few musty papers on the desk – nothing interesting – but it's odd to think that someone left so suddenly they didn't put away their stuff. My mom yells at me if I leave my toys out for a few hours – she'd be really mad if I left stuff out for years!

Something catches my eye in the corner – a reflection of light from the lantern. There's a brass doorknob. A closet! Aha! I'd bet anything that someone is hiding in there. Once I get them, we'll have two more people searching with us for the last group.

I'd really love to have someone else here in the dark. I mean, for Gail, not for me. I quietly creep up to the door, careful not to make a lot of noise. Oh, it's gonna be so fun to scare 'em down here! My hand touches the doorknob and I prepare to fling the door open and pounce.

Then behind me, Gail screams, "Eeek! It touched me!" She bolts out the door to the hallway and I follow. Oh gosh, oh gosh, oh gosh! Phil was right; ghosts are gonna get us! And then we'll become ghosts ourselves! My heart is pounding as I catch up to Gail, who has stopped a few doorways down and is frantically brushing something off her arm.

"Did you see the ghost?" I ask.

At first she barely seems to notice I said anything. The shock of it all was probably too much. After a few more seconds of rubbing, she finally speaks, "Oh my God! It touched me!"

"What touched you? The ghost?"

"What? No, that spider!" A spider. All that screaming over a tiny little spider? Ugh. I don't even give her time to grab my arm as I head back into the room.

"You are such a baby – do ya know that?" She shuffles back behind me and puts her hand on my shoulder again. "Sorry," she mutters. I don't say anything back to her. We make it back to the closet door, not caring about being quiet this time. The surprise is totally ruined now. No use sneaking up. I turn the knob, open the door, and stick the lantern inside.

Nothing. No kids, no coats, no shoes, barely even any spider webs. All that fuss for absolutely nothing. "They there?" Gail asks, pressing hard into my shoulder as she tries to peer into the closet.

"No," I say, turning and putting the lamp close to her, "at least you didn't ruin the surprise this time. But, if you scream any more, next time we have a sleep-over I'll find a spider and put it on your face while you sleep!" Her eyes open wide and she nods. I doubt she'll scream again now.

Just as I turn to leave the room, I hear a noise from down the hallway. It's very quiet at first, but then it gets a little louder. Somewhere, something is scratching the wall. This isn't like the scurrying of the rats or any other little critter. This is much bigger, almost – kid-sized! We've got em now. They messed up and we're gonna win!

I bring Gail into the hallway and follow the sound. It's coming from somewhere down the end of the hall. As we get closer, the sound stops. We check all the rooms along the way but find no one. There is only one room left: the last room in the hall, behind a closed door. That must be where they are.

Old filing cabinets line the walls to the sides of the door. Gail accidentally stubs her foot on one and it wobbles. She is about to yell from the startle and pain, but remembers my threat and catches herself. Suddenly the cabinet starts to tip forward from the jolt. Gail and I catch it and push it back up before it topples over, but it's sure heavy. These things are really old and beat up – and pretty dangerous. We stay further from the rusty cabinets for the rest of the walk to the door.

When we near the end of the hallway, I step right up, hand Gail the lantern, and push to open the door. It won't budge. "No fair!" I shout, "It's against the rules to hold doors! Open this right now! Let me in! Don't be a cheat, Chad!" Harder and harder I push. "Let me in! Let me in!"

I'm making lots of noise trying to barge in the doorway and soon Gail joins in. I can swear I hear a soft voice – almost a whisper – from the other side of the door. It almost sounds like, "let me out." Did the door get stuck after they went inside? I put my ear against the door and listen, but hear nothing.

I must've been hearing things. Chad and Lindsay are just being cheaters and keeping us from getting in to tag them. Plus everything sounds weird down here; things echo in the hallways and you never can quite tell where any sound comes from. It was probably just the sound of the lantern scraping against the door as Gail helped push.

Finally Gail and I work together and push hard at the same time. The door flies open and we rush the room. "Gotcha!" we scream. We shine the light in all directions, ready to pounce on the others as soon as we catch sight of them. The room isn't very big and doesn't even have any furniture. It isn't a really scary- looking room, but what's scary is that Chad and Lindsay aren't here. No one is.

As usual, Gail states the obvious, "There's no one here!" Was there something we were missing? A hidden door or tunnel for them to escape? I grab the lantern from Gail and start to look closely at the walls. I can't seem to find any secret doors, but there has to be! They can't just disappear. "Barb, if no one's here, who held the door shut? Was it a ghost? What else could do that?" I'll admit that she has a point, but I am not five. Ghosts don't exist and I am not a scaredy-cat.

I examine the door. It's a little bent out of shape from the inside and really scratched up from something (maybe a raccoon or possum), but it's just as covered in dust and cobwebs as everything else in the station. If our friends had been holding the door, there would've been handprints all over it. Then it hits me, "Of course! Look at how beat up this door is – the stupid door was stuck!" Gail looks a little confused, but quickly understands and begins to giggle with me, "All that yelling and it was just a stuck door! Wow, we are silly. I bet the others are laughing their butts off at all the racket we made."

Relieved that we aren't dealing with a ghost or monster, Gail takes the lantern and offers to go first for a bit. There's no chance anyone is hiding in this area. We'll head back down the hallway, past the stairs, and down the corridor to the right. Any noise we heard must've been the building settling or a rat or something.

I follow behind Gail. She was right about not being able to see. She's basically a black shadow and all that's visible is a little area in front of her. For some reason the hairs on the back of my neck begin to stand on end. Has it gotten colder? It was a pretty warm summer day this morning. We pass the stairway. There's only a little light shining halfway down the stairs, had I not been looking up at the walls, I would've missed the stairs completely. It's like a dragon's dungeon down here. We should play that next time we come here; I'll have to tell the others when we find 'em.

This time we walk all the way to the end of the hall and work our way back towards the stairs. The first room is just another office with a moldy couch and a fallen over desk. The second room is a bathroom. It's gross, but Phil and Maggie might be brave enough to hide in there, so we go in. Two stall doors are open, one stall has had its door fall off, and the last stall's door is closed. We'll have to go all the way into the room to see if someone is hiding there.

We past the first stall and I hear a "crunch" beneath my feet. "What was that?" asks Gail, "Do you want me to shine the light down there?"

I think about it for a moment and decide, "No." I didn't see or hear any other glass debris on the floor. If it wasn't glass, I don't want to think about what thing I stepped on - or have Gail freak out again. I'll have to remember to wash the bug guts off my shoe later.

We continue inching forward. Suddenly we hear a faint scratching again – just like from the other hallway – only this time it's clearly coming from the last stall. We have em now!

Gail reaches out her hand to touch the door and quickly pulls her hand away. "Eww," she whispers, "It's all slimy!"

"Just open it," I whisper back, "before they can get away!"

Gail raises up the lantern and reaches out her hand again. This time as her hand nears the door, it opens before she can touch it. The hinges groan as if they haven't been oiled in years and years. I jump forward and push past Gail, "We got ya!"

I fall right into the empty toilet. Even though there's no water, it's completely gross to be covered in dust and dried toilet crud. I'll have to find a way to wash up before I go home, but I don't have time to fret about it now. How can there be no one here? The door was closed, and then it opened! They couldn't have crawled away that fast, especially not without us hearing them run. What's going on here?

The room begins to feel colder. Not from wind, I don't even remember feeling any breezes at all down here – there aren't any windows or air conditioning. The air just seems to have suddenly had all the heat taken out of it.

I pull myself up from the floor and turn to Gail. She doesn't need to state the obvious this time. We both know that something's wrong. Maybe we should get upstairs and yell down to the others that we're done playing for now. Something isn't right here.

We start to walk fast towards the door. From the corner of my eye I think I see something moving behind us in the bathroom mirror. It looks almost like a woman, but too big and shadow-like to be human. Despite my terror, I turn and raise the lantern to try to get a better look.

The creature is in the form of a woman, but its legs twist in unnatural ways and its arms seem too angular. Its dark skin looks slimy and cracked, like a dead bug after you hit it with a fly swatter. Long black hair flows from its head, as if it were caught in a heavy wind, but the air is still around us. I can't see its eyes or face, but as Gail lets out a scream beside me, I see what must be its mouth open wide. Two rows of long silver teeth shine in the lantern light – and they look sharp! This isn't some joke or prank from the others, this isn't even just a white sheet ghost like Phil claims to have seen – this is a monster!

The thing lets out a roar and I can see its gangly arms reach towards us. Gail and I scramble to the doorway and run down the hall. Gail is swinging the lantern wildly as we head back towards the way out. I think we are almost there when in front of me, Gail trips. I don't have enough time to stop, so I fall with her. The lantern's flame goes out as it hits the floor and the glass shatters. Without the light, everything goes black.

"We have to get up Gail," I shout, "Come on!" It's pitch black and I flail trying to find where she has fallen so we can get up and get out. Finally I feel her dress and grab her hand. Her breathing is heavy and she is sweating like me. "Run!" I yell. With no light to guide us, I can only pray that we find the stairs and run up before whatever that thing was gets us. I scream and scream for the others. Gail screams too – our voices echoing through the halls. The sound and blackness is disorienting. It doesn't even sound like Gail's voice is coming from in front of me. If I wasn't hanging onto her hand, I'd be lost in the dark. I can't even see her without the lantern, I'm just going by feel. Gail holds my hand tight as she pulls me forward down the hall. We're running too fast to even waste energy on screams. Heavy breathing and footsteps – that's all I can hear. Our breathing, our steps, and then something else behind us. Something that is getting dangerously close.

How long have we been running? I don't remember being this far from the stairs. Have we missed it? Where are we heading? "Where are the stairs?" I yell to Gail. She keeps running, panting too hard to answer. "We need to get out of here or hide! Keep running Gail, keep running!" Please God, let us make it out alive. I'll listen to Mom, I swear. I'll even wear a dress to church on Sundays. I'll never play here again.

By now I know that we have missed the stairs. We need to find a room to hide in, to lock the creature out. "The door!" I scream, "that big ol door can protect us from it! Run to the end of the hall!"

Gail is running faster now, faster than I ever thought she could. Her hand grips me so hard it hurts and our sweat has pooled together to make our palms slimy. I hope she won't let go, though. Whatever is chasing us is right behind us now. I can only hope that she'll be able to find the doorknob in the dark and be quick enough to open the door and close it behind us before the monster can get in.

Suddenly, we slow down and I hear the big metal door open. We've made it! Gail rushes in and begins to pull me inside. Then something grabs me from behind. It pulls hard. I scream. Gail screams. The monster roars. Everything blends together. I can't even tell where each sound comes from. The sounds come from all around with the echoes. The monster's roar is deafening, sounding like a tiger and a train combined. The thing behind me pulls harder. I slip from Gail's grip and fall backwards away from the door. The thing from behind us runs in front of me, slamming the door closed with a loud thud. Next I hear the cabinet next to the door come crashing down. There is pounding and pounding from behind the door, but the cabinet must be keeping Gail trapped inside.

From down the hallway I hear more pounding movement and a cacophony of loud shouts, more of those things must be coming closer. I try to run, but fall and hit my head. The last thing I remember before I black out is a bright light in my eyes and all the creatures picking me up, ready for the kill.

When I wake up, I'm outside in the field around the train station. It's late afternoon and the sun is shining in my eyes. Am I dead? Probably not – I don't think you're supposed to feel anything when you're dead, and my head still hurts and I taste a little blood. How'd I get out?

I slowly try to sit up, moaning with pain. Gail, Phil, Maggie, and Chad gather around me. All of 'em look worse for wear. Gail's dress is torn in multiple places, Chad and Phil are scuffed up, and Maggie has a cut on her arm.

"Are you alright?" Maggie asks, "We barely made it out. We thought you might be dead!"

Confused, I ask, "How did we make it out? The last thing I remember is being dragged back by the monster and Gail was trapped inside the room."

Maggie looks nervously at the others. None of 'em say anything. Finally, Gail speaks, "It wasn't me in that room."

My heart skips a beat. I was holding her hand as she went in the room. I felt her sweaty palm, her dress. She was dragging me forward as we ran from the monster.

Wasn't she? If it wasn't her, then… The answer hits me and I feel tears running down my cheek. I don't even feel ashamed for blubbering in front of the others. I had been so close to the monster, I touched it. I'm lucky to be alive. I wouldn't be, without Gail.

"As soon as I heard you running, I followed after you," Gail continues, her voice shaky, "I tried to scream to you, but there was too much noise, and then I had to focus on running or else I wouldn't be able to catch up. When I heard the door open, I pulled you back as hard as I could and then slammed up against the door to close it." Gail tugs at the now frayed hem of her dress, still nervous. "Whatever that thing was, it was awful strong, so I knocked over one of those big cabinets to close the door. The others heard our screams and then helped me carry you up the stairs. We got this far out and then had to put you down for a second to catch our breath."

With Chad's help, I get to my feet and give her a hug. For once I don't mind admitting in front of the others that we're friends. I don't think I'll ever have that problem again.

Even though we're far from the building, I want to get out of here – who knows how far those underground hallways go, or what is beneath us right now. I want to see my mom and dad, and I never want to be on this side of the big ol' fence again. We don't talk much more as we make our way back through the hole in the fence and run back to our neighborhood.

I thank Gail one last time for saving me from the monster. I feel bad for all the mean things I said to her earlier. She isn't really that bad after all. She seems to know without me having to get all mushy. We hug one last time and then head our separate ways.

I'll never know for sure what that was down in the train station. Was it a ghost, a monster, something worse? What would have happened if Gail hadn't been strong enough to pull me back? I hope I never have to find out. From now on I'll join my mom in warning the children about going through that hole in the fence. Maybe that thing is the real reason why we're told to stay away. Part of me wants to ask Mom, but I doubt she'd give me the real answer if that was the case; she'd be too afraid of the nightmares it would bring. Ha, nightmares. I'm not sure if I'll ever be able to sleep again. All I can think about is how that thing is still there in that basement, only blocked by a big 'ol filing cabinet, waiting for a new set of brave kids fooling around down there. Waiting for the day it's let out of the basement and can come after me again.

FEAR OF THE DARK

BY EMILY LOUISE RUA

I'm hungry. My stomach grumbles. I should be having a warm meal, but instead I'm sitting in the dark basement waiting to teach my son, Grant, a lesson. For the past two months he has been terrified of the dark – especially our dark basement. Nothing can coax him down the stairs, even when the lightbulb at the foot of the stairs is on. Lately, I have taken to waiting in the shadows at the far edge of the basement, calling to him to join me. I'm determined to end his phobia before the big move to the new house, and I won't eat my damn dinner until he comes down.

"Grant," I begin, "Come on, kiddo. All you have to do is start with one step, then another. I'm down here – there's nothing to be afraid of."

I see him framed in the cellar doorway looking down into the basement. His light blonde hair is backlit by the sunlight coming through the windows in the kitchen. I don't know exactly what time it is – I've been down here for a while – but it's summer, so even this late in the day it is bright outside.

Grant's feet are firmly planted on the first-floor landing. Of course, after all these days of pleading, I didn't actually believe he would just run down on the first ask, but it was worth a try. I switch tactics for my next attempt: "The sooner you come on down, the sooner we can do something fun. If you hurry up, we can even go outside and play baseball. You'd like that, wouldn't you?"

I can see Grant perk up. Baseball is his favorite. We would spend hours throwing the ball back and forth in our backyard. Next year he'll be eligible for the minor league division Little League team in our neighborhood. I can tell he'll be a fantastic pitcher - the boy has quite an arm.

"Daddy," he calls out, timidly, "Let's just go play now. I promise I'll come down later if you play catch with me now."

"That's what you said yesterday," I reply. "I need you to come downstairs now." I pause instead of saying any more. I can see Grant is unsure of himself and considering what to do. My stomach growls loudly – it always seems to do that in silent moments.

Everything is in boxes down here, packed up for the move. I don't have much to work with to entice him. On the ground I find one of his baseballs – he always leaves them around the house. I can't count the number of times I've yelled at him for his carelessness, but today I'm happy to have one so close by. "I have an idea," I start, "Let's play catch down here. I'll throw the ball to you and you toss it back. How does that sound?"

Grant nods eagerly. I toss him the baseball. He catches it and throws it back to me with perfect accuracy, even though I'm in the far corner of the basement. That kid could make it to the pros someday. What an arm! We go back and forth a dozen or so times. With each throw he seems less scared of the darkness.

Then the second phase of my plan. I begin to throw it short, making him reach out further and further to catch the ball. Finally, he takes one step down the stairs to complete the catch. One step down, twelve to go.

A toss or two later, Grant stops before lobbing the ball back to me. "Daddy," he asks gingerly, "are you still mad at me?"

I sigh, knowing what he is referring to - early May. Even though I had spent all day telling him to put away his toys, he still left one of his baseballs out on the stairs. I've never been a man to yell or scream, but that day… well, I hadn't been proud of my response. I remember my foot rolling off the baseball, frantically grabbing for the handrail but missing, and hearing crack after crack as I tumbled down the stairs before hitting the cement. On the way down, I screamed and yelled, louder than I ever believed I could. I was furious at Grant's carelessness. I can still see his face twisted in sheer terror and devastation. No parent wants to invoke that in their child. I certainly don't look forward to it happening again, but I am hungry and if I don't eat soon…

"No," I say at last, rubbing my still sore leg with my good arm, "No, I'm not mad anymore." My stomach growls, "But, I am going to be very grumpy if I don't get my dinner." I laugh a little to put him at ease.

Grant looks relieved and his mouth curves in a slight smile. He takes another step down (eleven more steps to go). "I'm scared Daddy."

Not this again. "There's no need to be afraid. I'm here. There is nothing else down here – except maybe some more of your baseball gear." I smile, though I doubt he can see much of it in the dark.

Grant dips his foot down to the next step, balancing on one leg instead of putting any weight on it. "Mommy says I shouldn't be scared either, but she says she understands. When we move next week, Mommy says the new house won't even have a basement. Everything is on the same floor, she says." He lifts his foot back to the step he was balancing on. "Daddy, will you come with us when we move?"

"Of course," I lie. There's no need to worry him yet. I still have time. My wife and I have had a strained relationship for longer than I'd like to admit. She claimed I neglected her, spending my time prepping Grant for a life of baseball instead of being a husband. We fought often, usually ending with her accusing me of pressuring the boy to athletically perform instead of letting him enjoy his childhood. She never wanted this big house, this "lonely life" – as she called it – and the incident in May had been the last straw. She will take Grant away from here and I'll be alone. This week is my last chance with the boy.

Suddenly, I have a new idea. "But, you know," I start, "I can't leave here unless you come get me. I'll be stuck here forever and you'll leave without me."

"Why?" Grant asks, concerned.

"Because my leg and arm are still sore and I can't climb up the stairs alone. I need you to be brave and help me out. Please son," I add for effect, "I really need you now. If you do this, it will make up for leaving your ball on the stairs. Everything will be alright again. You, me, your mom – we'll all go out for ice cream. Wouldn't that be nice?"

It may have been wrong to use his anxieties against him, but the results sometimes justify the means. He needs to overcome his fear – and I need to eat my dinner.

"It can be just like it used to be?" He asks, hopeful.

"Yes."

For the first time in weeks, I finally believe I have gotten through to him. He takes a big breath and begins to shakily climb down the stairs.

Ten to go.

Nine.

Eight.

Seven.

Six.

Five.

Four – so close now I could almost grab him. It's almost done, and I'll get my dinner before sunset.

Three.

Two.

"Grant!" A voice calls out from the kitchen, "Grant! Get up here right now!" My wife appears in the doorway and Grant quickly climbs back up the stairs into her open arms.

Damn it – we were so close!

"What were you doing down there, Honey?" She asks, holding him in a tight embrace.

"I was playing with Daddy," My wife gives him a squeeze and he continues, "We were playing catch on the stairs. He says that I just have to get over my fear of the dark and we can all be a family again. Everything will be alright. Nothing will be my fault."

I can't fully see her face, but I hear my wife's voice quiver in response, "Oh Honey. None of this is your fault, but nothing can make things go back to the way they were. I am so happy you feel like your dad is still here – I feel him too – but when he tripped down the stairs back in May, well… he went to heaven. Do you understand?"

I hate it when she brings that up.

Grant looks back down towards where I am hiding before replying, "He's dead, but he still comes back to play with me. He's just down there in the dark. Maybe you can come with me and we'll bring him back upstairs."

Months ago, seeing my wife giving Grant a comforting embrace would have filled me with joy. Now, it just intensifies my unrelenting hunger.

My wife follows Grant's gaze towards my corner. I retreat a little further into the shadows, but I doubt she would have seen me in my previous spot – I'm as adept at camouflage now as Grant is at tossing to third base from the outfield. Both of them coming down wouldn't be ideal, but I think I could make it work.

I'd get my dinner.

a few words from

EMILY LOUISE RUA

As a designer of horror theatre or experiences, explain your process.

Whether I am writing a film, planning a convention, or designing a Halloween yard display, I focus on creating a coherent "world" for the viewer or attendee to experience. For film, I make sure all elements of set design and costuming reflect the characters and story in subtle ways. Character motivations must be consistent as well. For live events every booth, panel, class, and attraction must fit the overall theme of the event (no timeshare vendors at a Halloween convention). I want my creative endeavors to take attendees out of the normal everyday world and into something unusual and fantastic. There should not be any element of the experience that feels out of place or unnatural in the setting.

When is the last time you were genuinely scared by something someone created?

I believe I am the world's biggest scaredy-cat; I think I love horror because it can affect me so strongly. The most recent film I viewed that terrified me was *The Autopsy of Jane Doe*. It is an amazing slow-burn of a film that uses a tense atmosphere to set up anticipation for the chaos that occurs over halfway into the film. I love films where supernatural horrors terrorize people who just happen to be in the wrong place at the wrong time. I begin to wonder if I may soon be in such a situation as well. What will I see the next time I walk down my long, dark hallway at night?

Tell us about your contribution to our book. What was the inspiration?

Fear of what lays in wait for us in the dark is universal and timeless. I vividly remember always closing the basement door when I was alone as a child because I was certain that if I did not, something would slowly creep up the stairs to capture me and drag me down into the abyss. I thankfully do not have a basement right now, but still occasionally get that feeling when the closet door is left open or I am passing by an abandoned building. My tales concern those childhood fears and how opening those doors can lead to terrifying encounters.

What do you love about the genre of horror?

Horror unites us. Although the specifics of what scares us may differ, fear is universal. When you go to a movie theater to see a horror film, if someone screams or lets out nervous laughter, it is infectious. We get to confront the dark side of humanity and the unknown together but survive (even if our screen counterparts do not).

What is some of your favorite horror literature? Favorite author?

I love collections of short stories - from Alvin Schwartz's *Scary Stories to Tell in the Dark,* to Neil Gaiman's *Fragile Things*. Other volumes that hold a special place in my heart are *The Monster's Corner (edited by Christopher Golden),* John Collier's *Fancies and Goodnights*, and any of the manga compilations of Junji Ito's work. For novels, I love teen horror written by R.L. Stine (*Fear Park* Trilogy), Christopher Pike (*Whisper of Death* and *Gimme a Kiss*), and L.J. Smith (*The Forbidden Game* Trilogy).

What is your favorite Halloween treat?

Reese's Peanut Butter Cups are the way to my heart.

You are hosting the perfect Halloween movie marathon. What are the films you choose and why?

My favorite types of films to watch in a group have a mixture of spookiness and humor. For Halloween, I would choose some classics and personal favorites that feature the holiday. We'd start with the family-friendly films of *Hocus Pocus, Ernest Scared Stupid,* and *The Halloween Tree,* and then end the night with the adult-oriented *Trick R' Treat* and (a cult favorite among my Movie Night friends) *Satan's Little Helper.*

Describe the perfect Halloween.

Autumn leaves line the sidewalk and scatter across my front yard. As the sun sets, my neighbors and I light up our yard displays and come to our porches to greet the processions of ghouls and goblins. As I pass out treats to the costumed hooligans, I can smell pumpkin pie and bonfires in the distance. Before bed, I celebrate the Halloween traditions of yore with a few divination games and retelling of scary stories with my loved ones. At the end of the evening, I fall asleep cuddled with my (mostly) black cats, eager for the day-after-Halloween shopping spree.

SCARE CRED: EMILY LOUISE RUA

When most young girls wanted to be veterinarians or princesses, Emily wanted to be a vampire slayer and horror movie hostess. While she continues to hunt vampires in her spare time, she has pursued her interest in horror films, receiving a B.A. in Cinema-Television from the University of Southern California and working on various films and web series. In the upcoming horror anthology film Nine Ways to Hell, Emily both directs and stars in the "Gluttony" segment. Emily also works in the events industry, coordinating many horror/Halloween conventions and film festivals in the Los Angeles area. Her past events include ScareLA, Screamfest Horror Film Festival, HauntX, and many more!

ONE SUMMER NIGHT IN CHEROKEE

BY MATTHEW SANDERSON

In the summer of 2014, I travelled to the United States from the United Kingdom to propose to my wife-to-be, Tiffany. We originally met back in 2006 when we both attended a convention in Florida where we were both pretending to be vampires. It was a live-action roleplaying game convention – but putting it that way always makes us chuckle and it usually makes the listener do a bit of a double-take. Over time, our relationship grew and eventually I plucked up the courage to ask her to marry me. It only took eight years – a fact she often reminds me of.

In the lead-up to the big day, I arranged to spend a couple of weeks with Tiffany. She was living in North Carolina at the time and wanted to take me to some of the places she had visited when she was growing up. Her parents often took her camping in the Great Smoky Mountains around Cherokee and she knew the place well. We rented a car and she drove us out there. I made sure I carried the ring I intended to give her was discretely kept on me at all times, or at the very least within arm's reach. There was no way I was going to lose it just days before the proposal!

Rather than camping (as Tiffany knew I liked my creature comforts) we decided that our plan was to find a room at one of the many Bed and Breakfast establishments on Tsali Boulevard (Highway 441) that headed north from the center of Cherokee. Many of these backed onto the banks of the Oconaluftee River where Tiffany had frequently played during her childhood visits. Even though Tiffany was adamant that finding a room would be easy, we drove past one sign after another that all declared the same thing – "No Vacancy".

As we came to the end of what we thought were all of our options, we passed a hotel on the left-hand side of the road. It was part of a chain of hotels seen all across the country and certainly stood out compared to all the other buildings we'd seen on the road up until this point. Three-stories tall, all the front-facing rooms appeared to have balconies that flanked the main entrance in the middle of the building. Its grand appearance implied it might be expensive, but it was apparent it was our only option at that point.

Tiffany was a little disappointed that the hotel wasn't closer to the river, as it stood on the opposite side of the road, but nevertheless we pulled into the car park and within minutes had secured a room. It was a little more expensive than we'd budgeted for compared to the rates for a typical Bed and Breakfast, but our room was spacious and comfortable. There wasn't anything that would call "special" about the room. It was a standard hotel room layout. The bathroom was immediately next to the main door, it was pretty normal in every respect. We had two large beds to choose from and a large TV on the opposite wall. As far as I was concerned, it was money well spent.

After dropping our bags off in the room, we took a drive to one of the places in Cherokee that she knew I wanted to visit – the local casino. I've always enjoyed a game of poker and consider myself to be a moderately good Texas hold 'em player and had put aside some money specifically for the occasion. We spent a while waiting for a seat to become available at one of the tables but eventually my time came.

Lady luck was on my side that night and an Ace-high flush on the river earned me a $505 pot when several players had gone all-in ahead of me. That paid for the car rental, the hotel and left us with a little spending money for the next couple of days. We left the casino on a high note and went back the hotel. It had been a long day by that point and we were both ready for some rest.

What happened a few hours later has remained vividly in my memory ever since that night. I suspect it will remain that way until the day I die. Terror has a very acute way of making a lasting impression.

Having set the scene, I now want to take the opportunity to reassure you, dear reader, that I am not a person that has a history of "seeing things". In fact, the only time I ever hallucinated was in 2007. I'd flown out to Tombstone, Arizona, to take part in a poker game that was being held by the live-action roleplaying game society that both me and Tiffany were members of. Luck was nowhere to be found that night. Not only did the cards hate me, but I was rather ill throughout the trip, having picked something up from a visitor to the office where I worked a few days before I flew out to the States.

When I eventually got home, I was diagnosed with borderline pneumonia and spent much of the next couple of weeks in bed recovering. However, in Tombstone, with that diagnosis still a couple of days away and no medication to help me through the night after the poker game, I had a terrible fever and could hardly sleep. With the same vivid recollection of what happened that night in Cherokee, I remember my hallucination in that motel room in Tombstone. The door silently opened and a procession of five figures in hooded robes, their arms crossed in front of them entered the room. The third figure, the one in the middle of the row of five, held a huge block of ice on a purple pillow in front of him. The figure held it in much the same way one would carry a crown to a coronation. The five figures glided silently through the room and into the bathroom, and that was the last I saw of them.

I remember how ill I was that night in Tombstone. Thankfully, I haven't been that ill since, and I was certainly in good health when me and Tiffany visited Cherokee, so I cannot explain away what I saw in the hotel room as being a fever-dream or hallucination.

It was the middle of the night when I woke. I suspect it was the result of Tiffany moving beside me. A movement at the end of the bed caught my eye. Tiffany was there, naked, her long dark hair flowing down her back. She was looking away from me so I couldn't see her face, and she was walking casually towards the bathroom. She went inside the bathroom, which I thought at the time was a little odd. There was a bit of light coming through the curtains from outside, as we had a front-facing room, but it couldn't have been enough to see by in the bathroom.

The bed was comfortable and now that Tiffany had gone to the bathroom, I had it all to myself. I stretched out my arms to both sides of me, hoping to enjoy the space for a few moments. While my left arm dangled off the edge of the bed, my right arm hit something hard. At first, I thought it was the bunched-up duvet, or perhaps a very hard pillow, but quickly I realized it couldn't be, it was too hard to be either of those. In the dim light, I could see Tiffany's sleeping face pointed towards me as she still lay in bed. My right arm had collided with her elbow.

The question came into my mind no more than a second later, as I sat wide-eyed in bed, looking towards the bathroom door: who had I seen at the end of my bed?

The rational part of me quickly started to analyze what was happening. I had only thought it was Tiffany because the figure had similarly long hair. From behind, in the dark, that had been an easy assumption to make (especially as it was only supposed to be the two of us in the room!). But it had to be *someone* as I had *definitely* seen them. This wasn't a figment of my imagination or the confusion of some half-formed dream with reality in the moment of my waking from slumber. I was positive that I had seen someone in our room, and that person was now in our bathroom, waiting in the dark.

I don't know exactly how long I lay in bed, gripped by terror, staring at the open bathroom door, waiting for someone (or something) to emerge from the darkness. My mind raced with other questions. What if it was someone that had broken into the room to rob us? I couldn't see my wallet in the dark. Had they gone through it and taken the winnings from the poker game? Maybe it was someone that heard us talking about it when we got back to the hotel and had waited until we were both asleep to finally make their move? But, if that was the case, why were they naked? It didn't make any sense – no-one breaks into a hotel room naked. Likewise, what kind of burglar hides in the bathroom when they've been seen, putting them in a position with no way out? Surely, they would have made straight for the main door and run out. It didn't make any sense, but all the time I kept thinking that they were still in the bathroom.

Running through the various possibilities and discounting them, one by one, I finally settled upon one explanation that I couldn't build a strong enough counter-argument for. What if the figure I had seen had been a ghost? It seemed ridiculous at first. As far I could tell, the building looked pretty new. When we pulled up, the exterior looked bright and fresh with no sign of wear and tear. The rooms were tidy, the corridors showed no signs of age. Weren't hauntings supposed to happen in old places, places with history? That said, how many people had passed through this hotel over the years? I read somewhere once that deaths in hotels were not as rare as people think. How many had potentially died here? Was this a guest that had checked in and never left?

Once that thought had entered my mind, I couldn't get it out again. I just lay there, hoping that whatever (rather than whoever) was in the bathroom stayed there. If I'd had the courage, I should have got up to turn on the light and see for myself if there was anything in there, but I simply couldn't move.

Eventually, tiredness must have taken its toll and I fell back to sleep. When I woke the next morning, strengthened by the sunlight pouring through the window, I found my wallet untouched with all the winnings from the casino still present, and the bathroom was completely empty. The main door was still locked and the door guard latch still in place. It seemed pretty obvious to me; no-one had come through that door besides us last night.

When Tiffany was awake, I told her about what I had seen during the night. She replied, saying that she had woken up at some point as well, only to find a native woman standing beside the bed, looking down at her through long dark hair. There wasn't any look of hostility in her face, Tiffany said, she was just looking at her in bed. I was stunned and still am not quite sure what to make of it, even after the years that have passed. Could it really have been the same figure? After all, I never saw their face, but the long hair sounded the same.

We stayed in the hotel for a second night after visiting various places in the area Tiffany wanted to show me. Even though I spent what seemed like hours staring into the dark, scared of what might appear again, much to my relief, nothing happened that night. When we finally checked out, Tiffany asked the member of staff at the front desk if they had ever had any guests report any ghost sightings to them. The member of staff was perplexed but shook their head, saying that they weren't aware of any. I still remember Tiffany's excited reply to that before she went on to explain: "Well, you have one now!"

A few days later, we travelled to the Fort Raleigh National Historic Site, the location of the famous Roanoke Colony. In the Elizabethan Gardens there, I finally gave Tiffany the ring I'd been carrying around with me all the time around Cherokee. We married early the following year and have been happy together ever since – especially as neither of us has seen anyone else standing at the end of our bed or looking at us when we've woken up in the middle of the night.

a few words from

MATTHEW SANDERSON

As a designer of horror theatre or experiences, explain your process.

In my opinion, there are several core elements that can form the foundation of a tabletop horror roleplaying game scenario: an antagonist (e.g. a monster, a manic killer, an evil cultist, etc.); the setting (being a combination of the physical location as well as the time period); or something that has otherwise inspired the author, such as an event (e.g. a murder), or an item (e.g. a cursed doll), etc.

When one of these elements appeals to me strongly enough that I feel a story can be crafted around it, I start to think about how it could relate to the other core elements. For example, it makes sense for a scenario pitting the players against sea monsters to take place somewhere near or on the ocean, rather than in the middle of a dessert.

The rest of the story grows organically from there. The important thing about writing a scenario is to keep in mind that the players should be the stars of the story. It's my job as the writer to present as many opportunities as possible to unnerve, scare and terrify them from the start all the way to whatever climax they may reach. That's what makes it a "horror" game after all!

When is the last time you were genuinely scared by something someone created?

Honestly, I scare easily! That said, I detest jump scares. I much prefer spooky imagery and atmosphere above cheep shocks. The last time I think I experienced a genuine scare was when I went to watch *The Lady in Black* at the theatre. There is an incredible difference between watching a horror story in the safety of your own home, with a TV screen between you and the story, and being present when the story is physically unfolding around you. The stage production includes character walking through the audience, putting you within reach of the action, and some set-pieces that are chilling just to even remember. For me, it's the closest thing to being "real" and "intense" as it gets.

I won't soon forget the image of a rocking chair moving on its own in one scene, only to appear again later with the eponymous woman in black sitting in it as it moves, then rising in one fluid motion out of the chair and walking across the stage.

Tell us about your contribution to our book. What was the inspiration?

My contribution is taken from real-life. It's an event that occurred to me (and my wife, although she was blissfully asleep throughout the whole thing) and is the one time in my life that I was the most scared I have ever been. While part of me can think of a rational explanation to explain what happens, there's still enough doubt in my mind that it was something far from mundane.

What is some of your favorite horror literature? Favorite Author?

My favorite horror author is definitely James Herbert. What appeals to me so much about his work is that while all his books were horror, he interwove elements of other genres to provide a different feeling to a lot his books. *The Spear* includes elements of a spy thriller. *The Fog* has a disaster movie-like quality. *Shrine* has a distinctly religious theme. *Domain* is post-apocalyptic.

Herbert wrote my all-time favorite novel, *Haunted*. It's a fairly short book, but one that packs a lot in between its covers. As the title suggests, it's a ghost story, about a parapsychologist that debunks claims of hauntings. Without spoiling it for those that haven't read it (to whom I wholeheartedly recommend this book!), it has a twist that is unlike any other ghost story I've read, and one that puts it head and shoulders above the rest for me. Echoing what I wrote above about why I love horror so much – I live for those moments when the rug gets pulled out from under me, and *Haunted* does exactly that.

Describe the perfect Halloween.

It would have to be a ghost hunt for me. There's plenty of places that claim to be haunted in the area here, and several of then run ghost hunts overnight on Halloween. What better night of the year is there to try and experience a piece of the paranormal? Of course, if a spirit decided to appear, and my camera was able to capture the image… well, that would be the icing on the cake.

SCARE CRED: MATTHEW SANDERSON

Mathew Sanderson is a freelance author who has been writing for horror roleplaying games since 2012. To date, he has worked on more than 20 books for popular game lines including *Call of Cthulhu*, *Kult: Divinity Lost*, *Vampire the Masquerade* and *Fear Itself* among others. He can often be found at UK gaming conventions, running games to scare his players to the best of his abilities. Matthew lives in the UK with his loving wife, Tiffany, and a growing flock of adorable birds and chickens.

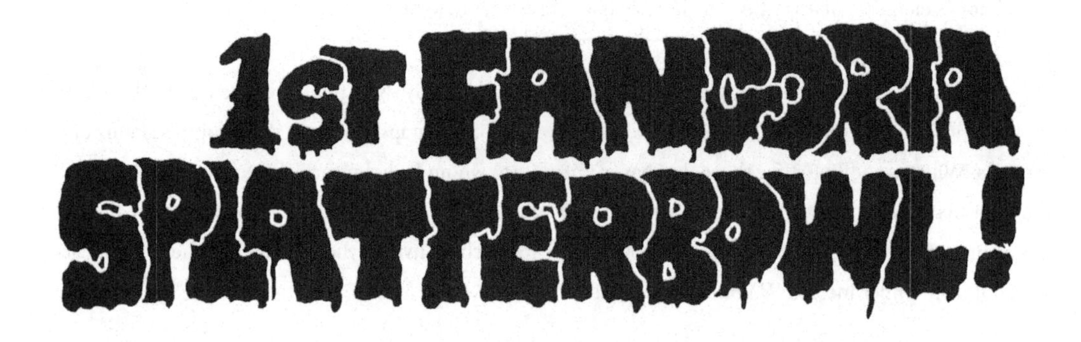

BY LINWOOD SASSER
& JOHN ARNOLD

HEY THERE, FANGO-FIENDS! THIS IS YOUR VERY OWN UNCLE BOB, BROADCASTING LIVE ON ASSIGNMENT FROM CAMP SLEEPAWAY IN TEXARKANA, ARKANSAS WHERE MICHAEL MYERS AND JASON VOORHEES ARE APPROACHING THE FINAL ELIMINATION ROUND, HAVING WADED THROUGH A HOST OF COMPETITORS AND-OH- ABOUT THIRTY-TWO HELPLESS VICTIMS IN THIS, THE
1st FANGORIA SPLATTERBOWL!

CHOMK!
JASON'S NOT EVEN WAITING FOR THE BELL! A BRUTAL THREE-QUARTER AXE SPIN INTO THE UPPER SHOULDER OF THE SHAPE!
DON POST
YOWP! THE SHAPE IS QUICK TO COUNTER WITH HIS PATENTED LARYNX-CRUSH NECK-HOLD...
...AND WE HAVE AN INSERTION! AND AN EXIT WOUND! MARVELOUSLY ENGINEERED EFFECT!
GOSH-ALL-HEMLOCK, FIGHT FANS! JASON HAS SLIPPED AWAY NOW AND IS STUFFING HIS INTERNAL ORGANS... BACK... ICK! OBVIOUSLY PREPARING...
FOR A COUNTER-STRIKE...
AMAZING TENACITY!
WHOOP! HE'S BACK WITH A... A... GOOD LORD! IT'S A DEEP FAT FRIER!!
LIL' FRIER
WOTTA COMEBACK! JASON'S GOT MYERS ON THE ROPES... HE'S DOIN' THE SHAKIN' SHAPE STAGGER!!
JASON SEEMS PREOCCUPIED WITH SOME SORT OF SHARP GADGET...
WOW! IT'S A BARBED WIRE BOLO! THE FLESH IS REALLY FLYING NOW!

THE SHAPE IS ON THE CARPET!!
STOMP
RASH
REND
AND -OWCH! IT LOOKS LIKE JASON IS AIMING TO KEEP HIM THERE!
YESSIR, WE'RE REALLY SEEING SOME WILD DIVERSITY IN METHODS TODAY... GAG CHOKE
REEK! RAAK! REEK!
OWP! AN UNEXPECTED TURN OF EVENTS! IT APPEARS THAT ONE OF THE "VOLUNTEER VICTIMS" FROM STARLOG'S "MEET THE ENTERPRISE" CONTEST ESCAPED THE EARLIER SLAUGHTER!
TREK LIVES!
AH... EXCUSE ME, SIR SNORT BUT THAT MASK YOU HAVE ON RESEMBLES THAT OF AN UNUSED DESIGN OF TH' ENTERPRISE ENGINEERING CREW...
REEEE! REEE! REEE!
HORROR HORN
HSS! HSS!
PANT PANT PANT
OOPS!

WOW! WHAT A SOCKO FINISH! JASON SHOULD'VE TAKEN A LESSON FROM HIS OWN FINE FILMS: "NEVER TURN YOUR BACK ON THE PSYCHOPATH!" AN OBJECT LESSON FOR THE YOUNGSTERS IN THE AUDIENCE!
AND NOW... ON TO THE KITCHEN FOR PLENTY OF MUNCHIES AND ONE BIG SURPRISE!!
MEEEEEK! MEEMEENIE MEEKEENIE! MEEEEK!
THAT'S RIGHT! IT'S LEATHERFACE, 250 LBS. OF PURE MALICIOUS MAYHEM! PURVEYOR OF PEERLESS, PRICELESS PSYCHOTIC SLICING 'N' DICING!! CANNIBAL, KILL-CRAZY FOOL WHO... WHO... SAY BWAH... BETTER GET THAT CHAINSAW HUMMIN'!
MEEEK! MEEEK! MEMEMEME MEEEE!
YANK
PRUT
YANK
PRUT
YANK
PRUT

OWCH! WE SEEM TO HAVE A PROBLEM HERE!
TUC! PRUT TUC! PRUT
SLASH!
HAVE YOU CHECKED THE OIL LATELY? ENOUGH GAS?
TUC!
COULD IT BE IN THE IGNITION?
TUC! CHUK!
WELP, THAT ABOUT WRAPS IT UP FOR THE FIRST ANNUAL SPLATTERBOWL! FINAL SCORE: SHAPE 34, PIECES O' MEAT ZIP!
SO THIS IS ADIOS FROM YOUR UNCLE BOB! -OH YEAH- AND DON'T CRY FOR ME, ARGENTINA... Y'SEE, I FIGURED THAT ONE OF THESE BOYS WAS BOUND TO GET FRISKY EVENTUALLY...
... BUT NOT TO WORRY...
SOME THING IS BOUND TO SAVE ME!
NYUK!! NYUK!!

a few words from

LINWOOD SASSER

As an artist or writer, explain your process.

John Arnold and I had a common background, loving horror in films, literature and comics. When *Fangoria* announced their contest, we were excited to give it a go. The challenge was to write a story or comic depicting Michael Myers Vs. Jason Voorhees. We knocked out the basic story and started to work on the panels. John would pencil and ink. I was the colorist. We bounced gags and dialogue off each other and generated the surprise ending. We were both big fans of *John Carpenter's The Thing*, so it practically wrote itself. Having Uncle Bob Martin as a commentator pretty much assured us of getting our entry noticed. Months after we sent the pages in, I bought issue #39 off the stands and was floored to see that we had won the contest. A few days later we received formal notice from *Fango* and a few copies of the issue. I still find it amazing that *Fangoria* devoted a good portion of their few color pages to our little comic.

When is the last time you were genuinely scared by something someone created?

All the time from shocks and surprises in films and attractions, but it's that lingering fear of the unimaginable that's harder to come by. Dead & Buried, a creepy little movie written by Alien scribe, Dan O'Bannon, comes to mind. There's a scene where rescue workers survey the scene of smoldering, flipped over, VW van, that has only one charred occupant. The burned remains are horrible enough, but when the "corpse" opens it's mouth and screams, that's shock, followed by the horror of the man's situation. A tip of the hat to Stan Winston for that nightmare effect.

Tell us about your contribution to our book. What was the inspiration?

Early Mad Comic books, not magazines. John and I always admired the amount of information and anarchy that artists like Wally Wood, Jack Davis and Will Elder could cram into the background of their panels. We really paid homage to that in our second strip for *Fango*, Suckerswamp.

What do you love about the genre of horror?

I guess I'm attracted to the type of horror that is possible, but unlikely to occur in my personal life. Be it grand old tales of terror and the supernatural or speculative fiction, based on dark reflections of our modern world.

You are hosting the perfect Halloween movie marathon. What are the films you choose and why?

Candyman. Tony Todd scared the hell out my two girls and me when we saw this one. There's also something romantically poetic about this first film. *Les Yeux Sans Visage* or *Eyes Without A Face*. Creepy and unsettling. The contrast between the B&W cinematography of the horrifying surgical scenes and the dreamlike interludes in which we follow Christiane, as she lives her life masked, conveying all emotion only through her eyes. Truly haunting. *Abbott & Costello Meet Frankenstein*. A good palette cleanser after *Eyes*. Excellent pace, makeup, sets, special effects, Lugosi as Dracula and Bud & Lou, still engaged in what they're doing. A respectful farewell to all of Universal's beloved, iconic creatures and funny too. Then time for bed, Roddy. I'm not staying up all night, even on Halloween.

If you could continue any horror story (book or film), what would it be?

Being a massive fan of the classic Universal horror films, I'd love a proper sequel to any one of their series. *The Monster Squad* came close, but was a tad juvenile. Universal's Dark Universe turned out to be a bust. I guess I should be grateful for Jeff Rovin's novel, *Return of The Wolfman*, a direct continuation/ sequel to *Abbott & Costello Meet Frankenstein*. It has its faults, but is, overall, a good read and a pleasant time spent with old fiends.

Describe the perfect Halloween.

I'd begin about a week before by attending a party dressed as whatever strikes my fancy. A Ghostbuster, Batman '66, a demon, or a masked Luchador Mexicana. Getting to see what other guests come up with is a big part of the fun. Winning a costume contest, in recognition of my effort, would cap it off nicely. The perfect Halloween night, for me, is staying home. I would decorate my house and entry way, in traditional spooky lighting, cobwebs, animated bats, skulls, and crawly things. Music from classic horror films plays in the background. Answering the door in a not-too-scary costume and giving out handfuls of candy. Acting scared of the little monsters and telling the little princesses, mermaids and super heroines how pretty they are. That's the Halloween I look forward to, now that I'm an old guy.

SCARE CRED: LINWOOD SASSER

Besides being a coauthor of *Fangoria*'s much beloved comic strips, *Splatterbowl* and *Suckerswamp*, you may also have seen him perform as Jake Blues, Oliver Hardy, W.C.Fields or Jurassic Park's John Hammond, at Universal Studios Florida from 1991 until 2001. He currently tours the country with John Mueller's Winter Dance Party, a recreation of the final show performed by Buddy Holly, Ritchie Valens and The Big Bopper. Linwood Sasser graduated from the Florida State University School Of Theater a long time ago, in a state far, far away. He has been directed by Steven Spielberg, Tom Hanks, Bob Goldthwaite and Alex Winter. Though born in the Panama Canal Zone, Linwood currently resides in Simi Valley, CA and works as an actor in Los Angeles.

a few words from

JOHN ARNOLD

When is the last time you were genuinely scared by something someone created?

The last film that actually gave me a nightmare was David Robert Mitchell's *It Follows* (2014). It avoided the usual story-telling mistakes we get in modern horror – not fully explaining the manifestation except as a sort of sexual bogeyman and gave us likable, fairly smart characters fleshed out enough to really embrace and care about.

Tell us about your contribution to our book. What was the inspiration?

My pal Linwood Sasser and I were both huge horror fans that met at Florida State University. He was staying with my wife and I shortly after our marriage in Lake Charles, Louisiana in August 1984 when we discovered that *Fangoria* magazine – the '80s replacement for Warren's *Famous Monsters* and Calvin Beck's *Castle of Frankenstein* magazines – put forth a challenge for the readership to create a "Battle of the Titans" sort of comic strip for *Fango* with Jason Vorhees facing off against Michael Myers or somesuch. Linwood and I had been submitting cartoons to various seedy men's magazines and suffering rejection slips and this struck us as something fun, as we were both raised on *Creepy*, *Eerie*, *Mad*, and *Cracked* magazines. We knocked it out over a few days, co-writing it. I drew it, inked it, and did the lettering, but I'm afraid that it looks somewhat empty without Linwood's really splendid colors and shading; your readers should seek out the color scans online for a view of the project in its printed glory.

What do you love about the genre of horror?

I think the feeling of being trapped – of trying to survive against an overwhelming force – is at the core of many of my favorite films: *Night of the Living Dead*, *Dawn of the Dead*, Carpenter's The Thing, Robert Wise's The Haunting, and particularly the non-horror classics *Zulu* (1964) and *Davy Crockett: King of the Wild Frontier* (1955) with Crockett and company cornered in the Alamo, which devastated me as a child.

What is some of your favorite horror literature? Favorite Author?

I love Stephen King and the great stable of EC writers of the 1950s, but the guy that really stands out to me as I get older is the late, great Archie Goodwin whose perfectly-spun little six-page stories in the early Creepy and Eerie magazines – illustrated by most of the former EC bullpen greats like Reed Crandall, Wally Wood, John Severin, Alex Toth, Angelo Torres and so on – fueled my horror engine for much of my life.

What are some of your influences?

All of the artists above – who are terrible as aspirational material because of their greatness. Not sure we'll have another John Severin, ever, and Reed Crandall's work was beautiful in any genre he attempted.

What is your favorite Halloween treat?

Hand-made popcorn sugary confections made by the mystery lady down the street. Sweetly dangerous.

You are hosting the perfect Halloween movie marathon. What are the films you choose and why?

I'd expect a party atmosphere, so really intense or cerebral horror films – most of my top ten, certainly – would all be out in favor of "fun horror": *Army of Darkness* (1992), *Drag Me to Hell* (2009), *Creepshow* (1982), *Poltergeist* (1983), and *Lifeforce* (1985) would all be strong contenders.

If you could continue any horror story (book or film), what would it be?

I would politely decline, because sequels suck. Try to name truly great sequels and you'll end up with no more than a handful and the number of decent horror films reduced to dreary crap is too many to count.

Describe the perfect Halloween.

You have to be maybe ten years old, with friends and family, going around your old neighborhood.

SCARE CRED: JOHN ARNOLD

John Arnold taught English at Leesburg High School in Florida for thirty years and thoroughly enjoyed it. He enjoys his retirement reading comic books, collecting horror and sci-fi toys, playing video games, and watching and critiquing films. He lives with his lovely wife Ann and his two dogs, probably until he is claimed by Death's sweet embrace, hopefully sometime around 2040.

McCLOUD STREET MEMORIES

BY SHARON SPRAGUE

I can't pee my bed. I can't pee my bed. Mom and dad will be mad.

There's nothing down the hall. Nothing.

It's my imagination. An old creaky house.

Wood and glass and dust and shadows.

And a guest room I must pass on my way to the bathroom.

One quite step at a time. The worn rug underneath my bare feet.

The moon is gone, there is no light.

And the guest room is open because dad doesn't want it closed.

And I won't look. I put my hand up beside my face.

But I know there's someone looking back.

It's a him. Looking back at me but if I can't see him he's not there.

And I don't pee the bed and the toilet seat is cold and wonderful.

And I creep back and shield the other side of my face but I can't help it …

I peek for a second and I see gray eyes and they aren't terrible, just sad.

They are just there and because they're there, I run back to my room.

And I'm under the covers and I try to remember prayers but I don't pay attention at church and mom and dad would be mad and the dust mixes with the shadows and there is no light and the door is always open and I didn't pee the bed and the grey eyes are there and always will be there … And I fall asleep buried under a comforter and two blankets and the cold Michigan air whips around outside and the century old house groans in the winter wind but the house is solid and constant and all its residents stay warm that night.

a few words from

SHARON SPRAGUE

When is the last time you were genuinely scared by something someone created?

Last year, seeing *IT*.

Tell us about your contribution to our book. What was the inspiration?

The short story I've submitted was my experience in my creepy Victorian childhood home. I'm certain as a toddler that I was visited by ghosts, because as I grew up, I just knew they were there, somewhere. Questionable shadows, coldness, sounds, and….a feeling. There wasn't a part of that house that didn't terrify me.

What do you love about the genre of horror?

Suspense. And that feeling of not being in control as a reader or viewer — anxiety adrenaline. If I start looking through my fingers, then I know it's good.

What is some of your favorite horror literature? Favorite Author?

Stephen King for sure – all of it.

What are some of your influences?

I grew up watching *The Twilight Zone* and *Alfred Hitchcock Presents* and just ate that up as a kid. My mom and I watched all the shows and movies together and it was a great bonding opportunity for us. I thought Hitchcock was creepy and weird and I dug it.

What is your favorite Halloween treat?

Candy pumpkins, but I have to eat the stem off first.

You are hosting the perfect Halloween movie marathon. What are the films you choose and why?

I'd want to cover it all so I'm going to go with *Texas Chainsaw Massacre* (original), *Night of the Living Dead, The Omen, It,* all the *Paranormal Activitys.*

If you could continue any horror story (Book or Film), what would it be?

Damien...today.

Describe the perfect Halloween.

I love a great Halloween party, but more than that, a party that is an experience. Maybe guests have roles to play, so it'd be a dinner theatre/party/installation. From the invitation to the moment they step into the party, a story unfolds. Actors, yes, I'd hire actors too. I once threw a *Friday the 13th* themed party at my friend's parent's lake cottage. It was intense. And dark.

SCARE CRED: SHARON SPRAGUE

Sharon Sprague is a creative powerhouse and Jane-of-many-trades. A lover of words, she's built her multi-decade career as a professional copywriter working for brands like Disney, Universal, Hilton, Leap Frog and Walgreens. Sharon's penchant for writing humor led her to the halls of The Second City in Chicago, where she wrote sketch comedy for a featured showcase. As a freelance artist, she shares her quirky and colorful paintings and illustrations through her design business, Ok Silly. When she's not creating, she's probably reading some nerdy non-fiction, enjoying the Florida sun, or chasing you down to pet your dog.

THE LIFE AND (almost) DEATH OF ELIZA PETTIGREW

BY JEFF STANDARD

The first rays of sunlight begin awakening the garden. Flowers sway in the morning breeze, as butterflies and bees dance from petal to petal. Every little morning ritual occurs as it always does. Life and Death entwined in an illusion that nothing ever changes. The sunroom door opens and swings out into the garden.

"Into the light," Eliza says to herself with a sense of hope for the day. After eighty-six years of life, the first rays of morning light, upon her flower garden, remind her everyday that she is still alive. She is truly blessed to have kept Death at bey for so long. She knows the day will come, but in the meantime, she will celebrate each day that she exists.

The gardening cart gets stuck on the threshold, as she rolls it out the door. At her age, even such a simple obstacle is an effort. Her ginger cat bounds out of the house, easily clearing the top of the cart, then sits to wait for Eliza. A couple of seconds later, the cart is bumping down the brick path, that weaves through the garden.

Everyday, even in the Summer, the path becomes littered with fallen leaves. Her first priority is always to sweep it clear. She enjoys the peaceful feeling of imagining she is sweeping all the negativity from the path of her life.

Having swept about three quarters of the path, she rounds the corner, by the Maple tree, heading toward the swing. Suddenly, the cat, grooming herself nearby, hisses and within seconds is on the top of the fence. Quickly she disappears into the neighbor's yard.

Before Eliza can really give it a thought, a sudden chill envelopes her. Not the kind of a chill an elderly person can get, even on a hot day, but the creepy chill that makes every hair on her body stand on end. Even without looking up, she knows it is there... silently there. If she could only sweep it away as easily as the dead leaves. Ignoring it is not an option, as it will soon insist upon itself.

"Just sitting there on my swing..." she mutters under her breath, "...casting such a depressing shadow on this glorious morning" Eliza's broom stops just short of the swing, "Lift your feet lazy bones," she waits with determination, until its literally bony feet slowly move from the path. She sweeps through, all the while watching from the corner of her eye, for it to follow. It remains unmoving and silent.

She grows inpatient, "You just gonna sit there and say nothing?" Eliza draws a deeper breath, "You show up, uninvited, and now you're gonna be rude?"

Its hooded head slowly lifts and speaks as if it had lips. "I really don't see the point in talking, considering the circumstances."

Eliza stops mid sweep, "So I don't have any say in the matter?"

Death sighs, " Small disclaimer...I can not be bargained with. I can not be cheated and I can not be outrun. You don't really strike me as the running type, but I always include that. Death is inevitable and irreversible...oh and I absolutely do not and will never, play chess."

Eliza looks back to the path and slowly sweeps away a few more leaves, "I see"

Death watches her for a few moments, "You sweep away those leaves today and there will be twice as many tomorrow. What are you going to accomplish with more life?"

Eliza stops and, while leaning the broom against her body, whips her hair up into her serious bun. She turns and walks closer to the cloaked skeleton slouching on her swing. She watches that his long bony fingers do not move in her direction, "what I accomplish is that for today...the path is clear, the weeds are pulled, the flowers are tended and for today my garden adds beauty to this world. Even if I'm the only one who sees it, I feel alive and that's what I accomplish. How can you take life with no compassion for what it means?"

Death is momentarily distracted, as a butterfly flutters passed its skull. Holding up a finger, it waits, as the butterfly circles and softly lands on the tip. The little wings fold up, as it then falls over dead and drops away.

"You stop that!" Eliza snaps

Death's empty eyes look toward the dead insect, "Stop that?...you might as well ask me to stop breathing."

"Is that an option?"

Death opens its cloak to reveal an empty rib cage, "Not really." It closes the cloak,

"No offense for your enjoyment of sweeping, but life with all its trappings still strikes me as mundane. I'm not sure why you cling to it so."

Eliza speaks with sudden inspiration, "Why I cling to it?... I was born. I was loved. I played. I danced. I loved with all my heart. I suffered loss. I brought life into this world and I watched it all again through their eyes. I have seen you more times than anyone should have to stomach, yet I never stopped seeing the beauty in this world... in life. The gift in every tomorrow is more precious than you can obviously imagine." She pauses, in vain, for some response, as if it could convey any type of emotion.

"Some of us," it replies, "were spared the 'life' experience, so forgive me if I don't have goosebumps from your heartfelt speech. My lack of flesh makes it difficult."

Eliza sighs, "Too bad you weren't spared your sarcastic sense of humor."

"It's kind of my thing," Death wryly answers, as it sits up straight and adjusts its hood.

"A quick heads up on how this will go. When I touch you, we will be pulled into the Ether, which has existed since the beginning of time. It fills the empty spaces between every living and spirit being, between every here, there, and nowhere. It's the whole river Styx thing, except not really a river, but a flow. Your destination is not my concern. The Ether will place you where you belong, so let's avoid the whole 'Are we there yet?' question because you'll know when I know, and it's just horribly annoying."

"Alright, nod if you got all that." it waits.

Eliza's head lowers at a slight angle, in thought.

"Good enough!" Death cracks it neck on one side and then the other, " Let's make this official." It clears its throat, as if it has one. Its voice begins to resonate deeply, "Eliza Pettigrew... It is time"

It's skeletal hand extends toward Eliza's forehead, but she is not ready to lay down just yet. To its surprise this frail little lady drops her broom, grabs its wrist with both hands and stops its movement dead, so to speak.

She stares intently into its hollow eye sockets with sympathy, "How can you have compassion for life, when you've never lived."

She pushes in closer to this mask of Death, for which she no longer has fear, turning its wrist as she does.

"It's time..." Eliza speaks in a soft, motherly way, that she has not used in so long, "... for you to grow up"

Its own bony fingertip is pressed to its forehead and with a sudden shock, it falls back into the Ether, surrounded by darkness, like usual. This time, however, it is its destination that awaits. Pulled by the sheer force of Eliza's intention, its journey twisting and turning in the flow so long, that it is annoyed by it's own thought of 'Am I there yet?'.

With a final whoosh, it is literally extracted from the Ether by a giant set of hands, into light...into warmth... flesh. Breath sucks into his lungs. Slowly his eyes open for the first time and he sees her face... his mother's face. He is alive... and as Death fades from his newborn mind, its last thought is registered, "Checkmate reversed...well played Eliza Pettigrew..."

Eliza sits on her swing, quietly enjoying life, as her ginger cat settles in on her lap. The birds sing and the butterflies float from flower to flower. She notices a leaf flutter on its stem, break free and drift down to the path at her feet. She contemplates it laying there and smiles warmly, "Tomorrow little one."

a few words from

JEFF STANDARD

Tell us about your contribution to our book. What was the inspiration?

The idea came to me as I was sweeping the brick path that winds through my garden. What if Death, jaded in his work, encountered a very old woman with no intention of dying.

What do you love about the genre of horror?

I like that the scares don't just come from the moment of confrontation, but can be drawn out and anticipatory of what lurks unknown in reality or in your mind.

What is some of your favorite horror literature? Favorite Author?

Stories from Ray Bradbury, Stephen King, Anne Rice, Clive Barker, JK Rowling.

What are some of your influences?

Richard Matheson, JK Rowling, classic Universal monster movies.

What is your favorite Halloween treat?

Reese's peanut butter cups

You are hosting the perfect Halloween movie marathon. What are the films you choose and why?

Hocus Pocus, Ghostbusters, Abbott and Costello Meet Frankenstein. The combination of horror and comedy best captures the childhood fun of Halloween.

If you could continue any horror story (book or film), what would it be?

The first *The Howling*. The idea of a colony of werewolves living among us is terrifying.

Describe the perfect Halloween

Decorating the yard, watching spooky movies and passing out candy.

SCARE CRED: JEFF STANDARD

While growing up a 'Monster Kid' in Georgia, I dreamed of visiting Universal Studios in California to see my monster friends. Although I never made that trip, eventually I found my way to the new Universal Studios in Florida, as a make-up artist working on opening 'The Beetlejuice Show' and Halloween Horror Nights 2. Twenty-eight years later, including fifteen more Halloween Horror Nights, I still find myself working with my monster friends, as well as a lot of goblins and creatures from a magical world as a part of the Universal Creative Fabrication / Figure Finish team.

HAUNTER'S TALE
KEEP GOING... THERE'S MORE FIENDISH FUN AHEAD...

THE HAUNTED HISTORY OF EREBUS

BY ED TEREBUS

In the late 1970s my brother Jim worked with one of the local JC chapters doing their haunted house. In the year 1980 my brother was laid off from Ford Motor Company. After the lay-off he decided to build his own haunted attraction. He was 28 and I was just graduating high school at the age 18. Our first haunted attraction was 1200 square-feet. It was a freestanding building set up in front of a local Kmart. We had all the exterior walls up on the first day but with one little problem, no internal supports. That evening, 60 mile an hour winds came through and wiped out the whole building. We spent three days reconstructing and setting up the rest of the attraction. Not to mention, we set up on the lower part of the parking lot, so every time it rained, the patrons walked through 3 inches of water. All part of the ambience that year! That first year we charged $1.50 for admission. We lost $500 when all was said and done.

We decided we needed to approach this a different way. Jim found some mobile home trailers that were 12-foot wide by approximately 50 foot-long that had been damaged by flash fires. We spent all summer stripping, repairing, building and decorating these trailers for the following Halloween season. That year we charged $3 and the haunted house consisted of 2800 square-feet. The following year we added a fifth trailer in the center of the castle to increase the space to 3500 ft.^{2}. We ran that unit for 13 years. We donated those trailers for a dollar to a church that ran a haunted attraction. We acquired 10 mobile offices that were 14 foot-wide by 70 foot long, approximately 9,800 square-feet. We ran that unit for seven years. While running this unit and looking at the cost of Storage, transport, permits, temporary electricity, temporary water, lot rental, set up time, available operating time and tear downtime, we decided to look for a permanent structure.

In 1998 we purchased a building with 113,000 square-feet. I sold my house and my brother remortgaged his because no bank was going to give us a loan for a haunted attraction. Living in that building, I went eight years with no paycheck, just so we could pay off the loans.

Working on the attraction still debating on what we should call it. We're looking for a single word, something like what Madonna represents in the music community. I was reading a vampire novel and it started talking about Erebus. I was not familiar with that and intrigued my interest, because if you put a letter T in front of it, that is our last name, Terebus. Erebus, by Webster's definition, is the darkness beneath the earth that the dead must pass to reach Hades. In Greek mythology, Erebus is the brother of night and son of Chaos. Perfect!

We opened in the year 2000. In the year 2005 we took the Guinness Book of World Records away from a haunted house in Japan for the world's largest walk-through haunted attraction. We held that record for five seasons until 2009. The record was 2,189 linear feet. We are now over 2600 linear feet, that's the equivalent of walking the length of over seven football fields.

Michigan has always been very popular for haunted attractions. At one point we had over 100 attractions within 50-mile radius of us. Because of that fact, we couldn't go to the trade show and buy the really cool stuff because everybody else would have the same thing. It forced us to be more innovative and create things here at Erebus that you can't see any place else.

Many years ago, we tried having the actors touch people. We soon found out that was not a good idea, so we created things that would grab you, bite you, land on top you and we will even bury you alive, how long can you hold your breath?

Haunted attractions are a tradition, a right of passage once you finish trick-or-treating. That is what keeps the Halloween spirit running forever in our young souls!

Erebus Definition:

- According to Webster's, Erebus is the darkness beneath the Earth that the dead must pass to reach Hades.
- In Greek mythology Erebus is the son of Chaos and the brother of Nye (Night).

According to Ron Leadbetter in Encyclopedia Mythica: Erebus was known as the embodiment of primordial darkness, the son of Chaos (who was the void from which all things developed, known also as Darkness). According to Hesiod's *Theogony*, Erebus was born with Nyx (Night), and was the father of Aether (the bright upper atmosphere) and Hemera (Day). Charon, the ferry-man who took the dead over the rivers of the infernal region, is also said to be the son of Erebus and Nyx. Later legend describes Erebus as the Infernal Region below the earth. In this version, Hades was split into two regions: Erebus, which the dead have to pass shortly after they have died, and Tartarus, the deepest region, where the Titans were imprisoned. Aristophanes' *Birds* says that Erebus and Nyx were also the parents of Eros, the god of Love. He is often used metaphorically for Hades itself.

The Name:

• The owner's last name is Terebus, remove the "T" and you get Erebus.

Story: Erebus is the result of Dr. Colber who worked for the government to build a time machine. After being fired and stripped of his certifications, he began work on the time machine on his own. Eventually he was successful at sending people back into time, with the only one glitch. The destination time period looked at the people as a virus and wiped them out. Determined to over come this glitch he sent in group after group of his own personnel. Ultimately unsuccessful, he ended up broke and lacking the proper personnel to run his machine. It is then that Dr. Colber came up with a brilliant idea, disguise his time machine as a haunted house and have the general public help fund his project and use the people going through as his human guinea pigs.

Stats:

- Erebus is 4 stories high!
- A walk through the attraction is the equivalent of covering a distance of 7 football fields!
- Erebus has 125 employees, 90+ of them actors, who work every night during the open season.
- In the off-season, six of them work part time while another five of them work full time all year long. (Many of Erebus' one of a kind props are built off-season)
- Most of the props in Erebus are one of a kind.

A Haunting History:

- Erebus was founded in 2000 by Ed and Jim Terebus, 40-year veterans of the Haunt Industry.
- Erebus has gained national recognition as being one of the top haunts as well as being placed in the Guinness Book of World Records.
- Erebus leads its Patrons through four stories of unique and terrifying paths with fear so intense some call it pain!

Haunting Facts:

- Erebus is four stories, three levels above ground and one under ground.
- Over a 1/2 mile walk inside the building.
- The owner's have over 80 years combined experience scaring people.
- Erebus is very interactive; there are sections where things will bite you, fall on you, touch you, jump out at you and scare you in ways you never imagined possible.

- Erebus appeals to all 5 senses: the smell of chainsaw gas, or dry, creepy air; the touch of textured walls; the sounds of screams and laughter; the taste of fear creeping all around you; and the sight of some of the most mutilated monsters and scenes you'll ever see.
- Erebus Haunted Attraction held the Guinness Book Of World Records for the longest walk-through haunted attraction from 2005-2009
- 90% of all our props are built by Erebus, guaranteeing our show will be different than any other in the world.
- Over 450 people chicken out and 56 people pee themselves per year... (Confirmed by Managers!)
- Since the beginning of Erebus, we've had 8,617 people chicken out and 1,074 people have peed themselves.
- Beaumont Doctors concluded that going through Erebus was like an aerobic work out for your heart.
- Looking to have some fun without fear! Check out Erebus Escape - Our Premium Escape Room Destination! Located just 6 blocks north of Erebus Haunted Attraction in Downtown Pontiac, MI. ErebusEscape.com

a few words from

ED TEREBUS

As a designer of horror theatre or experiences, explain your process.

It all starts off with selecting a theme. From there, we orchestrate what kind of scares will happen, from small to large, and what kind of reactions we can expect to see out of those scares. What directions will they be looking and moving while reacting? This is what allows us to keep everyone entertained and also moving forward. Lastly, the focus turns to the more creative aspect, decoration, lighting, sound and reset value.

When is the last time you were genuinely scared by something someone created?

Unfortunately, being in the haunted attraction business for 40 years has toughened my ability to be scared. So, it has been a long time since I've been scared from something someone created.

Tell us about your contribution to our book. What was the inspiration?

Many people think we just moved into this massive haunted house when in actuality we came from very humble beginnings. I would like to let people know that our first haunted attraction was very small and we grew little by little, year to year, from there. To share the story of our growth over the last 40 years and to look back and appreciate what it took to get here.

What do you love about the genre of horror?

Halloween is hands down, my favorite holiday, as you may have guessed. Not that I don't love the others, but Halloween carries this rare air of no-judgement. The Halloween season allows us to become something outside of ourselves, be it scary, goofy, funny, or just plain different. And for whatever reason, people are open and accepting of it. That is what ignites my joy and passion for Halloween and the reason I've dedicated my life to it.

What are some of your influences?

We live, eat, sleep, and breath haunted house every day of the year. Not sure it has much to do with influence, but more in the way of how we see things, our perspective of the day to day that people don't see through our eyes. The loud barking dogs that the neighbors had or the two guard dogs at the storage lot transformed into vicious undead dogs of the cemetery. Or a puddle up against a building in the middle of a parking lot after a rain storm, giving us motivation for one of our greatest displays, the bottomless pit. Lastly, speaking with likeminded individuals at the trade shows and sharing in the experiences and laughs over the years that might spark a new idea!

What is your favorite Halloween treat?

I know it is kind of a hate it or love it candy, but candy corn and I love it!

You are hosting the perfect Halloween movie marathon. What are the films you choose and why?

Alien and *Aliens*. These two movies were suspenseful and scary from start to finish. And the beauty is those two emotions stemmed from never knowing where the monsters were coming from or what was going to happen next!

Describe the perfect Halloween.

My family getting dressed up in our costumes. Sloppy joe's and chili on the stove filling the house with that unmistakable smell. Taking the kids out for trick-or-treating on a cool evening with Halloween music in the air from all the homes passing out Halloween goodies. The laughter and excitement on my children's faces. Returning home and then jumping into the car to drive to the haunt while my brothers holding down the fort. Approaching the haunted attraction, seeing searchlight sky for the entirety of the drive and finally, arrive to the line of excited people wrapped around the building.

SCARE CRED: ED TEREBUS

Edward Terebus Worked as a Locksmith and went to school for fine arts. Joined his brother James doing their first haunted attraction in 1981. Turned the Haunted Attraction business into a full time career in 1998, when they bought the building now known as Erebus. Erebus Haunted Attraction held the Guinness Book of World Records for the longest walk-through haunted attraction. 2005-2009. They were the first to bring that record into the USA. James and Edward along with their team have been instrumental in many of the advancement within the Haunted Attraction Community. Produced the Fear Finder Halloween Tour Guide since 1993. The paper, 40 pages and 600,000 copies featuring all the haunted attractions in southeast Michigan.

SadoMannequin

BY JIM TORRES

FADE IN:

EXT. WAREHOUSE -- EVENING

Lightning FLASHES followed by the BOOM of thunder. The rain is falling hard outside the old, junk warehouse on 52nd street. A sign out front reads: MORNINGSIDE SECURITIES

QUAID
(Off Screen)
There's a T.V.. It ain't got cable and there's no VCR. The one channel it does get plays shit all the time.

CUT TO:

INT. WAREHOUSE -- CONTINUOUS

QUAID is the day manager of Morningside Securities. He's in his early thirties, and is of medium height and build. With his slicked back hair, handlebar mustache and gold cross earring he looks just the like the kind if guy he is. A dork who thinks he's the coolest thing on two feet. Standing before him is PETER. Peter is another gem of a human being. He's in his early twenties and has 'eager to please' written all over him. At three hundred pounds, Peter barely fits into his double-XL uniform. His shirt looks as though it's engaged in a death-match game of tug-o-war. The buttons threaten to pop off at any moment.

This is Peter's first night on the job. He's seems to be more interested in his utility-belt than in Quaid's instructions. Quaid, not-so-playfully, SLAPS Peter on the face.

QUAID

Are you paying attention to me?

Peter quickly looks up.

PETER

Yeah...

QUAID

(interrupting)

Good. There's a phone in the front office. If you need anything don't call me. I don't care if the building is burning down. You call me, you're fired. I work this place from eight AM to eight PM. Anything that happens off my shift is not my concern. I'll handle it in the morning. There's a snack machine in the front, but I gathered you saw that on your way in.

Peter holds up his wrist showing a copper, medical ID tag.

PETER

I'm diabetic.

QUAID

So.

PETER

Who does all this stuff belong to?

QUAID

None of your business, but since you asked, Clem Garrison.

PETER

Old man Garrison?

QUAID

Yeah, the crazy hermit that lives in the cabin on LaGrange Mountain.

PETER

Why is all his stuff in here?

QUAID

You know, I didn't ask this many questions when I started which is why I'm still here.

PETER

Sorry.

Quaid pulls out a name tag from his pocket and pins it on Peter's shirt. Peter looks down at it. The tag is a laminated picture ID with a glum looking fellow on it. Obviously not Peter. The name under the picture reads: MILKY

PETER (CONT'D)

My name's not Milky. It's Peter.

QUAID

It's a boring job. You make it through the night and I'll get you your own tag. Until then, you're Milky.

PETER

Milky it is.

Quaid looks down at his watch.

QUAID

My shift's up. You got what you're supposed to do?

PETER

Yeah, yeah. Stay awake. Watch the stuff. If anything happens, don't call you.

QUAID

Good.

Quaid turns and walks toward the exit. Peter takes his gun out of its holster and looks at it with awe. Quaid stops at the door and turns back to Peter.

QUAID (CONT'D)

Oh yeah. One more thing.

PETER

(still looking at the gun)

What's that?

QUAID

Don't mess with any of that stuff back there, okay?

Peter looks up from his new toy.

PETER

Why?

QUAID

I mean it. Don't touch anything.

Lightning FLASHES.

A CLAP of thunder reports back.

CUT TO:

INT. WAREHOUSE -- NIGHT

The warehouse stretches out like a dark catacomb. There are piles of boxes stacked floor to ceiling, old television sets, antique furniture and random eccentricities strewn about everywhere. While the junk is random, there is a very gothic feel to this place.

Scattered amongst the junk are several mannequins.

They lie in different positions: scattered on the floor, propped up against walls, spread out on couches. Some are clothed and some are not. Most are not. Many of the mannequins are missing some of their limbs. In one corner, next to an old television set is pile of arms. Pale plastic.

CUT TO:

Peter stands in front of a pile boxes. He has taken the lid off one of them and is rummaging through its contents. His retrieves a stack of magazines. The usual fair for a place like this: FAMOUS MONSTERS, VAMIPRELLA, etc...

PETER

Cool.

He stands and picks up a plate full of chocolate covered raisins. With the magazines and candies in tow, Peter walks down the isles of junk. He unsuccessfully tries to eat, read and walk at the same time. He bumps into a stack of boxes and knocks a mannequin head to the floor. A few of his chocolates roll off the plate. Peter continues down the isle without missing a step.

Behind the fallen head sits an old velvet couch. On this couch lies a mannequin wearing a seductive black, leather cat suit. Black, leather gloves crawl up her long, plastic arms. A black, feathered mask covers the upper half of her face leaving only the painted blue eyeballs enough room to see. She stares without blinking.

Black boots cling tightly to her legs all the way up to her thighs where they flare outward. Her lips are painted black against her white, powder skin. She lies a still, and lifeless demoness.

A small silver chain hangs limp around her neck. Two small charms hang from the chain. One is a small silver cross, the other a word. A name. DEMONA.

Standing next to the couch is a dusty gumball machine. The glass bowl is filled with gum painted to look like eye balls. A closer look reveals that there might be more eyes and less gum in the machine. A leather whip hangs from one of the arms sticking out from the side of the gumball machine.

CUT TO:

PETER sets the plate of candies and magazines down on the table in front of him.

Another FLASH of lightning.

A clap of thunder rumbles outside as Peter flips on the old black and white TV set next to his plate of sweets. He picks up one of the magazines and crams a handful of chocolates in his mouth.

Images of old horror movies dance across the television set as though someone were changing the channels rapidly. Vampires. Zombies. Werewolves. Demons. Creatures. Peter slowly lowers his magazine and looks at the possessed television set. Zombies. Monsters. Aliens. The television stops on the image on a curious old man talking on a pay phone.

FORREST ACKERMAN

No, no! Not that chicken, the other chicken!

Thunder grumbles outside. The storm is passing.

Peter reaches up and slaps the television set. The image of a hairy man howling at the moon jumps on the screen.

Outside, the sky is clearing up. Clouds float past the full moon like ghost ships. Peter takes a sudden interest in the creature feature on the TV.

CUT TO:

Demona lies perfectly still on her velvet couch.

The last of the ghost ships pass by the full moon. A clear and perfect moon. The light from the moon shines through the only window in the warehouse not covered up with plywood or scum. The beaming light falls on the couch where Demona rests in suspended animation.

Demona's black, leather clad hand twitches.

CUT TO:

Peter aimlessly grabs another handful of chocolates and crams them in his mouth. The television flickers and then goes black. Peter looks at it with confusion.

CUT TO:

Demona's eyes open.

CUT TO:

Peter bangs the television. It blinks back to life. This time the image of a woman screaming blinks on the dirty screen.

The moon shines brightly into the warehouse.

Again, Peter grabs a handful of sweets. His hand quickly recoils from the plate as if something had stung him. He looks down and sees that his chocolates have been replaced with a pile of black, crawling insects. More confusion on the simple man's face. The insects crawl over each other in a frantic game of king of the hill. The lights in the warehouse blink off.

The moonlight pouring in from the window illuminates the couch Demona WAS lying on. Peter fumbles for his flashlight. He flicks it on and sweeps the warehouse with a beam of light.

Nothing.

Peter gets up and shuffles over to a wall with an ancient looking breaker box on it. He opens the panel and fidgets with the switches inside. Peter flinches as an arch of electricity shoots out from the breaker box. White sparks fall to the floor around Peters feet. The lights fade on. Their power only half what it was before they went out. Behind Peter stands Demona. Whip in hand.

Sensing someone is behind him, Peter slowly turns around. Demona stands a good six feet tall in her black boots. She works the whip in her right-hand like a snake. It slithers side to side at her feet. Peter stares at the seductive woman. He smiles.

Demona reaches out with her left hand and beckons him with her index finger. With a crooked smile, Peter straightens the tie he does not have on.

Just as he is about to take his first step toward the most beautiful woman he's ever seen, Demona CRACKS the whip around his neck! Peter jumps. His hands fly up to the black snake wrapped around his neck. Demona slowly reels him toward her. The corners of her black lips curving upward in an evil smile.

Peter stands before Demona, squinting through his inch thick glasses. Smiling his crooked smile, like a child on Christmas. Demona commands the whip off Peter's neck. She reaches up a hand and pushes him to the ground. Peter lands on his ass, still smiling. He is enjoying this. Demona loses the smile. Her right hand raises the whip high above her head.

Peter loses his smile. He turns onto his knees and starts to scuffle away from her. The black snake of a whip cracks hard against his back. He flinches at the sharp pain and continues to crawl away from her. Her hand raises the whip again. The whip cracks on Peter's back, again. And again. And again. And again.

Demona is breathing heavy with exhilaration. Peter scrambles to his feet and takes off running. Demona follows him with her eyes. Peter runs down the isles of boxes and junk. Past the couches and television sets. Past the creepy little man with an ax. Demona slowly walks after him. The click from her heels echoes throughout the warehouse.

Click, click, click... Peter reaches the end of the warehouse. He looks around quickly for something to hide behind. Nothing. Only boxes stacked to the ceiling. No doors. No means of escape. Demona flicks the whip out at her side as she descends upon her prey. Peter quickly fumbles for his precious, new sidearm. Demona stops feet away from Peter and watches him. Peter cracks the chamber of his revolver open. Demona lowers herself into a crouched position, like a cat ready to pounce on a helpless mouse. Peter pulls out a single bullet. The words: SILVER BULLET are etched on the side of the brass casing.

He quickly slips the bullet back into the revolver and snaps the chamber shut. Demona smiles wider, exposing her sharp fangs. Peter whips the gun up! Demona leaps toward Peter! Peter fires a single shot! Bang!!! The shot echoes loudly throughout the warehouse.

Demona crumples to the floor. Smoke leaks out from the hole in her black, feathered mask. Her painted blue eyes, stare blankly, without blinking. Surprised by his marksmanship, Peter stares at the woman he's just shot. Confused, he looks around the warehouse and notices the window. He turns and notices the full moon.

Peter looks down at the still Demona and then to the window and the full moon. He looks at Demona. He looks at the full moon. He smiles. Peter walks over to another mannequin. Another scantily clad, plastic female. This one is wearing a red gown. Peter picks her up and carries her over to the window. The moonlight pours over her white, plastic body. Peter rubs his hands together with anticipation.

Her pale blue eyes blink to life. She turns to face her new master. Peter smiles the widest, most crooked smile yet. This new vision of beauty walks over to him. He takes a step backward. She raises a hand to his chest to comfort him. Peter quivers with excitement. She pushes him down. Again, he bounces on his ass. Before he can lose his smile the lady in red is kneeling next to him.
She leans toward his mouth. Peter's eyes widen with excitement. he moves closer still. Peter puckers his crooked mouth into a crooked kissy face. Her full, red lips form a kiss inches away from Peter's lips. 3...2...1...

Lightning Flashes. A Clap of thunder reports back.

CUT TO:

EXT. WAREHOUSE -- EVENING

The rain is falling hard outside the old, junk warehouse.

QUAID

(Off Screen)

There's a T.V.. It ain't got cable
and there's no VCR. The one channel
it does get plays shit all the time.

CUT TO:

INT. WAREHOUSE -- CONTINUOUS

Quaid is standing before another young man named, JOHN. John is a seemingly normal guy. His uniform seems a bit large on his frame.

QUAID

There's a phone in the front office,
but don't call me. No matter what.
I work during the day and sleep at
night.

JOHN

Got it.

Quaid reaches in his pocket and pulls out a name tag. He pins it on John's chest. We see Peter's cooper, medical ID tag hanging from Quaid's wrist. John looks down at the tag. On it is a picture of Peter, looking glum. The name on the tag, of course, reads: PETER

JOHN (CONT'D)

But my name's John.

QUAID

Whatever. You make it through the night and I'll get you your own name tag, how's that?

JOHN

Alright, Peter it is.

Quaid turns to walk away. He stops and turns back to John.

QUAID

There's one more thing.

VAMPIRELLA
SUPER SPECIAL ISSUE

Palace
HORROR
MOVIES

The Splinter

BY JIM TORRES

In 1560 the first pencils were created using solid graphite sticks from the Grey Knotts mines in England. They were first used to mark sheep, but later the graphite became useful for making cannonballs. The mines were promptly taken over by the Crown and placed under heavy guard. Once enough graphite was retrieved the mines were flooded to prevent theft by the enemies of the Crown. The truth was they found something in the mines. Something with tremendous power. A threat capable of destroying the Crown and beyond.

A young boy from the Lake District recovered a splinter of graphite while exploring the fell around the Grey Knotts mines. He wrapped the slender stick in sheepskin and string - careful not to break the secret treasure. That night, by the thin light from a small oil lamp, he sketched a dragon on the wood floor beneath his bed. With each stroke of the graphite tip a sound arose from beyond the boy's room. A whooshing sound - a pulsing wave of wind followed by a low rumble. Once he finished his drawing he looked down at his creation with pride - a winged creature hovering over a house with the figure of a small boy in the window.

The lamp's light flickered as the pulsing rush of wind grew louder, and closer. Inspired by the dance of light the boy added a single embellishment to his creation - A flame at the mouth of the dragon. The boy smiled at his creation and marveled at the lead pen in his hand.

Growing tired, the boy withdrew from beneath his bed. He placed the pencil in an iron strong box his father had given him, careful not to break the delicate object.

The pulsing rush of wind grew louder. It beat against the house with increasing force. The window to the boy's room shuddered with each burst of wind. The boy moved to the edge of his window, oil lamp in hand. He was courageous, if not foolish. As the next wave of wind beat against the house the wooden frame of the window yielded to the pressure. Glass and wood splinters exploded inward knocking the boy down. He dropped the lamp as he fell. The flame was extinguished by the rush of wind. The lamp rolled to a stop beneath the boy's bed spilling its thick contents. The wood floor canvas soaked up the oil - a dark stain splashed across the boy's drawing.

Bleeding from cuts to his face made by the flying glass and debris, the boy looked with horror at the creature looming outside his bedroom window. The dragon, his dragon, hovered above the earth. Its wings beat against the night air sending wave after wave of debris and chill into the boy's room. Tears formed in the corners of his eyes, spilled over his cheeks and mixed with the blood from his cuts.

The dragon was larger than his father's boat - a Collingwood skiff he used to transport goods to the outer islands. The dragon's scales were a deep metallic purple that reminded the boy of his mother's finest gowns.

He smiled with pride at his dragon. His creation.

His destruction.

A flame appeared in the Dragon's mouth. Small at first, but it grew in size as the low rumble emanating from the dragon's chest became a roar. A flash of light followed by a stream of intense heat overwhelmed the boy. His bedroom burst into flames. The rush of wind from the dragon's wings fanned the flames spreading the fire throughout the house.

In moments the house was engulfed. The boy perished.

The flames began to consume the drawing under the bed. As the image of the dragon burned, so too did the creature beyond the house. It slowly broke apart into sparks of red and yellow embers. With a groan and a shudder the house collapsed inward and the dragon exploded in a shower of flame and ash. The thatched roofs of the village homes caught flame and burned. The fire spread and the small village was consumed.

The iron strongbox was one of the few items salvaged from the charred ruins. The intense heat from the fire fused the box shut. It was discarded and forgotten until many years later when the strong box was acquired by a strange man - a collector from the United States interested in the forgotten relics of calamity and pain.

He brought the box and its contents home and placed it on his mantle above the hearth in his living room. Where, inside, the graphite splinter awaits the hand of its next artist.

Another young boy perhaps?

a few words from

JIM TORRES

As a designer of horror theatre, film or experiences, explain your process.

My process is scattered. Sometimes I find inspiration for an idea when I'm not looking for it, sometimes I'm focused on crafting a story or character and the muse is with me. Music is very much a part of my process. The right song can spark a visual that peaks my curiosity. That is true for both *SadoMannequin* and *The Splinter*.

When is the last time you were genuinely scared by something someone created?

There's a lot of scary shit going on in the real world right now, but Jordon Peele's *Get Out* blew me away.

Tell us about your contribution to our book. What was the inspiration?

SadoMannequin was inspired by Forrest J. Ackerman, my dear friend Terry Pace, *Vampirella*, the *Eerie* and *Creepy* magazines and the song "Down" by *Gravity Kills*. I always loved the horrifying morality tales in *Eerie* and *Creepy*, and I had a crush on *Vampirella* (okay, I still do). I was driving one night, listening to *Gravity Kills*, and the idea of a mannequin coming to life to tease and torment an overly curious security guard popped in my head, and thus Demona was born.

The Splinter is a cautionary tale about being careful what you ask for, you just might get it. It was inspired by Ray Bradbury and his love of metaphors. It's also a continuation of *SadoMannequin*. In *SadoMannequin*, the security guard is supposed to be watching over a rare collection of oddities and antiquities that belong to a mysterious collector named Clem Garrison. The enchanted pencil in *The Splinter* becomes part of Garrison's collection.

What do you love about the genre of horror?

I love the catharsis I get from watching a really good horror movie or reading a really scary book. It connects me to my humanity and reminds me to savor and appreciate the goodness in life. The shared experience of watching a really good horror movie in a theater with strangers is pure movie magic.

What is some of your favorite horror literature? Favorite author?

Without a doubt Richard Matheson and Steven King are two of my favorite horror authors. King was my first exposure to horror novels, and I quickly fell in love with Matheson's work. *Hell House* is a genuinely terrifying book.

What are some of your influences?

I'm heavily influenced by music. If I'm inspired by a song while I'm writing I'll put it on loop and let it play over and over until it devolves into the background. As I write this the song "Letting Go While Holding On" by *Nine Inch Nails* is on loop.

You are hosting the perfect Halloween movie marathon. What are the films you choose and why?

John Carpenter's *Halloween* because it's perfect and Dean Cundey's cinematography haunts me. *The Conjuring* because it's my son's favorite, and *Young Frankenstein* because watching it with my father is one of my earliest memories.

If you could continue any horror story (Book or Film), what would it be?

It is my dream to do a live action adaptation of Ray Bradbury's *The Halloween Tree*. It would be interesting to see how Carapace Clavicle Moundshroud would torment and educate a new rabble of kids.

Describe the perfect Halloween.

A clear, cool Saturday night. Lots of kids trick-o-treating. Scary movies on the TV. A bottle of wine and friends to share it with. My dog on the couch beside me.

SCARE CRED: JIM TORRES

Jim Torres is a filmmaker and visual storyteller living in Huntsville, Alabama. His first feature film, the post-apocalyptic fairytale *20 Years After* starring Joshua Leonard (*The Blair Witch Project*) and Azura Skye (*One Missed Call*), won numerous awards, and was picked up for domestic and international distribution. Jim continues to work in television production and marketing. He is the co-owner of 4 Mile Post, a full service video production company in North Alabama, and the producer of numerous national television shows for the outdoor lifestyle market. He is currently in development on a new feature film project, *The Sympathetic Martian* which he intends to shoot in Huntsville in the near future.

LOW BATTERY

BY WILLIAM VAN CUYUCK

EXT. SUBURBAN HOUSE - AFTERNOON

MAGGIE, (30s) stands just outside the open front door with CARRIE (late 20s). Joyful sounds of Children can be heard coming from inside the house.

CARRIE

Are you sure you have to go?

Maggie glances at her PHONE. The time reads 3:47pm.

MAGGIE

Yeah. I really want to get home before dark.

Maggie leans back in to the open door.

MAGGIE (CONT'D)

Lucy! Come on honey!

LUCY (7-8) comes running out of the house with another girl in a BIRTHDAY TIARA, SOPHIA (7-8).

LUCY

Can't we just stay for a few more minutes? Please?!

SOPHIA

Yeah. I haven't even opened my presents yet.

MAGGIE

Lucy, you know we have to get going. Don't you still have that homework you need to finish?

LUCY

I don't have any home--

Maggie raises an eyebrow only Lucy can see. Lucy understands and nods almost imperceptibly.

Lucy turns to Sophia.

LUCY (CONT'D)

I'm sorry Sophia. You'll have to tell me what you get at school on Monday. Lucy and Sophia give each other a hug.

EXT. BACK ROAD - LATE AFTERNOON

MAGGIE'S SUV turns. A DETOUR SIGN can be seen pointing them down the back road.

INT. CAR - DUSK

Maggie glances at her CELL PHONE. She glances out the window at the late afternoon sun. She glances at her phone again as it flashes a LOW BATTERY 20% alert appears on her screen.

MAGGIE

(Mumbling to herself)
Where's the highway? Just keeps
taking us further and further away.
We stayed to long.

Lucy sits playing on a TABLET in the backseat, the sounds of the game she is playing can be heard lightly. SNACK WRAPPERS are littered around her seat.

LUCY

But Mommy it was a party.

MAGGIE

I know Lucy, but you know we need
to be home before dark.

Lucy continues to play on her tablet until the wilting sound of a dying video game character makes it last BLIP and BEEP.

LUCY

Aww. No fair.

Lucy looks up from her tablet.

LUCY (CONT'D)

I'm hungry Mommy.

MAGGIE

You finished all the snacks love.
We'll be home soon.

The battery bar on the little girl's tablet is in the red when it suddenly powers down.

LUCY

Awwwwww.

Maggie is about to place her phone on the PHONE CHARGER.

LUCY

Mom? Can I play on your phone?

MAGGIE

Not right now honey. It needs to charge.

LUCY

But you have Monster Kill on your phone and this just died.

MAGGIE

Not now. We need to charge up my phone a little. Just hang on baby.

LUCY

But...

MAGGIE

No buts! It's just the way it is.

Lucy pouts in the back seat. Maggie focuses her eyes back on the road. She sees another detour sign and has to turn on another back road. As she gets distracted with driving Lucy sets her tablet down, leans forward, and sneakily pulls the phone from the charger. She clicks it to mute and begins to play her game.

EXT. BACK ROAD - DUSK

The car drives down the road and around the bend.

INT. CAR - DUSK

The headlights and dash lights flicker and go out. She seems to lose all power and the car sputters to a stop.

MAGGIE

No. Please not now.

LUCY

What is it Mommy?

MAGGIE

I don't know. I'm sure it'll be fine.

EXT. BACK ROAD - DUSK

The sun is setting as the car coasts to a stop at the side of the road. Just a few rays of sunlight are still peaking through.

INT. CAR - DUSK

Maggie reaches for her phone and sees it's not there and that Lucy is playing on it.

LUCY

Do you need it Mom?

Mom snatches it from the Lucy's hand.

MOM

What did I tell you? It needed to charge!

Lucy starts to tear up.

LUCY

I'm sorry Mom. I just wanted to play Monster Kill.

Maggie feels bad for yelling.

MOM

I'm sorry. It's okay. Why don't you undo your seatbelt and come up here with me while I call the tow truck.

Lucy climbs up front onto Maggie's lap. She dials a number on her phone.

AUTOMOTIVE DISPATCH LINE (over phone)

Hi. Thank you for calling the Automotive Dispatch. Please hold while we connect you with the closest available driver.

There is a pause. Maggie looks at her phone again taking note of the low amount of battery again as CHEESY HOLD MUSIC PLAYS. The battery percentage drops from 20% to 19% as she looks at it. The music breaks up as the TOW TRUCK DRIVER comes on the line.

TOW TRUCK DRIVER (over the phone)
Hello?

Maggie quickly brings the phone back up to her ear.

MAGGIE
Thank God. Hi. This is Maggie Chaney. My club number is 814525 My car just broke down out on Thorn Road.

TOW TRUCK DRIVER (over the phone)
What seems to be the trouble?

MAGGIE
The car just lost all power and stalled out. We really need to get someone out here.

TOW TRUCK DRIVER (over the phone)
I'll get out there as fast as I can, but it is really backed up tonight. I had a guy call in sick, so it's just me. It might be a couple hours.

MAGGIE
A couple hours? No. I can't wait that long. (to herself) We stayed too long.

TOW TRUCK DRIVER (over the phone)
I'm sorry. There's nothing I can do ma'am.

MAGGIE
Alright, just please get here as
soon as you can.

Maggie hits end and looks at how low her battery is again, 18%, and then at the setting sun.

LUCY
Mommy. I'm really getting hungry.

Maggie looks frantic and nervous. She reaches over and opens the glove box. She rummages around in the glove box until she pulls out more empty SNACK and CANDY WRAPPERS and a FLASHLIGHT. She flicks it ON and OFF making sure it works. It FLICKERS. She hits it against her palm and the flashlight seems to brighten up. She digs through the messy glove box. She finds a BOX OF BATTERIES and excitedly pulls the box out only to discover that it is empty. She throws it to the floor disgusted.

Then she looks around seeing nothing but dark back road.
She clicks the dome light on and off in vain frustration. Nothing happens. Maggie looks anxious as she peers out the window. All she sees is a lonely drive way with a mailbox.

EXT. CAR -- SUNSET
Maggie looks at the car's engine with a fruitless look. She peers at the setting sun and then around the hood and looks at Lucy sitting quietly in the car. The Little girl smiles and waves at her, flashlight in hand.

She comes to a decision and slams the hood closed. She opens the car door.

MAGGIE

Alright. We're going to walk up that driveway and see if somebody's home. Someplace with some lights maybe, so we don't have to wait here in the dark. They might even have a snack for a cute little girl.

LUCY

Yeah.

MAGGIE

Can you look cute in the light?

Lucy gives her "cute look" and hands her mom the flashlight.

EXT. DRIVEWAY - NIGHT

Maggie and Lucy get out of the car and walk over to the end of the driveway. Maggie is careful to keep the flashlight beam on Lucy.

LUCY

I'm cold.

Maggie hands Lucy the flashlight.

MAGGIE

Wait here. I'll go grab our sweatshirts. Keep that sweet face in the light.

Maggie reaches back in and grabs her LUCY's SWEATSHIRT and her own SWEATSHIRT laying on the seat inside the car. She rummages in her PURSE and pulls out a JACKKNIFE. She debates for a moment before sliding it in her pocket. Stepping back up to Lucy, she kneels down in front of her and helps her put her sweatshirt on. Lucy nods.

MAGGIE (CONT'D)

Sweetie. See how dark it is?

MAGGIE (CONT'D)

Perfect for a game of "Be Bright Flashlight."

LUCY

Ok. I know.

MAGGIE

Remember, whatever you do, you have to stay in the light.

LUCY

I know.

Maggie and Lucy turn and start walking down the driveway. Maggie is freaked out by the dark as they walk and rushes Lucy along towards the house. Lucy happily jogs down the driveway, careful to stay in the flashlights beam. She looks back towards Maggie. Maggie is busy looking at her phone again. Maggie looks at the phone again. The battery bar reads 16%. Lucy GROWLS and ROARS a big pretend roar at the Mom as she steps up to her. Maggie jumps and looks up from her phone. She looks truly terrified for a moment---

Her hand darts into her pocket. Clutching the jackknife.

Lucy smiles up at her. Her face spotlighted by the flashlight under her chin. Maggie pulls her hand from her pocket-- And quickly covers her fear with a big Mom smile.

LUCY (CONT'D)
Ha. I got you good Mom. I really scared you.

MAGGIE
Yes you did sweetie.

Lucy turns and starts to walk back down the driveway. Maggie looks after for a moment. Her smile gone.

EXT. ABANDONED HOUSE - NIGHT
When they reach the house Maggie can now see it is rundown and dark. The flashlight flickers and dims for a moment...

MAGGIE (under her breath)
No, no, no!

The flashlight brightens again. Maggie sighs. Maggie KNOCKS on the door and waits. After a moment she wipes the glass of the front door with her hoodie's sleeve and then peers in to see an OLD CHAIR, LAMP, and PHONE in the dim light. Maggie debates a moment and then wraps the sleeve of her hoodie around her hand and breaks the glass on the front door, reaches in and unlocks the door.

LUCY
Mommy. Why did you break that?

MAGGIE

Don't worry. We'll pay for the
window. I just want to see if there
is maybe a phone we can use.

INT. ABANDONED HOUSE - NIGHT

Maggie and Lucy enter.

MAGGIE

Hello? Anybody here?

When there is no response Maggie steps over to the lamp and clicks the switch. Nothing happens. She reaches for the old phone on the counter and checks for a dial tone. Nothing. She slams the phone back into the cradle.

MAGGIE (CONT'D)

Damn it! Damn it!

LUCY

What's wrong Mom?

MAGGIE

I just was hoping that we'd find
something here. Let's just go back.

In her rush to head towards the door Maggie catches her foot on something on the floor. She TWISTS HER ANKLE and falls to the ground.

MAGGIE (CONT'D)

Shit!

LUCY

Mommy! You ok?

Maggie stands up and tries to put some weight on it.

MAGGIE

Yes baby. I....

She flinches.

MAGGIE (CONT'D)

Maybe not. Okay. Help me over there.

Lucy helps her over to the old recliner.

MAGGIE (CONT'D)

I guess we're waiting here.

Mom brushes off the dusty old recliner and sits down.

MAGGIE (CONT'D)

Here. Sit on my lap.

LUCY

What's wrong Mommy?

Just then her cell phone RINGS. She pulls the phone out and answers.

MAGGIE

Hello. Are you here?

TOW TRUCK DRIVER (over the phone)
I'm sorry ma'am, I seemed to have gotten a little lost. Where on Thorn Street are you?

MAGGIE
Not Thorn Street. Thorn Road!

TOW TRUCK DRIVER (over the phone)
Well that would explain it. I'm sorry. I'll head out that way right away.

MAGGIE
I can't wait that long! I need someone now. My phone is about to die!

TOW TRUCK DRIVER (over the phone)
Once again ma'am, I am sorry for the inconvenience. I'll get out there as soon as I can.

MAGGIE
I'm sorry. I didn't mean to yell. I'm just a little flustered out here. It's dark and my little girl is frightened. We are waiting in the house across from the car. I hurt my ankle. Could you please come and help me back to my car when you get here?

TOW TRUCK DRIVER (over the phone)
Of course ma'am. Like I said, I'll
be there as soon as I can.

She looks at her phone as she hangs up. The battery on her phone is at 12%. Distracted by her phone, Maggie doesn't notice as Lucy slips out of the circle of light into the dark.

LUCY (guttural)
So hungry.

Maggie realizes her mistake.

MAGGIE
Lucy. Come back here with Mommy.
Come back to the light.

Lucy doesn't look up. She just looks sullenly at the floor. Her hair dangles over her face. Do we see teeth?

LUCY (guttural)
I don't want to! Hungry!

MAGGIE
Please honey. I know you're hungry...

Maggie searches desperately through her pockets and finds a GRANOLA BAR she hadn't found earlier.

MAGGIE (CONT'D)
I found a snack! Lucy. Listen.
Here's a granola bar. Just come here.

Lucy looks up, and seems to debate stepping back into the light.

LUCY

No...hungryyyy.

MAGGIE

I'll let you play Monster Kill.

This seems to do the trick. Lucy's head slowly perks up.

LUCY

Really?

MAGGIE

Yes. Just come sit here with me.
I'm sure the tow truck will be here soon.

Lucy sits in her Maggie's lap and plays her game until 10% BATTERY LIFE pops up.

MAGGIE (CONT'D)

Okay. Time to take a break.

LUCY

Aww Mom!

MAGGIE

Just in case the tow truck driver calls.

LUCY

I still feel my hunger.

MAGGIE

I'm sorry honey. I'm---"

The flashlight providing their little bit of light finally flickers and dies for good. Maggie shakes it, but it's no good. Now it's just the light of the cell phone with the low battery sitting in the red. 10%

MAGGIE (CONT'D)

Just a few minutes longer.

(Almost to herself) A few minutes more.

Suddenly a voice is heard outside the door.

TOW TRUCK DRIVER (OS)

Hello? Ma'am? Are you in here?

MAGGIE

Oh, thank god. Yes. Right in here.

Just a moment.

The door to the house opens. The silhouette of a man in the doorway. His FLASHLIGHT BEAM pointing across the room and into the Mom's eyes. Excited, Lucy jumps up and rushes into the dark.

MAGGIE (CONT'D)

Wait! Don't! Wait for me!

Maggie stands up on her bad ankle and cringes, sitting back down on the chair. The Tow Truck Driver looks over at Maggie. His flashlight focused on her.

TOW TRUCK DRIVER

Sorry about the mix up. Are you okay?

Something skitters through his flashlight beam. Lucy?!

LUCY

SO hungry...the hunger.

MAGGIE

NO! Leave the man alone! Flash light!

TOW TRUCK DRIVER

What the hell!?

MAGGIE

Get her in the light!
(to Lucy) The light!

Something latches onto his leg. He screams. And although it doesn't seem possible Lucy pulls the big man down. She bites his leg. He tries to pry her off, but he can't

TOW TRUCK DRIVER

What the hell! Sweet Jesus!! Please just make it sto--

He SCREAMS again as Lucy pounces again on his stomach. His flashlight tumbles to the ground and the BULB SHATTERS. He continues to SCREAM and there is a sound of GNASHING TEETH, TEARING FLESH, and CRUNCHING BONES until finally the screaming subsides. The CHEWING and SLURPING takes a little longer. Maggie slowly slides down the wall, horrified.

MAGGIE

Lucy. Lucy! Stop!

Lucy just GROWLS at her from the shadows. The phone's battery symbol moves from 7% to 6% to 5%. The chewing is still going on as Maggie notices the tow truck driver's flashlight on the floor a few feet away. She looks over in the direction of Lucy and the tow truck driver's body and then crawls across the floor, cellphone in hand, and grabs the tow truck driver's flashlight. She opens the battery compartment and quickly dumps the BATTERIES into her hand. Then opens her own flashlight, excited she might be able to still get out of here. Using her phone so she can see what she's doing.

MAGGIE (CONT'D)

It's okay baby. I know it was an accident. It'll be okay. We can move. Just like we did last time. We can start over again. Just as soon as I....

She dumps her BATTERIES out. They are the wrong kind. She breaks down. She screams and throws the batteries across the room. She sobs quietly for a moment. After a moment Maggie collects herself and looks at the time on her phone. Still a long way till daybreak.

LUCY (OS)

Mommy?

Maggie doesn't say anything. She just stares ahead into the darkness. Her cell in her hand. The light on. The battery reads 2%.

LUCY (CONT'D) (OS)

Mommy?

Maggie seems to break from her stupor.

MAGGIE

Yes baby?

LUCY

Can I sit on your lap?

Maggie reaches out her arms. Tired. Defeated.

MAGGIE

Of course sweetie.

Lucy moves into the glow of the cell phone. BLOOD is smeared all around her face as the girl climbs onto her lap.

LUCY

I'm still a little hungry Mommy.

Mom fumbles out the jackknife, flipping out the blade and sadly looks at her daughter.

LUCY (CONT'D)

Can I play Monster Kill?

Maggie looks at her phone. The battery reads 1%. She pauses.

MAGGIE

Sure.

Lucy takes the phone and opens the game. Maggie seems to come to a decision behind her and, with tears coming down her face, reaches up with the opened jackknife to kill her daughter...
The phone powers down.

LUCY

Aww.

And they are thrown in pitch blackness. Maggie SCREAMS and the CHEWING begins.

INT. ABANDONED HOUSE - NIGHT

A slurping, chewing sound continues in the darkness.

A phone RINGS. Muffled. Skittering FOOTFALLS are heard moving across the floor. A LIGHT GLOW can be seen through a shirt pocket reflecting across the BLOOD POOLED on the floor. Small bloody hands roll the body over and reach into the pocket for the phone.

She brings it to her face. The glow from the TOW TRUCK DRIVER's PHONE picks up the blood smeared around the little girls face.

LUCY

Hello?

END CREDITS

a few words from

WILLIAM VAN CUYUCK

As a designer of horror theatre or experiences, explain your process.

In my early twenties I was lucky enough to work at Terror on Church Street, one of the best live action horror attractions at the time. In watching the guests as they made their way through the labyrinth this job taught me more about the horror genre than I could have ever imagined. I had always loved horror. I don't think you apply for a job like that without enjoying the genre. I had already devoured hundreds, if not thousands of novels and movies. Each sinking into my psyche, but working there was like a class in the psychology of fear. Each impact or scare on a group helped me understand the different things that scared people and why. I use the things I learned there in my own creative process every time I sit down to write a new scary story or make a new horror film.

In writing a story or making a film you want to meet them down at the most basic level. People may react differently when they are scared, but it is the same basic things that scare them. Whether it is the supernatural or a masked knife wielding serial killer the thing that scares them is the things that are out of their control. That is the really scary monster. The Uncontrollable. So I like to give people a taste of the uncontrollable. Play on those basic fears and attack. One of the other things that that it taught me is that even in the darkest depths of drama or fear there is humor. It is our coping mechanism. How we fight the tide of desperation and fear we feel in a scary story or movie. I like to use this the same way I did at the haunted house. After you scare them, you make them laugh. They relax a little, let down their guard which just sets them up for you to get an even bigger scare the next time.

When is the last time you were genuinely scared by something someone created?

I recently watched *Betaal*, an Indian zombie horror series. It was a fun and interesting take on the zombie concept and it was great to see it viewed through the eyes of another culture. There were a couple moments, things they did with the zombies that I found unnerving just because it was against conventions and not what I expected.

Tell us about your contribution to our book. What was the inspiration?

Low Battery is a short film script I first wrote (and wanted to direct) as a vehicle for my daughter, Marion, but never got a chance to film. She is an actress and could pull off the perfect creepy little girl and I wanted to be able to take advantage of that and showcase her. She can still pull off the creepy girl look, she just is not so little anymore having reached her teenage years. It came from me thinking about how protective we are of our children. How we will do anything for them, even if they are little monsters sometimes. Even if it will come back to bite us someday.

What do you love about the genre of horror?

I think my love of the horror genre comes from the way it really speaks to the human condition. How our "monsters" are analogies for deeper issues of humanity and society. Oh, and also I love the scares. When something makes the hairs on your arms and the back of your neck stand up and pay attention. The sense of mystery and the things that no matter how hard you try you just can't explain that comes with a good book, movie, or just a good scary story that someone tells you around a campfire or with a flashlight under the sheets late at night.

What is some of your favorite horror literature? Favorite Author?

I would say my favorite horror literature is eclectic to say the least. I love the classics. I mean Edgar Allen Poe's *The Tell-Tale Heart* and W.W. Jacob's *The Monkey's Paw* are a couple of my favorites. Shirley Jackson's The Haunting of Hill House is another phenomenal piece of work. More recently I think *John Dies at the End* by David Wong has a snarky appeal I cannot deny and House of Leaves by Mark Z. Danielewski is almost indescribable in how detailed and multilayered it is. My favorite author is probably no surprise though, Stephen King. I love his work because of his ability to intertwine genres so easily. The ability to accentuate the normal and the monsters of society that don't even touch upon the supernatural and create such strong, real characters. Then to take those relatable, human characters and present them with incredible horrific situations.

What are some of your influences?

I have been interested in horror since I was a kid. My father first introduced me to the classic movies like *Frankenstein*, *Bride of Frankenstein, Dracula, The Wolfman* and the *Mummy*. I can still remember building the classic glow-in-the-dark Frankenstein model with my dad and then it's glowing body parts freaking me out as I tried to fall asleep. As I got older and started to read voraciously. Stephen King, Peter Straub, Edgar Allen Poe, Ray Bradbury, and Shirley Jackson all had a place on my nightstand or in the dark confines of my backpack on the way to school. More movies defined me too. There was, of course, *Poltergeist* and *Evil Dead* but how could Michael Myers, Jason, and Freddy not dig their claws into me as well. Movies like *Jaws, Alien*, and John Carpenter's *The Thing* were my some of my favorites and I still watch them every chance I can. In recent years Guillermo del Toro has been an inspiration. It is hard for his love of the genre not to make you just fall in love all over again. I dug deep into the lore of monsters because of these. Vampires, werewolves, and demons to aliens and the Bermuda Triangle. They all inspired and entertained me on my creative path and they still do to this day.

What is your favorite Halloween treat?

My favorite Halloween treat has to be Reese's Peanut Butter Cups, but I also love a good Peppermint Patty too.

You are hosting the perfect Halloween movie marathon. What are the films you choose and why?

My own personal Halloween movie marathon would start with *The Changling*. I remember the hairs raise up on my arms and the back of my neck the first time I watched it. Even better, the second, when I knew exactly what was about to happen. Second on the list would be *Evil Dead 2*. It would lighten the mood while still making you jump in all the right spots with lots of gore and a little demonic possession. Third would be some more possession with *The Exorcist*. There have been many demonic possession movies in recent years with exorcisms, but I don't think any have beat the original in the way they bring the feels. The first *Conjuring* would be next. I loved how it brought a bit of haunted history while being just a great creepy movie. As for the fourth, it would depend on the group's mood, either *Poltergeist, Get Out*, or John Carpenter's *The Thing* would probably get the call.

If you could continue any horror story (Book or Film), what would it be?

I think it would be interesting to take a swing at what happens next after John Carpenter's *The Thing*. It would be a challenge considering where things are left. What could happen next? Hmm? The possibilities are limitless.

Describe the perfect Halloween.

Halloween is by far my favorite holiday. Over the years, my perfect Halloween has changed. Whereas once it would have been out with friends for the all-night movie marathon, now it is a little different. I imagine the perfect Halloween now would be my wife and I handing out a few treats before heading out to meet up with friends and watching our kids enjoy trick or treating with some of their friends and younger cousins. Cruising the neighborhoods and seeing whose decorations are the best. Seeing all the kids in their costumes as they make their way from house to house filling their bags with candy goodness. Then, when their bags are full and their feet are sore heading home and introducing the kids to a horror movie classic.

SCARE CRED: WILLIAM VAN CUYUCK

William Van Cuyck is an award-winning writer and director of short films and author of the unproduced short screenplay *Low Battery*. As a lover of anything nerdy or scary, William started writing stories about superheroes and things that go bump in the night back in elementary school. An actor trained at the American Musical and Dramatic Academy, he realized that even though he loved acting he preferred life behind the camera. He studied film at FullSail University while scaring tourists on the weekends at a year-round live action haunted attraction. Now, happily married with two kids, William can be found either working on his next project, teaching his son to drive, or driving the freeways of Los Angeles taking his actress daughter to her next audition. You can also find him at @wvancuyck on Instagram and Twitter.

I SING BRADBURY ELECTRIC: A LOVING, PERSONAL REMEMBRANCE

BY STEVE VERTLIEB

He was a kindly, gentle soul who lived among us for a seeming eternity. But even eternity is finite. He was justifiably numbered among the most influential writers of the twentieth century. Among the limitless vistas of science fiction and fantasy he was, perhaps, second only in literary significance to H.G. Wells who briefly shared the last century with him. Ray Bradbury was, above all else, the poet laureate of speculative fiction. He shared with Ernest Hemingway the simplicity of phrase inspired by genius. No more legendary literary figure ever claimed Earth as his home, and yet Ray Bradbury was a childlike gargantuan whose life and artistry were shaped by the wonder and innocence of curiosity and tender imagination.

He was born into a world of rocket ships and monsters, a universe traversed by BUCK ROGERS, FLASH GORDON, FRANKENSTEIN, DRACULA, and a miraculous primordial ape called KING KONG. His boyhood was transformed by the promise of distant worlds and stranger creatures whose outward malevolence masked secret torment, the sadness of being deemed somehow different.

Ray Douglas Bradbury was born in Waukegan, Illinois (a home he shared with Jack Benny) on August 22nd, 1920. From birth he shared an affinity with the magical realm of motion pictures. His middle name was dedicated to the imagery of screen swashbuckler Douglas Fairbanks, and so Ray always knew that his spiritual ancestors consisted of pirates and colorful masked swordsmen. Coming of age during America's great Depression, the gregarious youth was lifted by the seat of his pants by silken images painted in celluloid. His heroes consisted not only of daring cavaliers such as Fairbanks, but by the pervasively exotic characterizations of Lon Chaney Sr., Boris Karloff and Bela Lugosi. The mystic lure of far away worlds beckoned the impressionable adolescent with the promise of tomorrow, while monstrous cinematic cadavers and rockets to Mars replaced the mundane scenery of a Depression stricken America.

As sympathetic souls and kindred spirits came together in pre-destined unison, Bradbury found himself drawn to the early worlds of science fiction, fantasy, pulp fandom and, together with fellow teenagers Ray Harryhausen and Forrest James Ackerman, began their journey of discovery, forming what has come to be recognized as "first fandom," in pursuit of creative profit and recognition. Bradbury would later state that he owed everything to Forry Ackerman who sold his first published story. The third member of the imaginative trio, Ray

Harryhausen, formalized their creative partnership with the visual realization of Bradbury's short story "The Fog Horn." Published in a celebrated issue of *The Saturday Evening Post,*the short story concerning a sea beast consumed by the tantalizing image of an isolated light house, became the basis for Harryhausen's first solo screen effort, THE BEAST FROM 20,000 FATHOMS.

Rod Serling encouraged the celebrated writer to join his literary enclave at CBS Television as the decade reached its conclusion and, while Bradbury submitted several scripts to Serling's classic science fiction/fantasy anthology series, THE TWILIGHT ZONE, only one was aired as a part of the series. "I Sing The Body Electric," inspired by Walt Whitman's famous poem, served as the basis for a Bradbury story in which an electric grandmother is hired by a wealthy widower to work as his children's nanny. The episode aired as a part of the series on May 18th, 1962 and was later included in a famous Bradbury anthology of the same name published in 1969. While this remains the only episode of the series penned by Bradbury, Serling managed to include an affectionate reference to the writer in his own melancholy tale ("Walking Distance") of an advertising executive on the verge of a nervous breakdown, coming home once more to the small town in which he had spent his boyhood. As Martin Sloan (Gig Young) walks along the streets of Homewood, he makes a casual reference to the Bradbury house standing prominently in his gaze. Homewood sweetly represented small town Americana from which both writers had migrated.

Ray Bradbury turned his adolescent energy and enthusiasm into poetic imagery, and brought a human face to Man's exploration of the stars. When Neil Armstrong took his first small steps upon the lunar landscape in July,1969, generating a giant leap of faith for all Mankind, Bradbury's frustration over the lack of excitement shown by the television networks covering the monumental story exploded into headlines, and a memorable tirade by the world's most eloquent innocent. Bradbury sat solemn and quiet as a guest on a network Lunar themed telecast, struggling to fill time with inanity after insanity. Unable to contain his rage at the proliferation of stupidity filling the national airwaves, the child in a man's body rose to his feet...outraged by the lack of understanding and exhilaration being exhibited by David Frost and his disinterested panel of guests...and threatened to walk off of the live telecast. His contempt for the bland assemblage of guests apparent, Bradbury admonished them as he would a poor student in the gaze of a disappointed teacher. "This is the greatest night in the history of the world," he raged. The lack of excitement over this cherished, awe inspiring moment in time, was just too much for this child of wonder either to accept or to absorb. The moment that Ray, and millions of children around the world, had dreamt of and imagined since BUCK ROGERS and SUPERMAN had first flown into space some thirty years earlier was finally here. That these simple, uninspired talk show guests were consumed with themselves, rather than this extraordinary moment of mortal achievement and exploration, was more than Bradbury could endure.

Like millions of imaginative children inhabiting Bradbury's world, I revered his name and legend. Ray Bradbury signified everything I'd ever dreamt of or aspired to.

As a quiet, introspective boy growing up in Philadelphia during the nineteen fifties, I became a poster child for what would one day become known as "A Monster Kid" -- a generation of "baby boomers" weened on, and inspired by, television, the huge monster movie craze of the fifties, and the introduction of a genre movie magazine with the unlikely name of *Famous Monsters of Filmland.* The progenitor of this magical publication was none other than the editor who had first brought Ray Bradbury to the attention of publishers. Forrest J Ackerman, or as he was known to his millions of adoring children, "Uncle Forry."

Forry was the Hans Christian Anderson of science fiction, fantasy, and horror, a Walt Disney father figure who, like the proverbial "Pan," would lure willing children to worlds and concepts beyond the stars, filling their imaginations with inspirational promise and invitation. He was a joyous Pied Piper who, together with his boyhood friends, Ray Bradbury and Ray Harryhausen, would cause generation after generation of youth to embrace their dreams, and create their own fantastic lives and careers. Steven Spielberg and George Lucas were only two of the many artists who found their singular paths among the clouds inhabited by Bradbury, Harryhausen, and Ackerman.

Ray Bradbury with Steve and Erwin Vertlieb

It was during the wonderful Summer months of 1974 that I traveled for the first time to Los Angeles, and came face to face with the land of fantasies, dreams, imagination, and motion pictures that had so consumed and mesmerized my own impressionable childhood. I was like the proverbial kid in the candy store. Everywhere I turned represented the reflection of my own childhood longing and wanderings.

Among my friends of the period was composer and orchestrator John Morgan. John announced one afternoon that he had received an invitation to Ray Bradbury's house that evening, and he wondered if my brother Erwin and I would like to join him for the royal summons. I swallowed my singular exhilaration, and excitedly accepted his generous invitation. Bradbury's residence was a large yellow structure in a quiet residential neighborhood. We nervously climbed the outer steps and rang the door bell. As the door opened, Ray greeted us personally and ushered the three of us into his living room. I was both thrilled and frightened, for here within my gaze was the legendary writer smiling at me and extending his hand. His hands, I remember, were very large and inviting and I became lost inside their welcome grasp. Ray asked me about my own career, and I told him that I was a published writer and minor film historian. My day job was, I explained, a film editor at a Philadelphia television station.

He asked if I knew that he had written the screen play for John Huston's magnificent 1956 production of MOBY DICK. I assured him that I had. He was very proud of the gift that Huston had given him after the picture had been released. It was a 16 millimeter Technicolor print of the Warner Bros. release given him personally by the director. Ray was like a little kid proudly showing off his Hopalong Cassidy pistol. He asked if I'd like to see a few minutes of the film. I said yes, of course, and he ran to find the print. His joy was infectious as I watched him delicately thread the projector and share his treasure with us.

As the film began to un spool on the screen in his living room I could see that the print was immaculate. My film editor's eye, however, noticed just the beginnings of an emulsion scratch in the otherwise gorgeous Technicolor print. I took my life in my hands, and asked Ray to stop the film for a moment. I don't know if it was courage on my part or youthful arrogance. It's difficult now to say which. Ray looked at me with a puzzled expression. I asked him if he ever cleaned his projector "gate." He asked what I meant. I said "Ray, do you have a box of cue tips and some Isopropyl Alcohol?" Here was one of the most important writers of the twentieth century going dutifully to fetch a box of cue tips for this young upstart transgressing his hospitality. I honestly thought he would lift me bodily from my chair, and hurl me out the door to the street below. Instead, like the gentle soul he was, he went out into another room to bring what I had requested. I took a cue tip from the box he had handed me and immersed it in the accompanying bottle of alcohol. I showed him how to clean the "gate" of the projector in the areas that came into contact with the film print and assured him that this procedure would help to keep his beloved Technicolor print from being torn and permanently scratched. He thanked me for this simple lesson in film maintenance, and appeared grateful, but I was thoroughly convinced at the time that I would soon be black listed all over Hollywood, and forbidden from ever encountering or confronting this splendid ICE CREAM MAN again. That was Ray. He was just a big kid...a gentle, enthusiastic child with the talent and intellect of a genius.

During that same trip out West we had the unique opportunity to sit in the audience with Ray and his wife for a live, small theater production of FAHRENHEIT 451. Ray told me that he adored Bernard Herrmann's original score for the Truffaut film version of his famous novel and, at his insistence, the small theater troupe used excerpts from the Herrmann recording of his score for London Phase 4 Records, with the composer conducting The London Philharmonic Orchestra. The experience was surreal.

After that, Ray and I maintained a sporadic, yet steady correspondence for the rest of his life. I remember running into him at one of Forry Ackerman's Famous Monsters Of Filmland conventions in Virginia in 1993. I hadn't seen Ray in years. He was surrounded, as he always was, by a burgeoning crowd of awe struck fans. I approached him and asked if he remembered an arrogant young man some twenty years earlier who had had the temerity, in his own living room, to lecture him on the care and feeding of his 16 millimeter movie projector. He looked up at me from the hotel couch on which he was sitting and grinned somewhat impishly, pointing his finger in my direction. "Was that YOU?" I assured him that I was, indeed, that brazen young lad. We both chuckled over the recollection of that embarrassing episode so many years earlier. He might have cringed at my appearance, but he didn't. He simply chuckled in delight. He was A MEDICINE FOR MELANCHOLY.

Among the many ties that bound us together was Ray's passionate interest in symphonic motion picture music written for the screen. We shared a love for the music of such composers as Bernard Herrmann, Miklos Rozsa, and Max Steiner among others. I had known Miklos Rozsa as a friend for nearly thirty years, and Ray not only admired his music, but had worked together with the composer during the filming of KING OF KINGS for MGM in 1961. Rozsa had won a richly deserved Oscar for his magnificent 1959 score for Metro-Goldwyn- Mayer's BEN-HUR, and so was asked to write the music for the studio's early sixties remake of the original 1927 Cecil B. DeMille silent classic. Ray was hired by Metro to write the narration spoken by Orson Welles scattered throughout the picture, and attended some of the recording sessions with Rozsa.

In 2007 the historic Castro Theater in San Francisco was preparing a special film festival honoring the work of the legendary composer, and I was asked to choose the films for the presentation, write the liner notes for the program, and co-host the festival. As it turned out, the Miklos Rozsa film festival became a major San Francisco event in late 2007 and early 2008 with seventeen motion pictures presented to packed houses over a nine day period. The composer's daughter, Juliet Rozsa, along with his granddaughters Nicci and Ariana, all drove in from Los Angeles and appeared with me on stage during the introductions. I was honored to read proclamations from both the Mayor of San Francisco, as well as the Hungarian Ambassador to The United States. However, the introduction that thrilled me the most was one written expressly for the event by Ray Bradbury.

Knowing Ray's love for film music, I wrote him about the festival. He wrote me back asking if he might contribute his own written introduction to the festival. I was honored to accept his lovely request. After all, who was I to say say "no" to Ray Bradbury. Consequently, I felt a tingle of excitement as I read Ray's brief, loving words from the stage to an audience of some seven hundred people just prior to my "live" interview with Juliet Rozsa, and a 35 millimeter screening of the composer's masterpiece, BEN-HUR.

Over the years that followed I continued to correspond with Ray, both my mail and through the internet. Each Christmas would bring Ray's newest holiday poetry which seemed to arrive not through conventional mail delivery but, rather, upon wings of angels within a snow covered sleigh. On one memorable occasion, after sending him an article I'd written pertaining to the science fiction genre we both so adored, he wrote me a lovely note thanking me for continuing to write about the worlds of fantasy and science fiction. He felt a singular obligation to keep the faith, so to speak, through his own place in literary history, and wanted to thank me, as well, for continuing to carry the torch along with him. Despite his advancing years and assorted health problems, which included a debilitating stroke in 1999, he was still the same little boy who had discovered the wonder of other worlds and galaxies so many decades before. Like Ray Harryhausen and Forry Ackerman, with whom he had shared his first spiritual journeys to outer space, he wrote "Steve…You're a good pal." I nearly cried when I read that, and wanted to reach out and hug this gentle soul whose life and work had so touched and impacted my own.

Ray continued to find wonder in the music of the movies and particularly loved Jerry Goldsmith's valiant score for THE WIND AND THE LION. His affection for Goldsmith's exhilarating musical themes for the romantic Sean Connery adventure film inspired his own work, and he proudly acknowledged his debt to the composer's symphonic poetry in creating NOW AND FOREVER: SOMEWHERE A BAND IS PLAYING , published by William Morrow Company in 2007.

I published my own tribute to Jerry Goldsmith and his music for another epic score, FIRST KNIGHT, in June, 2011, at Film Music Review, and discussed Ray's love for that earlier Goldsmith music. I sent the article to Ray's beloved daughter, Alexandra (Zee) shortly after its online publication. I think that one of the greatest thrills of my life, perhaps, was when Zee took my work along with her during a trip to her dad's home a few weeks later, and read it to him. She wrote me that he smiled from ear to ear and offered his own enthusiastic comments as she read him my words about the Goldsmith music.

Several weeks later I received a small parcel from Ray in the mail. On the face of the large white envelope were two postage stamps honoring Edgar Allan Poe. Next to the stamps, Ray had drawn an arrow pointing toward Poe, and written in big letters "My Pa." Inside the envelope were a photograph of Ray standing next to a painting of Poe, along with a handwritten note which read...

Steve:

Thanks for "Mickey" (Miklos Rozsa) 4E (Forry Ackerman) Xmas & ME!

Love,

Ray

I got to see Ray a couple of more times, and those visits were the most wonderful love fests that I could have imagined. After the death of his lifelong friend friend Forry Ackerman, I sent Ray my Rondo nominated tribute to my own forty seven year friendship with Uncle Forry and, as I sat at his side, Ray said "I owe him everything." I visited Ray shortly after his ninetieth birthday in late August, 2010. He was busily involved in numerous tributes, interviews and appearances honoring his birthday, but he told Zee to please somehow fit me into his schedule... and so I traveled with my little brother Erwin to Ray's house to spend a loving hour at his feet. It was difficult for him to speak due to ill health, but he was obviously happy to see us and felt invigorated by our visit. I continued to feel astonished that this world renowned literary figure, this giant of a writer, was still living within the confines of the very same humble home he'd shared with an unsuspecting, quiet residential neighborhood for some fifty years. When I asked him about it, he told me that he'd raised his family and enjoyed much of his fame and success in his beloved house. Why would he ever wish to leave it?

In January, 2010, I discovered that my own health had been dramatically failing and that I would need major open heart surgery quite soon if I were to survive. In mid February of that year we scheduled surgery for a few weeks hence. I wrote Ray of my impending procedure, and he playfully instructed Zee to write me of the poetic irony of my requiring heart surgery right around Valentine's Day. He further instructed her to tell me that he would not allow me to die. Who was I to contradict Ray Bradbury?

I was able to visit Ray one more time during the closing days of August, 2011. Once again, the demands on his time had become nearly impossible, as the world around him was beginning to understand and respect the significance and singular importance of the solitary inspiration who had so profoundly influenced the better part of their lives. Once again, Ray grew excited at the prospect of my impending visit and asked Zee to please arrange his schedule so that he might find time to see me. When Zee wrote me that "Dad" was excited about seeing me during my visit to Los Angeles, I humbly pondered the reasons why Ray Bradbury...this living legend...would grow excited over seeing me, of all people. I think the reason for his enthusiasm had little to do with me personally. It was just that Ray had never truly grown up. He was still the eternal innocent...still the little boy possessed of childlike awe and wonder who was eager to stop time and simply visit with an old "pal."

Ray had just turned ninety-one and was visibly excited over the news that a film production company had just purchased the rights to his novel *Dandelion Wine*. As we entered the house, Zee told me that her dad was thrilled by the report and that he couldn't wait to tell me about it. When I entered his den I found him in good spirits and quite animated. We talked of the sale, and of our nearly forty year friendship. As the time wore on, and Ray was growing tired, I grew unusually sentimental as we were to preparing to leave. I filled up with tears as I told Ray how deeply I loved him, and how he had so profoundly impacted not only my life, but the lives of literally millions of friends and admirers all over the world who loved him as well, and owed him so very much. I arose from my chair and embraced this frail, gentle soul. I kissed him on his cheek, and told him how much he meant to me. He said "I love you, too, Steve" as each of us smiled and fought back the inevitable tears. As we left the modest home on Cheviot Drive, I turned once more to see the façade and stood there for a moment, deep in thought and contemplation. As we got into the car, I said to Erwin "I have a terrible feeling that this is the last time we'll ever see Ray."

The remaining months of 2011 slipped quickly away. A new year was dawning but, with it, came new health concerns...not only for me, but for my beloved mom who had celebrated her one hundredth birthday six months earlier. In the early morning hours of February 1st, 2012, I received the dreaded telephone call that my mother had passed away. Among the treasured notes and letters of condolence that I received was a touching E-mail from Ray and Zee Bradbury expressing their sadness over the loss of my mom.

Nostalgia for things past and for a simpler time, perhaps, has become a common thread shared by so many so called "baby boomers." In December, 2011, I was interviewed in my home for two hours by film director Robert Tinnell and a camera crew for a new film documentary concerning the "Monster Kid" phenomenon inspired by Forrest J Ackerman, his groundbreaking *Famous Monsters Of Filmland*Magazine, and the hugely popular, affectionately remembered monster movie craze of the 1950's. Such luminaries as Steven Spielberg and George Lucas owe their careers to the phenomenon, as do such decidedly minor players as myself. While the film has not yet been completed, the producers released a theatrical trailer promoting their forthcoming documentary in the Spring. I sent the link for the trailer to Zee Bradbury, inspiring her to write back that "Dad should really be a part of this." I telephoned Bob Tinnell on his mobile phone while he was driving in West Virginia to let him know that Ray Bradbury was interested in appearing in his film. He pulled off to the side of the road in excitement over the news. I put Bob in touch with Zee, and they arranged for Bob to come and visit Ray either in late May or early June, 2012, to interview him for the film.

In the meantime, I had spoken with Zee about my own impending return to Los Angeles in late August, 2012 and, as usual, she wrote back that her dad was excited about seeing me, and had asked her to re-arrange his schedule so that he might find the time to do so. While at work on the morning of Wednesday, June 6th, I received an E-Mail from Bob Tinnell letting me know that Ray had passed away during the night before at his home in Los Angeles. I stared at my Blackberry phone in stunned silence, unable to fully grasp the news. Ray Bradbury was gone. I began to cry. My lifelong hero and friend had died. I would no longer behold his wonderful face and childlike smile, nor would I ever again find my own hands lost in his. He had joined Forry and his other pals in what must surely be Science Fiction Heaven. Ray shared our lives and existence for an all too brief and shining moment in eternity, and now he had departed, leaving us to face a world sadly dreary in his absence.

Ray has found peace in another realm of immortality, having joined THE GHOSTS OF FOREVER, and yet his work lives on beyond his fabled physical presence, and we shall continue to sing Bradbury Electric in joyful celebration and chorus for the remainder of our own solitary sojourn upon this wondrous sphere.

THE MOST 'FAMOUS MONSTER' OF THEM ALL: A PERSONAL REMEMBRANCE OF FORREST J. ACKERMAN

BY STEVE VERTLIEB

In a child-like land of dreams and dragons dwelt a Pied Piper of imagination, a Santa Claus of fantasy and horror, who lived in the mythical kingdom of Horrorweird, Karloffornia. His name was Forrest J. Ackerman but, to his friends and colleagues, he was simply "Forry." A generation of wide- eyed children grew up under the spell of his magical influence beginning in 1958, at the tail end of the horror, science fiction and fantasy cycle of motion pictures that had dominated movie screens across the country. Famous Monsters of Filmland Magazine made its premiere appearance on news stands that year, an enchanted pictorial ticket to a fantasy domain unprecedented at the time.

Famous Monsters, or F.M. as it came to be known, was the first magazine devoted entirely to the horrific legacy of classic horror films, covering five decades of the misunderstood genre with loving attention. For lonely, imaginative children all over the world, Famous Monsters became a wondrous destination. Within its modest pages dinosaurs returned to life, werewolves and vampires stalked the vivid tableau of illustrated nightmares, and gargantuan creatures reached out from beyond their printed domain and pages to excite and exhilarate the senses. Famous Monsters of Filmland became home to millions of boys and girls, a refuge from the mundane, and a tantalizing invitation to unrealized realms of wonder and imagination.

Born November 24th, 1916, Forry reportedly picked up an issue of Amazing Stories Magazine in a drug store located at the corner of Santa Monica Boulevard and Western Avenue in Hollywood at the age of nine, and was instantly hooked. At least, that's the legend.

In 1929 he began the "Boy's Science Fiction Club" and, by 1932, had become a founding member and Contributing Editor of The Time Traveler, the original fan publication devoted to sci-fi. First Fandom seems to have begun in Clifton's Cafeteria in downtown Los Angeles with the formation, by Ackerman and others, of "The Science Fiction Society," a celebration of the genre by teenage boys who included Ray Harryhausen and Ray Bradbury.

Their amateur magazine, Imagination, edited by a youthful Ackerman, published the first story by Ray Bradbury in a 1938 issue. During the Second World War, Ackerman edited a military newspaper at Fort MacArthur in San Pedro and, by the end of the war, had opened up his own literary agency. His reputation, honesty, and love for the genre attracted many of the top writers in the field to his representation, including Bradbury, Hugo Gernsback (the avowed "Father" of modern science fiction), Isaac Asimov, A.E. Van Vogt, and L. Ron Hubbard.

The original publication of Famous Monsters of Filmland Magazine ran from 1958 until 1983, under the auspices of publisher James Warren and Warren Publications. As the magazine continued to garner success, it was joined by a happy coterie of brother and sister publications such as Monster World, Screen Thrills Illustrated (devoted to Saturday matinee cliffhangers, and edited by Sam Sherman), and Spacemen (devoted exclusively to science fiction films).

Forry was officially credited with inventing the term "Sci-Fi," claiming that the inspiration came to him while listing to the radio in his car with wife, Wendayne, one afternoon out on the road. The disc jockey on the air referred to a recording as being played in "Hi-Fi." Hence, a youthful generation of fans came to regard their cherished genre as "Sci-Fi."

I began buying copies of Famous Monsters Of Filmland at the news stand, and at my local pharmacy either with issue six or eight, but quickly ordered the previous back issues as soon as I came to understand what I had lucked into. I was immediately lost in a special treasure trove of joyously terrifying apparitions, and poured over each new issue as an archaeologist might have relished the discovery of an ancient Egyptian mummy. It was somewhere around 1964 when I first encountered Forry Ackerman.

Growing impatient for a more serious or scholarly approach to imagi-movies, and immersed in the cocky deceit of adolescent arrogance, I wrote him a self- righteous letter decrying the juvenile approach of the magazine I had once loved without judgment. To my utter delight, (yet astonishment) came back a lengthy, two-page letter in scholarly defense of my petty diatribe. "Every couple of years or so," he wrote, "someone writes me this same kind of complaining letter about the magazine, and I'll be happy to tell you what I have told them."

He went on in a genuinely kindly manner to explain that he would have preferred to take a more scholarly approach to the subject, but that both his young readers and his publisher had made it clear that they wanted an easier, more accessible approach to the subject of monstrous movies, and that his hands were tied.

I was immediately struck by his gentle honesty and felt guilty that I had been compelled to attack a man and a concept that had given me such immeasurable delight and pleasure over the past four or five years. We began a wonderful correspondence over the next twelve months which I treasured and enjoyed.

Then, during the early days of September, 1965, I received a tiny envelope post marked from New York. It was addressed to the Vertlieb Brothers and, despite its eastern origin, led me to suspect that it was from Forry. Inside was a note in gold printing that read, simply, "An Invitation from Forry Ackerman." With mounting excitement I opened the folded paper and gasped as I read its contents. The folded note beckoned my little brother Erwin and I to come to New York City for the first Famous Monsters Convention. It was billed as the 1965 New York Monstercon, and was being held on September 18th of that year from 1 pm until 4 pm at Loew's Midtown Motor Inn at 8th Avenue and 48th Street in Room 201. I was just nineteen years old. My brother was sixteen. We had never ventured outside of Philadelphia by ourselves. My father had taken us to the New York World's Fair the year before, but we had never made this kind of an epic journey by ourselves. I can still remember the nervous excitement we felt the evening before. I lay awake all night, unable to sleep. As morning approached, we bravely boarded a bus to 30th Street Station and stepped onto the Pennsylvania Railroad car to the biggest city in the world.

We were strangers in a strange land, innocents abroad, maturing quickly as we walked the busy streets of the sprawling metropolis in search of our monstrous destiny. We arrived at the hotel early, and bravely rode the elevator to the 2nd floor. As we walked through the empty corridor my heart pounded so loudly that I thought it would burst through my chest.

There...we found it....Room 201. There was no noise emanating from within and, when I reached down my hand and grasped the door handle I found that it was locked. Were we too early, I wondered? Was this the right room? Were we even in the right hotel? We walked back to the elevators and pressed the lobby designation. We were lost and scared, knowing no one in New York. The doors parted when we reached the lobby and there, staring back at us, was the grinning face of an older man I'd come to recognize from the yellowing pages of Famous Monsters.

There he was in the flesh...well, sort of...glasses, moustache, dark hair...wearing a jacket and dark tie.

He was 48 years young, and his face bore a faintly mischievous grin. Although I was Jewish, I knew that I had just come face to face with Santa Claus. My brother was busily staring at the elevator floor when the door parted. I nudged him with my elbow, and he looked up. I pointed in a not terribly nonchalant manner at the Draculean figure blocking our path to the lobby. As I did so, the distinguished gentleman before us gave me the "finger," as well, in mock recognition of the importance of this historic moment, pointing to us as I had done to him. "Forry?" I asked. "Yes," he answered with a grin. "Are you the Vertlieb brothers?" "Yes," I answered. I was eloquent even then, you see.

Forry joined us on the elevator as we rode once again to the second floor. By this time, the door had opened to Room 201 and several guests had already arrived. For me and, I suspect, my brother, this was to be a magical afternoon and our introduction to the world of organized fandom. There were many of Forry's adopted children there and it was, I'm sure, the beginning of a wondrous, fanciful voyage for them, as well. There were young fans by the unlikely names of Allan Asherman, George Stover, Gary Svehla, and Walter J. Shank who preferred to be called "Wes." We all reached out to Forry and to each other, as brothers finding our elusive twins after a lifetime of separation. We were no longer different, or alone. We had found others like ourselves, and it was an invigorating realization. We had found a homeland that none of us ever wanted to leave again.

It was as though the "Book People" in Ray Bradbury's visionary tale of Fahrenheit 451 had discovered others like themselves and had settled into a new reality in which "monsters" were not only okay, but loving and respectable. Frankenstein and Dracula were, in sweet actuality, soft spoken actors bringing culture and artistry to their profession, while The Wolfman and The Mummy brought simplicity to the screen in their portrayal of very normal human insecurity and fear.

We learned that day that being "different" was being special. It was a healthy education, presided over by the gentle writer and film fan seated at the head of the class. We grew to know him as Uncle Forry for he was, indeed, the kindly uncle we had never known; generous, giving, and able to visualize hitherto unknown worlds that sparkled radiantly within our young imaginations.

A year or two after that memorable afternoon, perhaps in 1967, Uncle Forry was appearing at a Philadelphia convention as a guest, I believe, of the Philadelphia Science Fiction Society. I asked my mom if I could invite Forry to lunch at our house, and she said yes. I then asked Forry if he'd like to join us for lunch at my house because I wanted to show him my own small, but growing collection of movie and fantasy memorabilia.

He agreed to come, but was concerned about the menu. He had recently suffered a slight heart attack, and was feeling understandably fragile. A tuna sandwich on white bread seemed to fill the bill, and he joined us for a couple of unforgettable hours in my personal dream domain.

I couldn't believe it! Forry Ackerman was appearing live and in person at my house. I would have announced it to the neighbors, had they known who he was. I took Forry upstairs to my bedroom where I had proudly displayed my own movie treasures, and he politely acknowledged their importance. I had a small record collection of movie soundtracks, and wanted to play "Name That Tune" with my infamous guest. I pulled out my used recording of the suite From Things to Come by Sir Arthur Bliss on RCA records and he, of course, recognized the familiar themes immediately. The Ackermonster was a guest in my house, and I couldn't have been more proud and happy.

I had always enjoyed writing, and probably began a journal when I was a little boy, writing entire plots for the films I had seen in order to preserve them in my memory. It was the 1950s, and at least one or two hundred years before the advent of home video.

I had attempted more serious excursions in writing by the mid sixties, and had brazenly put together a mercifully short story intended as an unofficial sequel to Bram Stoker's novel Dracula. It was called Dracula Revisited, which wasn't, in retrospect, the most original title for a sequel. Forry liked it, however, and wrote me about a major horror anthology that he was editing for a Spanish publisher in Barcelona. He asked if I'd like to have my short story included in the volume. At his request, I worked very hard at tightening and revising my original story.

Las Mejores Historias De Horror appeared on book shelves in Spain in 1968, and 1969, with a cover credit that read "Recopiladas por Forrest J Ackerman." It was a massive paperback edition that featured a virtual who's who of horror authors and literature, compiled by Forry himself, that included stories by Tennessee Williams, Bram Stoker, Ray Bradbury, A.E. Van Vogt, Theodore Sturgeon, Robert Bloch, John Wyndham, Jack London, Donald Wandrei, Donald Wolheim, Val Lewton and, for fifteen glorious pages beginning on page 79, the newly titled The Second Death Of Dracula by a youthful writer by the name of Stephen Vertlieb.

I was never directly involved in either the creation or production of Famous Monsters of Filmland Magazine, merely its loyal servant. However, during the run of its sister publication, Monster World, I achieved a dubious fifteen minutes of fame in the Fang Mail, or letters to the editor section, in which the assistant editors would often fill the column with fabricated letters from friends. They would change the names, however, in order to protect the innocent. One such name that appeared periodically, you should excuse the expression, was "Steve Liebvert." Ron Borst and Mark Frank had tremendous enjoyment poking fun at their friends and fellow fans in this manner. In the many ensuing years, I spent considerable time with Forry. We'd meet frequently at conventions held in New York City, and would often talk until dawn about films, actors, music, and our favorite monsters. We'd usually follow up these marathon sessions by going out for breakfast at four or five in the morning at a nearby cafe diner. Forry loved to tell stories about his friendship with Boris Karloff, or about owning the Lugosi Dracula ring and cape.

However, his favorite story was of once having attended a lecture by the immortal H.G. Wells. Wells, he related, was in his latter years and spoke in a high-pitched, rasping voice. Forry mastered his impression of Wells with studious effort, wishing to preserve the legacy of one of our greatest writers by duplicating his voice for future generations to hear. He would grow quiet for a moment, as though emerging from a portal to another dimension, and begin... "I wish to speak to you for about an hour." It was a thrilling moment as Wells spoke to us softly from beyond the grave.

I'd sometimes find invitations from Forry to birthday parties held in his honor, usually in New York. I joined Allan Asherman for one of those memorable evenings in which we were regaled by stories of his youth and love for the genre. Publisher Jim Warren was there, as well, and thanked everyone for coming. I couldn't help feeling special for being asked by Forry to join him at these storied events.

During my first trip to Los Angeles in 1974, I found myself honored to be in the company of two of my own personal heroes and friends. I had begun a passionate correspondence with Robert Bloch, the celebrated author of Psycho, in 1970. Bob wrote me that if I ever visited the city of angels, he'd volunteer to act as a tour guide, and drive my brother and I all over Hollywood to see the landmark sites. When I arrived, Bob was true to his word.

We drove to Paramount and walked the western streets that John Wayne had once commanded, and visited George Pal's office where the legendary producer/director was working on a teleplay for CBS based upon In The Days Of The Comet by H.G. Wells. Among our stops was a trip to the Ackermansion where Forry Ackerman played host to Bob, Erwin, and I. It was an afternoon I don't think I'll ever forget.

Forry's mansion was a gargantuan museum of treasured, priceless artifacts from the golden age of cinema and science fiction, and he was a jovial, congenial host, pointing out and highlighting the most famous crowns in his fantasy jewel of a home. The day ended with a dinner invitation from Bob and his lovely wife, Elly, to their home for a wonderful evening of conversation and food.

In the early nineties at a Fanex sci-fi convention, either in Baltimore or Virginia, I was asked to host "An Hour with Forrest J. Ackerman." Gary and Sue Svehla had put the convention together with loving hands and, knowing my friendship and history with Forry, asked if I'd consider hosting the hour long presentation. I happily agreed, and spent a delightful hour seated next to the irrepressible story teller.

Knowing Forry's penchant for puns and corresponding punishment, I began the hour by telling the assembled crowd that I had searched high and low for my guest throughout the hotel grounds, but was unable to find

Steve Vertlieb and his brother Forry Ackerman and Robert Bloch

him. I walked out into the hotel parking lot, adjoining a nearby park, but "I couldn't find Forry for the trees." Forry stood up, pretending to be offended by the joke, and started for the door. I pulled him back to his chair, promising to control myself in future.

Then Forry uttered a terrible, groan worthy pun and, in revenge, I arose in mock outrage and headed for door. He pulled me back to my seat as the audience laughed in understanding approval. When the hour ended, Forry asked me if I'd provide him with a copy of my remarks for his files. I did so happily.

Not long after that, Forry returned to Virginia for The Famous Monsters Convention held, I believe, in 1993. It was an all star conclave featuring hundreds of his best friends. Among the guests was Robert Bloch who, now frail and fragile, mesmerized the crowd with his tales of working on Boris Karloff's Thriller television series. Sadly, I realized that it would probably be the last time that I'd ever get to spend time with Bob. It was.

During the course of the weekend, there was an affectionate presentation to Forry from each of the countless magazines and fanzines he'd happily inspired. Among these was Cinemacabre, a wonderful magazine I'd played a small part in producing and creating, along with publisher George Stover, and editor John Parnum. John made the speech honoring both Forry and his influence on us "kids." George and I accompanied him to the stage, however, and when the time came for us to leave, I reached down and kissed Forry on his forehead. He smiled, and the audience laughed. It was just my way of saying thank you to a gentle soul who had changed my life.

It wasn't long after that that Forry suffered what may have been a stroke. He never entirely recovered from his illness. He continued to make appearances along with his lifelong friends, Ray Bradbury and Ray Harryhausen, but his health had grown precarious and he appeared skeletal in photographs I'd seen of him. He was forced to give up the Ackermansion, and sell much of his storied collection. He moved into a quiet bungalow, retaining merely a few of his most precious possessions.

In 2007, during the Labor Day Weekend, I read that Forry was attending World Con, the world science fiction convention in Los Angeles. A film that I had appeared in, Kreating Karloff, was being screened at the convention, and I wanted Forry to have an opportunity to see it. I contacted his personal assistant, Joe, and asked him to make sure that Forry was seated in the auditorium when the film was presented. Dutifully, Joe notified Forry of the screening and he sat through the one hour documentary. The following week I sent Forry an E-Mail asking if he had enjoyed the movie. He wrote back that he enjoyed it very much, but that he was perplexed by the appearance of the gray-haired old gentleman in the movie who bore my name. I chuckled, and wrote back that "You should talk."

At Thanksgiving, 2008, we all learned that Forry was, perhaps, ringing down the final curtain of his celebrated life and my prayers, as well as the prayers of thousands of boys and girls around the globe, went out to him. "Little Stevie Spielberg," George Lucas, and John Landis were among the countless fans, friends, and admirers who reached out to Forry in his final days to thank him for a lifetime of imagination. I telephoned him, but he had retired for the evening, exhausted but gratified at the expression of love and homage filling both his telephone and mailbox. I left a lengthy message on his machine in which I told him of my love and affection for him, and how deeply he had impacted so many generations of creative artists. I spoke with Joe the next day to ask if Forry had heard my message. He told me that Forry had indeed listened, and that he had smiled at the sound of my voice.

Forry seemed to rally for another couple of weeks, confounding his doctors and, for a time, it appeared that he was growing stronger. I thought that he might beat the odds after all. I put it out of my head for a few hours. I was visiting some old friends in Baltimore on Friday, December 5th when I heard the news. As fate would have it, I was sitting in George Stover's living room, seated next to the friend I had first met those endless years ago in New York at the very first Monster Con in 1965, when the text of a heartbreaking E-Mail message appeared on his screen. Forry Ackerman had died. We both sighed. It was a very sad and deeply felt sigh. Uncle Forry was gone. The lives we had so joyously inherited from this sweet, youthful old man would simply never be the same again. He's resting now in the fabled "Metropolis" of his favorite film, traveling above the futurian cities of a fantasy sky line along with Boris Karloff, Lon Chaney Sr., Lon Chaney, Jr., Bela Lugosi, Peter Lorre, and Fritz Lang. The narrator's voice is a familiar one to Forry, as H.G. Wells and company welcome him home at last.

For Steve + Erwin Vertlieb,
2 extremely fine young men
I am happy to have as
friends.
Forry Ackerman

FANEX 15
FANEX 15

a few words from

STEVE VERTLIEB

As a designer of horror theatre or experiences, explain your process.

I try to imagine things that would scare me, and then begin to outline the story or article from its roots to conclusion.

When is the last time you were genuinely scared by something someone created?

I found the first two *Conjuring* films quite frightening. Stephen King's *The Mist* was similarly terrifying with unmistakable roots derived from the classic horror/science fiction films of the nineteen fifties.

Tell us about your contribution to our book. What was the inspiration?

A lifelong, enduring affection for fantasy, science fiction, and horror films.

What do you love about the genre of horror?

I've always been fascinated by the unknown, and by circumstances beyond the realm of complacency. Things that derive from unhinged origins, or from beyond acceptable definitions of intellectual sobriety hold fascination for me. If we cannot name it or classify it, then we cannot control it. That is a terrifying concept.

What is some of your favorite horror literature? Favorite Author?

My favorite novel will always be Bram Stoker's *Dracula*. I read it in its maleficent entirety three times. As for my favorite authors, I would choose H.P. Lovecraft, Robert Bloch, Richard Matheson, Ray Bradbury, Arthur C Clarke, Charles Beaumont, Ray Russell, and James Herbert.

What are some of your influences?

Robert Bloch was not only a mentor, but a cherished friend.

What is your favorite Halloween treat?

Watching the classic Universal horror films with Boris Karloff, Bela Lugosi, and Lon Chaney, Jr.

You are hosting the perfect Halloween movie marathon. What are the films you choose and why?

I shall always consider the Robert Wise classic *The Haunting* the single most frightening movie ever made, simply because of what you don't see, as opposed to what you do. Nothing could ever surpass the boundaries of your own unbridled Imagination, and *The Haunting* derives its terrors from one's private inner demons and terrors. After that, I would choose *The Uninvited* (Paramount, 1944) and *Night of the Demon* (Columbia, 1957) for their similarly proportioned servings of things unseen that go "bump in the night."

If you could continue any horror story (Book or Film), what would it be?

Bram Stoker's *Dracula*. In my youth, I did write a short sequel to Stoker's book which was actually published by Forrest J Ackerman in a Spanish anthology of horror stories.

Describe the perfect Halloween.

Wall to wall classic Universal and MGM horror films from the thirties.

SCARE CRED: STEVE VERTLIEB

An award-winning writer, film historian, critic, archivist, musicologist, and poet, Steve Vertlieb has been writing about motion pictures and symphonic film music in a variety of books, magazines, journals, tabloids, and on the internet since 1969 and has been profiled in "*Who's Who in Entertainment in America*." His work has appeared in such publications as "*Cinemacabre*," "*Midnight Marquee*," and "*Penny Dreadful*." Inducted into The International Association Of Film Music Critics, he is also the subject of a forthcoming, feature-length motion picture documentary entitled *Steve Vertlieb: The Man Who "Saved" The Movies*...currently filming on both coasts, and scheduled for film festival release in 2021. Steve Vertlieb is the recipient of the "Rondo" Lifetime Achievement "Hall of Fame" Award.

NOT ALL GIRLS LOVE PINK

BY BOSTON WHITE

a few words from

BOSTON WHITE

What do you love about the genre of horror?

Horror, to me is a "safe scared," in the same way that people love to ride roller coasters; it is a controlled danger. For that 3 minutes experience, 30-minute episode, 2-hour movie, (3 nights of sleeping with the light on) adrenaline is pumping. I am a creative: when I'm watching a horror film, attending a horror event, reading a book, I'm not just looking for a quick scare that I'll forget about a few days later. I appreciate the story, the cinematography, admiring the effects, the costumes, the set design. Horror, for me is a lifestyle. It's a lifelong passion that has shaped me as a person. From my first horror love - the *Universal Classic Monsters*, when I was just a small child, to watching the making of Michael Jackson's *Thriller* on a loop - which opened my eyes to the worlds of John Landis and Rick Baker - to my pre-teen years, discovering the horror greats like George Romero, Alfred Hitchcock, John Carpenter, Tobe Hooper, leading to the present day with my work on podcasts (The Halloween Half Hour, Universal After Dark) and youtube (Bostonwhite) covering the horror genre and Halloween / Horror events.

What is some of your favorite horror literature?

Mary Shelley's *Frankenstein*. It's so beautifully written and a wonderful example of gothic horror literature. This has been my favorite ever since I can remember. I could read it over and over and never be bored. It's incredibly emotional, romantic, filled with sorrow. So many emotions are felt for the monster—a real rollercoaster. I also love the tale of how Mary Shelley came up with the story of *Frankenstein*. She was on holiday in Switzerland with her fiancé Percy Shelley and their friend Lord Byron, and they had all challenged each other to come up with the scariest story. Mary came up with the story of Frankenstein. Over the years, there have been many different interpretations of *Frankenstein* from many different creators, different films, different stories, different layers - if you have never read this original story, I highly recommend buying a copy.

What are some of your influences?

I adore makeup and special effects. My biggest influence is Rick Baker. He is such a pillar of the industry. His work is beautiful and unmatched. Milicent Patrick, she designed the Creature From the Black Lagoon, although she wasn't credited for it for many years. A woman named Mallory O'Meara recently wrote a book about her called *The Lady from the Black Lagoon*, I recommend reading it!

What is your favorite Halloween treat?

I love York peppermint patties. They're not widely available here in the UK, but during my most recent trip to the US in Autumn, I found pumpkin shaped ones. I had to have them and of course pumpkin spiced everything!

You are hosting the perfect Halloween movie marathon. What are the films you choose and why?

Halloween (1978), I heard Bruce Campbell describe it as the Cadillac of Halloween movies once - and he is spot on! No *Halloween* movie marathon is complete without this John Carpenter masterpiece. *The Shining* - one of my all-time favorite films, I still get goosebumps when I hear that title music. Such a fantastic example of what I've often heard referred to as "gateway horror". This is one that would please the hardcore horror fans as well as the scaredy-cats. *Scream* - I have such a love for this franchise. *Scream* was the first "new" horror film that I watched. My dad rented it. I was around seven and definitely shouldn't have been watching but it amazed me.

If you could continue any horror story, what would it be?

The Bride of Frankenstein, it always blew my mind that the Bride was such an iconic classic monster, despite only appearing on screen for around 3 minutes. In *Son of Frankenstein*, we see Frankenstein's Monster revived by Wolf. I always wondered how her story would play out if she was found and revived too.

Describe the perfect Halloween.

We don't celebrate Halloween in the U.K with the same kind of vigor and spirit as our U.S friends, and it's something that I've always been jealous of. I find ways to celebrate all things Halloween all year round. I guess in my head, the perfect Halloween is the kind that you see in films; a quaint New England town, orange leaves all around and the streets filled with trick or treaters, pumpkins lit on the porch and throwing a Halloween party in the style of Alison's family from *Hocus Pocus* .... a girl can dream. This past Halloween, I spent my day carving pumpkins with my toddler nephew, which I loved. I then spent the night at the most haunted hotel in the U.K. It was my favorite Halloween for many years.

SCARE CRED: BOSTON WHITE

Boston White, also known as Amanda, is a horror fan, contributor, Queen of Halloween, and social media superstar from the UK. In addition to her popular YouTube channel, where she posts travelogues of her adventures into horror, she is the co-host of the popular podcast *The Halloween Half Hour*.

KERSEY VALLEY SPOOKYWOODS HAUNTED ATTRACTION

BY TONY WOHLGEMUTH

Take a trip back in history through one of America's most well known and most respected haunted houses in the entire haunted attraction industry: Kersey Valley Spookywoods, a haunted house in North Carolina that is far more than just a haunted house attraction. At the time of this publishing, Kersey Valley has four year-round attractions: Zipline Tours, Escape Games, indoor and outdoor Axe Throwing, and High Ropes Course. Plus, Kersey Valley Attractions hosts two seasonal fall events: Maize Adventure and Spookywoods. Centrally located in the state of North Carolina, it's easy to find location is just off of I-85.

I was just nine years old in 1979 when my family moved to a sprawling, 60-acre farm that had been used to grow tobacco. My family moved from Switzerland to NC—and the dream was to own a farm. Purposed as a Christmas tree farm, the property had several tobacco barns, a hay barn, farmhouse, and a main residence. The property was an amazing backdrop to grow up on, and it became a popular hangout with all of my friends. We used one of the old barns to camp out on summer nights. We pulled power from the farmhouse—and one night in the summer of 1985 even to the loft of one of the barns.

Just after midnight, the chandelier fell from the top of the barn and stopped just inches from our faces as we lay in our sleeping bags. The end of the drop cord was caught by the window seal, keeping the heavy iron fixture from hitting us! This frightening occurrence spawned a dare between us friends to enter the old farmhouse to restore the power, insisting someone must go upstairs to satisfy the dare. One of the boys took the dare and, once upstairs, a family of bats got stirred up and one latched onto the back of the brave boy. This incident shook our group to the bone, creating an idea for a haunted house in the fall of 1985.

So, we worked on our big idea… with a budget of zero and only free items donated or found in a dumpster with walls painted white and splattered with "blood." Tickets sold for $2.00 each, and we sold a total of just over 1,000 tickets our first season, which was a two-week straight run. Marketing efforts were limited to hand-drawn fliers given out at our high school. The wait in line was four hours long by the time we hit our fourth season in 1989. I realized that we had to expand to more than just a five-room haunted farmhouse. So, we added a walk through the haunted woods. The catalyst that launched the hobby of a group of 10 friends and I started from a dare and exploded into a real business opportunity.

I met my future wife, Donna, in our third season—and she thought it was a cute hobby. But when I refused to give up the yearly effort of building the haunted house, she decided to join in and focus on marketing the attraction. The hobby quickly began to show its potential after we made an effort to advertise outside of the hand-drawn flyers. The growth was incredible! And we were at capacity, faced with a choice to either reinvent the process or be limited to just a 125-per-hour capacity.

In 1996, we transitioned away from a guided group format to a free-flowing, no-guide haunted experience. This not only changed the way we did business, it transformed our lives. The capacity leap leapfrogged from 125 fans an hour to more than 700 fans per hour. We continued to expand the attraction in order to extend the time of the experience. This is when the idea of planting Christmas trees came full circle. The trees we planted when I was nine years old were never harvested, as my father moved back to Switzerland and we just let them grow. The trees were now growing together and made a really spooky walking trail. So, in 1996 I registered the domain spookywoods.com, and we became one of the very first haunted attractions with an official website.

Donna and I finished college, and we both started working full time on our careers. But haunting was always our side job. We started researching ways to expand our business beyond October, and the next attraction idea came to life as a massive corn maze in 2001. We named this attraction Maize Adventure. We focused on daytime programming for young families as well as school field trips as an educational off-campus experience. Now we had two seasonal events that kept growing yearly—and each fed the other in cross-promotional efforts.

The time came to look for another attraction that would turn us into a year-round attraction. On a cruise in 2008, we decided to take a zip line tour in Belize. I fell in love with the idea, and over the next year, I designed and lobbied our local county officials to open a zip line tour across our farm. The time came to jump into entertainment full time and focus on our own growing business.

A first of its kind in NC, we opened a 1.5-mile-long zip line tour across 10 engineered sky towers in 2010. This was an amazing success, which helped us become full-time, self-employed entrepreneurs. With the added boost to our bottom line, we were finally able to hire full time artists and builders for our first love: Spookywoods. The business model was simple: keep adding fun, family-focused attractions and build them at a level of quality that had not been seen before. We now had the capital to try new and exciting attractions. The next attraction was Outdoor Laser Tag in the woods, built like an indoor arena with surround sound and highly themed play areas. This venture also took off and became a hit with all ages. Since we had invested heavily in the industries best-in-class laser tag, it was an easy decision to add a laser tag experience to the haunted house in order to cross-promote the attractions.

Then we added a High Ropes Challenge Course and Escape Games in 2015. We built the escape games just like we do the haunted house sets, utilizing the artists and builders we already had on staff year-round. We kept adding escape games and building them like never seen before. I always try to cross-promote all of the attractions whenever possible. So, building a five-room haunted mansion from the ground up that doubles as an escape game and as a walk-through haunted house during the Spookywoods season was just smart marketing.

It has become easy for us to try new attractions, since we own the land and we can market each new venture to our ever-growing database of loyal fans. The next attraction on the horizon was indoor and outdoor Axe Throwing. We were the first in the Triad to capitalize on this hot and growing trend.

The key to our overall success is to be different and build attractions with top-quality craftsmanship with a major focus on customer service. I'm always looking to add exciting and new attractions to the farm to keep our fans coming back every year. Now, in 2020, we are finishing a two-year project of building a railroad around the farm and adding a ghost town along the tracks. The 104-passenger Kersey Valley Express railroad is available as part of our Maize Adventure daytime attraction—and during Spookywoods, it becomes an interactive outlaw laser tag shootout from the train.

The farm property continues to grow as surrounding land become available. Kersey Valley Attractions currently sits on just over 80 acres of usable land. The 20 acres of land we purchase in 2020 will become home to two massive sunflower fields during Maize Adventure. The sunflowers are planted using a GPS planter to create amazing designs as the flowers grow. One of the fields is designed for selfies and the other for pick-your-own flowers. The future looks even brighter as, once the timing is right, a Christmas hayride experience is on the wish list.

To all young dreamers, it may be a cliché… but dream until your dreams come true. I would have never imagined what started out with 10 of my childhood friends would turn into my life's work that employs more than 350 team members yearly for over three decades and counting. Don't listen to the people who say "no." No doesn't mean never. It only means not right now. Be the leader, listen more than you talk, treat everyone with respect, and create something fun!

www.kerseyvalley.com

a few words from

TONY WOHLGEMUTH

As a designer of horror theatre or experiences, explain your process.

I imagine myself as a customer walking through the environment.

When is the last time you were genuinely scared by something someone created?

When I entered the farm house after shutting down the haunt to turn off a breaker that was left on. It was pitch black dark and I was using my cell phone light and I walked around a corner into the bear costume propped up, that I forgot was in there.

Tell us about your contribution to our book. What was the inspiration?

I was inspired to give insight to other dreamers that a hobby can turn into a lifelong business.

What do you love about the genre of horror?

I loving taking people out of reality even for a moment to invoke the flight or fight emotion.

What is some of your favorite horror literature? Favorite Author?

The Hound of Baskervilles.

What are some of your influences?

The nightly news.

What is your favorite Halloween treat?

Haystacks, a butterscotch chocolate treat Donna makes every year.

You are hosting the perfect Halloween movie marathon. What are the films you choose and why?

The *Friday the 13th* series, for me it all started in the 80's and it was what scared us growing up.

If you could continue any horror story (Book or Film), what would it be?

Stephen King's *In the Tall Grass*

Describe the perfect Halloween.

Clear skies with a full moon and no rain.

SCARE CRED: TONY WOHLGEMUTH

Tony Wohlgemuth owner and operator of one of America's longest running haunted attractions, Kersey Valley Spookywoods established in 1985. He has been a leader in the haunted attraction industry sharing his experiences for the betterment of the industry, founding member of the Haunted House and the America Haunts association (https://americahaunts.com).

He still lives on the 80+ acre farm with his wife Donna where as a teenager a dare to enter 1930's farm house sparked the idea to create a haunted attraction that is now internationally known for its creative and unique setting. They both have a passion to bring smiles and screams to their league of fans to their ever-expanding list of fun attractions. Just as their email signature promotes, Tony's "Comes up with the fun stuff" and Donna's "Brings the fun stuff to life". They are a force the industry references to keep the scare and business of fun on the farm thriving.

LIFE'S A BEACH UNTIL YOU DIE

BY JAY R. WORTHAM

It's not easy being undead, besides all the raw flesh-eating, making new friends is nearly impossible. Well, it was impossible until I got my new phone and met the girl of my dreams. Funny story, I pre-ordered it right before the tragic events that led me to my current state of rotting fleshy-ness. So, the mailman delivered it just about the time I ran out of neighbors to dine on and was feeling decidedly peckish.

The doorbell rang, I answered it and he reached out to have me sign for my new phone. Thanks to the poor lighting in my entry hall, he couldn't see much of me until I was right up to him. He tasted wonderful.

A few weeks later while wandering the beach at night, I came across an old group of nighttime sunbathers. No idea. Anyway, being a foodie before my change, I opted to take pictures of my pending meal and to my delight, the phone revealed them to not even be human. Finally, some new friends that don't look appetizing at all.

So go figure, the latest phone technology has the added benefit of seeing right through whatever magic they were using to disguise their real selves. What a beautiful bonus feature. You just have to love technology.

Slowly I crept up to the lovely blond with the red bathing suit on. Not only was her human disguise the most attractive, but she was also the only one all alone. You know, just in case. Truly being approached by a member of reanimated is very disconcerting for most of the living. I had no idea what these things are or how they would react. Better to play it safe.

"Hey there," I said. I suspect it came out more like a grown, but she didn't seem startled or at all dismayed by my arrival. She slowly examined me with her eyes moving from my rotting flesh head to my poorly shoed toes. She then returned her gaze to my face. Meeting my eyes. She stretched her arms in the air as she spoke.

"Who were you? Do I know you?"

"No, I don't think we've met before," I retorted, "As far as I know, I've only met humans up until this point." Her eyes widened as she processed my words.

"You see me, I mean the real me?"

"I see something that's not human when I look through my phone."

"Well, that's no fun, I prefer my food to be surprised, right before I bite into it." This time my eyes widened as I processed her words. "You're a clever one, however, so I won't eat you today and I'll be your companion until the day I decide to eat you."

That was the day I met the love of my life. It's been a few weeks now and things are wonderful. I do on occasion catch her out the corner of my eye licking her lips, so I know it's only a matter of time. Who would have thought, this undead life isn't half bad after all, for now at least.

a few words from

JAY R. WORTHAM

As a designer of horror theatre or experiences, explain your process.

I've always felt that horror has the most opportunity to just escape and let your freak flag fly. When I'm creating my dark and twisty works, I put my music on blast and I escape any limitations that my "normal" life pushes on me.

When is the last time you were genuinely scared by something someone created?

Halloween Horror Nights Walking Dead haunted house at Universal Studios. Here's the thing, I love zombie/undead horror films, but zombies genuinely bug me. I was good with going in until my lovely wife, the very person that laughs at my zombie fear and even says, "how can you be afraid of something so silly?" started pushing into each walking dead we encountered. The irony being that she wasn't doing it to be mean or funny, she was doing because she was terrified from the experience. Now isn't that silly?

Tell us about your contribution to our book. What was the inspiration?

Being that zombies are me weak spot, I've always wondered what it would be like to capture my experience as being a self-aware zombie. I also wanted to explore what nature would introduce into the world to balance things during a zombie apocalypse. Seemingly unstoppable killing machines that spread like a virus would only by stopped by something supernatural that fed on the dead. Now that's a love story.

What do you love about the genre of horror?

Like I said before, I love the freedom that horror brings. In horror, it's absolutely acceptable to have the bad guy win at the end. In horror the motives can be simple, complex or unknown and not diminish the horror. Not to mention, horror always has the flexibility, in my opinion, to borrow from or even enhance other genres.

What is some of your favorite horror literature? Favorite Author?

My true love for horror fiction was cemented by Clive Barker, *Books of Blood* and *The Great and Secret Show*. Later I added authors like Peter Straub - *KoKo*. I also love lesser known classic short horror fiction writers like Frederick Brown (*Night of the Jabberwock*) along with big names like Dean Koontz - *TikTok*. I even love mixed genre horror writers such as Laurel K. Hamilton and Anne Rice. Brown crossed a lot of his short horror fiction with science fiction while Rice is a shining example of letting your freak flag absolutely fly.

What are some of your influences?

My biggest influences are most likely people like Frederick Brown, Orson Scott Card and Harlan Ellison. I do love genre genius like John Carpenter (*The Thing*) and of course Robert Kirkman of *The Walking Dead*.

What is your favorite Halloween treat?

Free full-size candy bars. That's all I give out and that's all I want!

If you could continue any horror story (Book or Film), what would it be?

Years ago, I really enjoyed a book called *The Relic*. So, imagine my excitement and trepidation when a film was announced. Needless to say, the book completely missed the point of the book. The message in the book was about nature finding ways to restore order. Sometimes those ways are horrific. I'd love to fix the film by first reimagine the lead characters much closer to the book characters and build the the suspense to horror like the book did. And solidify to message that nature truly always get the last laugh.

Describe the perfect Halloween.

I'm that guy that loves to go all out for Halloween. Animatronic zombies, talking busts at the door, and a multitude of spooky lights and sounds. One year I went as far as making a full fledge haunted house in my garage. I built fake walls, some of which had animated blood. I had plenty animatronics all through It with one wall covered with webs, a giant spider and animated body wrapped in web. My whole family played characters at various points in the experience. It would have been a perfect Halloween If more than half a dozen kids were brave enough to actually enter It that year.

SCARE CRED: JAY R. WORTHAM

Jay R Wortham has spent thirty-five years behind the scenes pushing other artists to find their own unique voices. Now that he is over half-a-century-old himself, he has finally found a voice of his own. A dark and twisty mix-up that combines classic and contemporary horror tropes to vividly captured scenes. He paints imagery that is humorous, captivating, retro while contemporary, frightening and fanciful, forcing the viewer to juggle their own conflicting interests as they experience his works. He's always struggled with the standard artistic crisis of confidence that can hold any artist hostage. He has set aside this strange relationship and is driving his ambitions toward new opportunities to present his view to the world.

HORROR THROUGH THE EYES OF A TEEN

BY CADEN AIELLO

I grew up in a family that was tied to horror. My father was part of the Art And Design team for Universal's Halloween Horror Nights, so growing up I was always slightly fascinated by the idea of being scared. At that time however, I was too frightened by my dad's creations to really appreciate them. Fast forward to 2016 where I finally took a chance to see what my dad had been up to all these years. He took me to a HHN/theme park auction that was held in Orlando, where he had a panel with the rest of the creative team. Seeing the props and my dad talking about his passion for horror and Horror Nights really stuck with me and it has ever since. A year later I finally gave HHN a try, and I absolutely fell in love with it. The set design, the music, the fog, and the atmosphere made me realize that horror isn't just about getting scared.

Since then I've been to countless nights of HHN and seen even more horror films. Overtime I have gathered a new perspective on horror. Initially I had just thought that getting scared was just that, just getting scared. But I have come to realize that's not the half of it. The way I see it, facing your fears and coming face to face with horrifying monsters is all a metaphor. A metaphor for conquering your inner demons, a horror we all have to come to face at some point. Why does the jock in the slasher always die? Because of his need to feel wanted and acting like a jerk to stand out, his insecurities overtook him because he wasn't dealing with them the way he should have.

At the end of the day, horror is interpreted in so many different ways and none of them are wrong. I will forever thank horror and horror films for giving me a new way of looking at films in general. I also thank my father for being the coolest guy around and showing me this amazing, frightening, creative genre.

A FEW WORDS FROM

CADEN AIELLO

As a designer of horror theatre or experiences, explain your process.

Whenever I write a short film or short story, I love to make my main character grounded in the real world. No matter what supernatural monsters or curses get thrown their way, they are relatable to the reader.

When is the last time you were genuinely scared by something someone created?

The ending to *The Summer Of '84* was absolutely bone-chilling. Without spoiling it, the main villain does an incredible horrifying monologue about his killings and it's incredibly well done. The nights that followed watching that scene, it kept me up!

Tell us about your contribution to our book. What was the inspiration?

While reading the first volume and particularly the interview questions, it was nice to see how adults thought of horror and how it changed their life. I wanted to do the same thing but, from a kid's perspective. As I was writing my contribution I had realized how drastically different both viewpoints were.

What do you love about the genre of horror?

I love that under any circumstance, horror movies always make you feel something! Weather that be fear, disgust, hatred, humored, whatever it may be. The horror genre always finds a way to make you feel tons of emotions in an hour and forty-five-minute span.

What is some of your favorite horror literature? Favorite Author?

To this day some of my favorite horror literature are the *Goosebumps* books by R.L. Stein. They are the embodiment of early horror and a lot of veteran horror fans I know had this series to thank for their love. Some of them are silly, but some of them are downright gruesome!

What are some of your influences?

My dad, Michael Aiello is probably the best person to introduce me to this genre. His work with HHN inspired me to get interested in the genre and I can't thank him enough for bringing this integral part of who I am into my life,

What is your favorite Halloween treat?

It not a sweet treat, but the most iconic Halloween treat for me is Halloween Horror Night's pizza fries!

You are hosting the perfect Halloween movie marathon. What are the films you choose and why?

Killer Klowns From Outer Space (a classic), *Child's Play* (it's my favorite), *Halloween* (a perfect horror film), and *Saw III* (it's the best in one of my favorite series).

If you could continue any horror story (Book or Film), what would it be?

Killer Klowns From Outer Space! It will be a triumphant day when we get to see Shorty, Jumbo, and Slim on the big screen again.

Describe the perfect Halloween.

A full moon in the sky, me in a costume acting as a scareactor in front of our house. Constantly going inside to bring handfuls of candy out front. A nice breeze and Halloween soundtracks blaring from a speaker we have outside. Yeah, that's Halloween magic right there.

SCARE CRED: CADEN AIELLO

Caden Aiello is the son of Universal Creative member Michael Aiello. He is a huge fan of the horror genre and horror events. He is an aspiring Universal Art and Design team member, and is currently working on several screenplays for short horror films.

FINAL THOUGHTS

We're Here, For Fear, Get Used to It!

BY JOE MOE

Like many of you, I've been immersed in the horror genre ever since I was a little kid. Up to my neck in it and ready to be up to my ears and beyond. Like many fellow fans, I found that horror movies embodied the most exciting elements that sparked Hollywood ambition in every kid across the country. Horror movies demanded a level of craft and artistry that wasn't often found in more mainstream titles. Horror required hyper-imaginative subjects, visionary design beyond the pale, transformative makeups, otherworldly set-pieces and iconic actors commited to portraying mad creators, hapless victims, and, most importantly, monsters! My love of this form would grow up with me to become more meaningful with every year that passed and each horror movie I eagerly experienced. I hope those of you who share this passion had at least one best friend or parent who was a willing accomplice in your off-beat obsession. Ultimately, horror movies led me to the origin stories; the written word, deepening my understanding of the genesis of cinematic storytelling by the great authors. I came to view classic horror as our noble morality tales and many of the monsters that populated these stories as sympathetic creatures. Misunderstood and often victimized. Seeking love or acceptance while rebelling against a fate they never asked for. Slasher movies of the 80s, grew from "classic" horror to distill the most titillating elements of the genre. These were so concentrated and entertaining. The product of a generation before mine, throwing their "bats" into the ring to make a new breed of bloody good entertainment.

When I finally made my move to the mythical city called Hollywood in the 80s, I met and befriended my childhood hero Forrest J Ackerman. He and publisher James Warren's landmark magazine, Famous Monsters of Filmland, began in the late 50s and had influenced a legion of fans for generations. The number of films and filmmakers "Uncle Forry" and his "FM" inspired are endless. Forry's clawprints are forever fused with the accomplishments of the kids he mentored through the pages of his magazine that grew up to be Stephen King, George Lucas, Guillermo Del Toro, Steven Spielberg, John Landis, Joe Dante, Rick Baker and many more. In Forry we found an omnipresent, knowledgeable and generous benefactor who was a tireless promoter of the genre we treasured. He was also the consummate collector. A purveyor of artifacts from the movies we loved. Every Saturday, he opened his 18-room home to hungry fans to roam the rooms, getting up close and personal with 800,000 treasures including the stop-motion animated dinosaurs from King Kong (1933) to Bela Lugosi's Dracula cape from stage and his final appearance in Ed Wood's Plan 9 From Outer Space! I, and any lucky visitors to the "Ackermansion," furthered our education in horror, sitting at Uncle Forry's feet as he told us first hand stories of his friendships with our idols. From Boris Karloff to Fritz Lang. Vincent Price, Vampira, Christopher Lee, Peter Cushing, Ingrid Pitt and on and on. Forry's philosophy of generosity brought fandom together in a collaborative community who dared to follow in the footsteps of the men and women who made our cherished nightmares.

Today, horror has ascended to a place it hasn't occupied since the silent film era of 1920s and the Universal monster movies of the 30s-40s. It is the trifecta of show-biz success: Mainstream entertainment value, incredibly profitable and Oscar winning! Directors like Jordan Peele and Guillermo Del Toro make no apologies for loving horror or making horror movies. Independent filmmakers still cut their teeth and seed their careers on making horror movies. The biggest stars in Hollywood step from in front of the camera to make their directorial debut making horror movies. And the horror fan remains the most fiercely loyal and supportive you will ever meet. Whenever I have the privilege of participating in a panel at a horror event, I always ask, "How many of you fans aspire to make movies, be a makeup artist or write?." A good 75% of hands fly up, without hesitation. You see, there is no more sophisticated fan than the horror head. Most fans want to be involved in some way or, at the very least, be the most informed and knowledgeable audience member possible. The partition between the youngest fan and the most accomplished old-timer melts away as we talk about the things we love in common. As in most traditions, there is a narrative string threaded through the legacy of horror. As I grow older, I feel Uncle Forry's influence more and more acutely. I strive to inspire a younger generation to find their voice because they owe it to themselves, and then, to share that voice because they owe it to the rest of us. This is the kind of encouragement I hope you find in the pages of this book. The pages populated by ideas, stories and experiences expressed by fans turned pros. People who have successfully created the stuff our most nutritious nightmares are made of. Their efforts are born of a common love of high stakes suspense, fatal morality tales, inescapable justice and unfathomable tragedy.

I hope we'll one day see your name among those of your horror heroes. It can't happen unless you take a chance on yourself. Tell your story. One that's informed by all the stories you've loved that came before. Stories that had an impact on you. Create! You won't be doing it in a vacuum. A whole horror community will be right here waiting for you like ravenous ghouls ready to slurp up anything you dare to serve us!

With Loathing Hisses,

Joe Moe

J.MICHAEL RODDY'S
HAUNTER'S TALE

Special Thanks

A special and heartfelt thanks to the following fiends:

Nick and Beverly Pappas
The best of us. This book is because of them. In my book, they are the official Halloween Ambassadors.

Dustin McNeill
Your passion and talent are immeasurable.
I appreciate your support and friendship.

Lon Smart
You are a master of art and one of the dreamers of dreams. Your appreciation and genuine love of visual storytelling are inspiring.

Michael Aiello
My brother, my friend, and my favorite collaborator.

Daniel Roebuck
If we were going to have an official Haunter's Club, I would want Danny to be the spokesman. He is a MonsterKid, tried and true who made good, and has never lost sight of how wonderful and pure the month of October is.

Doug Jones
The modern-day Lon Chaney. The world is a better place with you in it.

Greg Nicotero
His friendship is as legendary as his talent. Thanks for giving a fan a chance.

Tom Savini
Thanks for showing me the meaning of "grande illusions."

Scott Swenson
Who would have thought?

Nancy Hutson
Eternal rewards…

My Family – The trinity of Roddy Gals
Cathy, Ellie, and Jessie, you encourage support and inspire me every day.

And, a heartfelt scream to all of those titans of terror and fright – the haunters that have brought so many countless hours of fear and scare in the dark.

THANKS FOR
SPENDING SOME TIME
WITH US. PLEASANT
SCREAMS.

James Michael Roddy

WE'LL BE LURKING FOR
YOU IN HAUNTER'S TALE
VOLUME 3 IN 3-D

Made in the USA
Monee, IL
03 November 2020

46652739R00280